Wind & Water

in the Middle Ages

༄

Fluid Technologies from
Antiquity to the Renaissance

MEDIEVAL AND RENAISSANCE
TEXTS AND STUDIES

VOLUME 322

Penn State Medieval Studies
Number 2

Wind & Water
in the Middle Ages

∽∾

Fluid Technologies from
Antiquity to the Renaissance

edited by
Steven A. Walton

Publications of the PSU
Center for Medieval Studies

Senior Editor
Norris J. Lacy

ACMRS
(Arizona Center for Medieval and Renaissance Studies)
Tempe, Arizona
2006

Library of Congress Cataloging-in-Publication Data

Wind & water in the Middle Ages : fluid technologies from antiquity to the
   Renaissance / edited by Steven A. Walton.
      p. cm. -- (Medieval and Renaissance texts and studies ; . 322. Penn State
Medieval studies ; no. 2) (Publications of the PSU Center for Medieval Stud-
ies; 15)
   Includes bibliographical references and index.
   ISBN-13: 978-0-86698-367-9 (alk. paper)
   ISBN-10: 0-86698-367-8 (alk. paper)
   1. Water-wheels--Europe--History--To 1500. 2. Water mills--Europe--His-
tory--To 1500. 3. Windmills--Europe--History--To 1500. I. Title: Wind and
water in the Middle Ages.

   TJ840.A2W56 2006
   621.2'10940902--dc22

                                                            2006028810

This book is made to last.
It is set in Adobe Caslon Pro,
smth-sewn and printed on acid-free paper
to library specifications.
Printed in the United States of America

Contents

List of Illustrations and Tables

ooooo

About the Cover

The image on the cover is redrawn from Sebastian de Covarrubias Horozco, *Emblemas morales* (Madrid: L. Sanchez, 1610), emblem III.55. Covarrubias (†1612) was a church official and lexicographer in Madrid who published what is considered the first Spanish-language dictionary in 1611 (other Spanish-Latin dictionaries preceded it). His *Moral Emblems* was dedicated to Don Francisco Gomez de Sandoval and Roxas, Duke of Lerma, and, like emblem books from across Europe at the time, included woodcuts of an image, typically with a moralizing motto, and an edifying poem below. The emblem tradition can be said to date from 1531, when Andrea Alciato published his *Emblematum liber* (*Book of Emblems*), a collection of 212 emblem poems. It went through a number of expanded editions in his lifetime, was translated into numerous languages, and developed into a genre (in Latin and most vernacular languages) over the next two centuries. For an online English-language version of Alciato, see <http://www.mun.ca/alciato/>. For more on the cover image (which does not appear in Alciato), see the introduction, below.

Cover layout and design by Todd Halvorsen of ACMRS.

ACKNOWLEDGEMENTS

This book originated with the *Wind & Water: the Medieval Mill* conference at Penn State, April 16 and 17, 2004, although only about half the contributions in the book were presented there. For that conference, we gratefully acknowledged the support of Penn State, The Worldwide University Network (WUN), and 11 Centers, Programs, Institutes and Departments across the university; it was truly a collaborative effort. Vickie Ziegler, Ben Hudson, and Norris Lacey here at the Penn State Medieval Center had the conviction in my ability to get this done and have never groused at some of the delays. To my colleagues in STS, especially Wenda Bauchspies, I offer thanks as well, particularly for putting up with my endless discussions of *InDesign* and the editing of this book.

In the production of this book, I have to thank the contributors first and foremost for their timely delivery of chapters and images and for answering seemingly endless small questions. Thanks also to Roy Rukkila and Todd Halvorsen at ACMRS for providing templates for *InDesign* and helping me work out the page standards. Once I had figured out how to do the layout process, they helped smooth the production process along quickly. The world of copyright is at once simple and confusing, and numerous people around the world assisted with obtaining images and their permission to use them: I owe a favor to William Sayers at Cornell for finding an image in their library system; Sandy Stelts at Penn State Special collections helped me and a contributor with images; and Terri Torretto at Dover Publications helped me understand public domain images in their publications. Also, to a number of others who suggested and assisted the various contributors, thank you ever so much. As usual, remaining errors or omissions are mine, although each contributor retains copyright on their articles.

Steven A. Walton
State College, March 2006

Introduction

Steven A. Walton (Penn State University)

A long time ago, came a man on a track,
Walking thirty miles with a sack on his back.
And he put down his load where he thought it was the best;
Made a home in the wilderness.
He built a cabin and a winter store.
And he ploughed up the ground by the cold lake shore...
The other travelers came walking down the track—
They never went further, no, they never went back.
Then came the churches, then came the schools;
Then came the lawyers, then came the rules;
Then came the trains and the trucks with their loads;
And the dirty old track was the telegraph road.[1]

Although embodying the growth of an American frontier town from dusty track to twentieth-century connectedness, "Telegraph Road" misses one of the most important elements of that growth. When the traveler "ploughed up the ground by the cold lake shore", there is a good chance he planted wheat or corn. That grain had to be ground to meal or flour and put into the "winter store", especially once all the other travelers arrived. The watermill or windmill and in fact all agricultural activities, centerpiece of a medieval, colonial, or any pre-industrial village, is absent from the Telegraph Road. Not to distract from the poetry of the piece, but in order to fully understand the growth of communities as well as the growth of industry—indeed the very next line of the poem is "Then came the mines, then came the ore"—one should look to the humble mill that bound communities together.

Beyond this—or actually, *before* this—"Telegraph Road" does not mention the fundamental tasks of new settlements: digging the wells for the water, as well as managing the waste, industrial effluents, smoke, and all the other concomitant markers of civilization. At one level, this is understandable, as the cathedrals of the world are admittedly more grand than the mills. But on the other hand, we do pay great attention to the mundane technologies of some civilizations (the aqueducts of Rome come to mind). Regardless, it is now time to focus our attention on these humble and crucial technologies. In this collection of essays, we offer a number of views of the water systems, including the mill, laws surrounding them, waste, nuisance, economics, as well as the symbolism and meanings associated with these centerpiece technologies to fill in omissions along Telegraph Road.

Before the steam engine and electrical generator, wind and water powered everything beyond human or animals' muscles. Quite beyond the hydrological and solar cycles responsible for life in the first place, humanity has been singularly successful in harnessing these two natural forces of wind and water to our will. Water has for millennia formed the lifeblood of communities; indeed early theorists of civilizations posited that it was such "hydraulic civilizations" that gave us organized societies in the first place.[2] Such a fundamental resource, then, deserves study as more than just a technology.[3] In the pre-industrial era (and even for a good portion of the era of modern factory production)[4] mills were everywhere: they ground grain, sawed lumber, fulled cloth, pulped paper, pressed cider and olives, and incorporated gunpowder. They were adaptable but also remarkably stable and yet malleable both technologically and socially over time; it is for these characteristics as well as for their motive forces that we punningly use the term "fluid technologies."

"Fluid Technologies" is more than a pun, however. Waterwheels, water lifting devices, pumps, fountains, windmills, and other hydraulic and pneumatic machinery flow into one another in their geography, their technology, their chronologies, and their fortunes, as well as in their overall meanings in law, art, politics, economics, and other human endeavors. Further, it is clear that they moved fluidly between cultures: from the Greeks to the Romans, from the Romans to the Arabic world and to the medieval Europeans, and in some cases such as Spain, back and forth between those groups as well. In short, one element we wish to demonstrate in many aspects of this volume is the continuity between these technologies. If anything, we hope that no reader will come away from this book understanding that in terms of the larger system of wind and water power and use, there ever was much of a technological rupture in Europe as we have sometimes been taught[5]—rather, what had been invented and innovated in the ancient world grew, changed, and morphed throughout the Middle Ages to provide necessary sustenance and opportunities of industrial capacity. When new inventions certainly did appear during this period (the windmill is the obvious case), they became enmeshed in the network of those earlier systems rather than necessarily triggering a truly revolutionary change in the structure of society.

Figure 1: **Emblematic noria: "One rises and the other falls"**; redrawn from Sebastian de Covarrubias Horozco, *Emblemas morales* (Madrid: L. Sanchez, 1610), century III, no. 55 (p. 255)

This metaphor of fluid technology precipitated my choice for the cover image to the volume (Fig. 1). As you might imagine, finding a single image that encompasses the concepts of both wind and water and makes some connection across the centuries from Greece and Rome to the Elizabethan world was no simple task. This emblem from *Emblemas Morales* (1610) bears the motto "Unos suren y otros baxan", or "some rise and others fall." The accompanying explanatory text offers,

> Los bienes desta vida transitoria,
> Que van corriendo bien como los rios,
> Son arcaduzes puestos en anoria,
> Al subir llenos, y al baxar vacios.
> No puede consistir aqui la gloria,
> Siendo todo mudança y desvarios,
> Aqueste priua, est ortro està en desgracia,
> Y quando el uno hinche, el otro vacia.

The fortunes of this transitory life, which keep on flowing just like rivers, are like the pots on a *noria*, ascending full, descending empty. In this there is no glory, for all is change and caprice; For every pot that's favored, another is disgraced, [and] When one fills up, the other empties.[6]

This invocation of the medieval concept of *fortuna* embodies some of the concepts addressed by the authors in this volume. While none are principally concerned with the typical "rise and fall" approach to history of technology, a number do very explicitly look at the rise and fall of our understandings of these technologies. Whether we are speaking of the perception of waterwheels across the centuries, or the rise and fall of an actual miller and his dubious financial dealings, it is clear that over the millennium and a half examined in this volume, the world changed quite dramatically; the world of Vitruvius was not the world of Shakespeare, although interestingly enough, one standing of the Tiber in the former time and another on the Thames in the latter might have looked at effectively the same water technologies in front of them.

In all this fluidity there seems to have been little of the glory Covarrubias refers to as far as mills and aqueducts were concerned, although irrigated gardens certainly did become wonders of the world. From this, however, we should not assume that the stories of such technologies are inglorious. Rather, the story of wind and water in the Middle Ages relies primarily upon the constant ebb and flow of these fundamental underlying technologies that kept society functioning. The water-lifting wheel—whether a *noria* which uses buckets along the perimeter of the wheel or a chain pump with a chain of buckets dropping deep into a well—spanned cultures from Hellas to Hibernia, from Sweden to Spain, and most importantly spanned time from the Romans and before to the modern world.

One might look to an early example from the ancient world recently reconstructed in London that symbolizes the importance of these sorts of technologies both to our culture and to another two thousand years ago. In 2001 an excavation at 30 Gresham Street came across the well-preserved remains of a Roman bucket-chain water-lifting machine. It was deemed both such an important find and of sufficient interest to museum-goers that the Museum of London recently rebuilt a working replica in their courtyard which was the subject of a *Time Team* television episode on BBC4.[7] (Fig. 2a) Similarly, even the fluid technologies of the less distant past generate pride and excitement today. In the nineteenth century, D. Gines Valcarcel Rodriguez commissioned the engineer Francis Eugene Mansy to build a giant, 8m high water-lifting *noria* to raise the water to a steam locomotive rewatering station at Tedelche, Spain (just west of Murcia). The *noria* also provided drinking water for the local population and became such a landmark that in 2002 the town of Hellin erected an exact replica prominently displayed in the central market square. (Fig. 2b) Thus, visitors today in places like London or Hellin or numerous other places around the world can marvel at the hydraulic technologies (re)built as fundamental building blocks of civilization.

Figure 2: **Water-lifting engines, old and new**; photos by the author.
[Top] Reconstructed Roman bucket-chain pump at the Museum of London, based upon an original excavated at 30 Gresham Street, London; [Bottom] Replica of a nineteenth-century *noria* on display in the public market, Hellin, Spain.

As the most emblematic symbols of the wind and water we seek to understand, medieval wind- and watermills offer the linchpin to understanding attitudes towards such technologies in the millennia straddling either side of the year AD 1000.[8] Mills were the core of society, the object of concern (both legally themselves, or indirectly in the concern over millers as necessary but less-than-reputable members of society), and yet also remarkably invisible. For a large, creaking technology that was expensive to build, a central meeting place for many, and a crucial component of the agricultural cycle for the vast majority of people, it may seem surprising that they should be so. Like so many things that form the bedrock of society, they are taken for granted and rarely discussed. Even the Bible points out their *un*importance: "All the firstborn in the land of Egypt shall die, from the firstborn of Pharaoh that sitteth upon his throne, even unto the firstborn of the maidservant that is behind the mill" (Exodus 11:5). How often after all do we discuss plumbing, or lighting, or central heating today? Then as today, we are much more likely to focus on the ephemeral, the *extra*ordinary, and the surprising. Here we want to bring out the importance of and the interest surrounding the underlying and mundane necessaries of civilized life.

Mills and Wind and Water

The unifying themes of this volume are the environmental power of wind and water to turn mills and their ability to offer useful and necessary services for communities. Additionally, we offer some understanding of their social consequences and how people perceived them in context. We take seriously Miquel Barceló's exhortation that "the whole hydraulic set-up, its design and implementation, should be the unit of analysis," but we will go further and say that its social context is important as well—even more important, in fact.[9] From grinding grain, sawing wood, fulling cloth and offering water for growing communities, water and wind are oft-neglected prime movers and natural resources that allowed western society to grow at rates other civilizations had not matched. Since the late classical world, western society has taken nearly every opportunity to harness these resources wherever and whenever they occur. Whether the wind on Aegean islands or on the American littoral from the St. Lawrence to the Caribbean, the water flowing from the Alps, or the tides ebbing and flowing on the Irish shore, wind and water became indispensable natural resources for industry and community. Contributions in this volume range from the antique world to Elizabethan London; from Egypt and Spain to Ireland and northwestern Germany; and the contributors themselves come from disciplines as far-ranging as history, history of technology, art history, garden history, legal history, environmental history, and literary studies.

Few of our contributors are strictly interested in the nuts and bolts view of mills as technological artifacts. To be sure, the contributors include an archaeologist and a number of technological historians, but we have steered clear of this area which is well served by other constituencies.[10] Here you will not find detailed technical investigations of individual sites, or mechanical studies of mills or millstones; technophobes need not fear to enter. Our group of contributors, however, bring mill studies from the physical world into the textual domain, although not so far as to lose the real-world connections that are sometimes lost in the academy. The contributors here all recognize that mills can be inspiring, can act as metaphors, and can even provide symbolic meaning, but they also realize that these inspirations, metaphors, and symbols were based in all cases on real, functioning, fluid-powered technologies. Consequently, their understanding of the wider meanings and implications of wind and water are firmly grounded in their investigations into the realities of the past.

Another strong theme running through a number of the contributions is the devotion to the ongoing debates of what has come to be known as the "Lynn White thesis" (or the "medieval technological revolution thesis" which was really more strongly trumpeted by Jean Gimpel), most pithily encapsulated in his phrase, "The chief glory of the later Middle Ages was not its cathedrals or its epics or its scholasticism: it was the building for the first time in history of a complex civilization that rested not on the backs of sweating slaves or coolies but primarily on non-human power."[11] Mill studies in the last decade have quite conclusively demonstrated that the simple model of the Middle Ages as having rediscovered the watermill (or reinvented, it is even sometimes claimed) and then applied it to industrial processes undreamt of by the Greeks or Romans cannot stand. This perception is more a function of the differential survival of remains as well as the differing predilections of the record-keepers in Rome and the Middle Ages. The long-recognized survival of the milling complex at Barbegal in southern France near Nîmes stands as a case in point. What were eight pair of sequential overshot waterwheels doing in a relatively out-of-the-way Roman province if the Romans had in fact not "discovered" the advantage of mechanized production?[12] Clearly they had; they simply were not interested in discussing it at length.

Our work also obliquely addresses the question of technological change, in which the mill is often seen as quintessential. As the first centralized power source, the industrial potential for mills has always been seen as transformative of the human condition. How that condition was transformed by various people at various times was hardly constant.[13] A case in point concerns the so-called "Norse mill". Generally understood to be a vertical-shafted, horizontal water-wheel, it had been thought that it came from the extra-Roman lands and for some reason became conceptually linked with the Scandinavians, despite no particular evidence that they had invented or even widely exploited it. More to the point, the Norse mill appears with no obvious diffusionary connection from the Caucasus to Ireland and, at least in historic times, from the Arctic circle to the Sahara.[14] In different places the same basic principle was advanced and found to work with subtle differences in blade shape, positioning, and overall relationship of the water source, wheel, and working area (Norse mills were almost exclusively used for flour milling). This does not even touch the story of the diffusion of the vertical watermill across the Eurasian land mass. Suffice it to say that mills are often the poster children for technological change, industrial development, and for the very concept of "progress" (however that might be defined).[15] We hope to offer at least a few new perspectives on how that technological change happened and was understood by contemporaries.

Once Europe had recovered in population, trade, agriculture, and other hallmarks of civilization after the decline of Rome, wind and water were indeed harnessed by mills and waterworks and put to good use. Bernard of Clairvaux's commentary of the work done by the River Aube in his monastery in the twelfth century is often repeated,[16] but Bernard was not alone in noticing how effectively the Cistercians had harnessed the water:

> This water...is supplied by the tireless course of the river Aube, of famous name, which flows through the many workshops of the abbey. Wherever it passes it evokes a blessing in its wake, proportionate to its good offices; for it does not slip through unscathed or at its leisure, but at the cost of much exertion. By means of a winding channel cut through the middle of the valley... by the hard work of the brethren, the Aube sends half its waters into the monastery, as though to greet the monks and apologize for not having come in its entirety, for want of a bed wide enough to carry its full flow.... As much of the stream as this [fronting] wall [under which it must flow], acting as gatekeeper, allows in by the sluice gates hurls itself initially with swirling force against the mill, where its ever-increasing turbulence, harnessed first to the weight of the millstones and next to the fine-meshed sieve, grinds the grain and then separates the flour from the bran.

The stream now fills the cauldron in a nearby building and suffers itself to be boiled to prepare the brothers' drink.... Nor does it hold itself acquitted yet. The fullers, next door to the mill, invite it in, claiming with reason on their side that, if it swirls and eddies in the mill, which provides the brothers with food, it should do no less by those who clothe them. The stream does not demur, nor indeed refuse any request made of it, Instead, raising and lowering by turns the heavy pestles..., it frees these brothers from their drudgery [and] after driving so many noisy and swiftly spinning wheels, it flows out foaming, as though it too had been ground and softened in the process.

The tannery is next to capture the stream, and here it displays its zeal in the fashioning of all that goes to make the brothers' footwear. Thereafter, its water decanted into a succession of channels, it carries out a dutiful inspection of each workshop, diligently inquiring where it can be of service and offering its ungrudging help in the work of cooking, sifting, turning, whetting, watering, washing, grinding and softening. Lastly, to ensure that no cause for gratitude be wanting, that its tasks be left in no respect unfinished, it carries the waste products away and leaves everything clean in its wake...while Clairvaux renders it thanks for all its blessings.[17]

The wondrous power of the water further inspired the author to extol its great benefit, arguing that not only did the water free the brothers from their toils of grinding and brewing and tanning, but "it frees them too from punishment for their sin" as well. Asking, "from how much backbreaking travail for horses and arm-aching labor for men does this obliging torrent free us, to the extent that without it we should be neither clothed nor fed?" the author sees the ultimate selflessness in the river's water: "It is most truly shared with us, and expects no other reward wheresoever it toils under the sun than that, its work done, it be allowed to run freely away." Given the ecstasy of this passage, and similar enthusiasm shown by many medieval Europeans towards this and other technologies, we should not lament that the "medieval Industrial Revolution" thesis may not be as strong as it was once believed to be. Instead, we should concentrate on the fact that while they were using mills and watercourses as their predecessors more or less always had, now they sang praises to them, they included them in their schemes of knowledge for the first time, and they bragged about them.[18]

Before turning to our contributors' thoughts on specific themes, one further point is worth making for the non-specialist coming to this volume. For most of us, the principal association of mills in the Middle Ages comes from Chaucer's thieving miller. We would do well, however, to remind ourselves that this image of mills and millers was hardly the only meaning medieval commentators attached to mills. In fact, mills took on a wide array of meanings in the wider world of mental images. Mills figured in some creation stories and were seen as both liberating or enslaving (millstones around the neck, for example). In emblems, for example, mills are equated with many virtues and moralities. The windmill, or *mola pneumatica*, could be equated to the grace of God, human life, speedy work, false friendship, or abundant humility. The watermill could be linked with obedience, impertinence, avarice or assistance, evil conscience, war and soldiers, orators or hecklers, and magnanimity. And both could be linked with both ambition and dependency.[19] Multivalent indeed!

Finally, the association of power was inescapable. One emblem from late in our period depicts a man trying to turn the sails of a windmill with a pair of hand bellows (Fig. 3). The futility of the task is reflected in the motto attached: "What labours that to bring to passe / That cannot be, is but an Asse". The moralistic poem below ties this futility to questions of ability, planning, and wisdom towards this powderful fluid technology fo the day:

> The cannon charg'd with less then doth behove,
> The heavie bullet farre off cannot throw:
> And none hath seene the weighty windmill move
> If one but with a paire of bellowes blow:
> This shewes we should in every action prove,
> With due proportion how each thing should go:
>   As wise men never will attempt the thing,
>   That first they know to passe they cannot bring.[20]

––––

Like the mill of fortune, this volume began with some papers from the 2004 Penn State Medieval Conference, "Wind & Water: The Medieval Mill" with the intent of showing the development and continuity of the mill from the end of the Roman world to colonial America. About half of the papers in this final volume owe their genesis to that conference (some were presented there, some authors merely attended), and some of the papers presented there did not make it into this volume. Other authors joined the project along the way, broadening and enriching the mix until, like the product of the mill, the wheat was threshed and ground, mixed with a leavening of other contributions, and has risen slowly. Now baked into a final loaf, we hope and believe our product is a wholesome multi-grain bread that all should enjoy.

Figure 3: **Emblem of Futility**; redrawn from Guillaume de La Perrière, *The Theater of Fine Devices Containing an Hundred Morall Emblemes*, trans. Thomas Combe (London: Richard Field, 1614), emblem lxxxv.

This book, it should be noted, is not a straight forward history of technology. Many such works have been written, and they all are important and useful. Our goal, by and large, is not to investigate the gearing or business history of individual sites—although gearing and business histories do appear at various places here—but rather to step back and consider the larger picture of how water and wind worked within the Middle Ages. We care about the power they provided, of course, but are more interested in how their uses, legal status, workforce, depictions, and meanings in essence helped form the modern world. We hope, in the end, the reader will take away a broader and deeper understanding of the "fluid technologies" of the Middle Ages.

This volume of essays is divided roughly into three parts, although at many points the contributors engage with one another's arguments and conclusions. The papers have not been arranged strictly chronologically, but rather thematically, drawing upon the strengths and arguments of each contribution to bind them into a cohesive whole. We begin with the more "archaeological" papers: those that look at the physical and textual evidence for mills at various points over a span of nearly two millennia. GEORGE BROOKS opens the volume with a consideration of the origins and lasting quality of the Vitruvian mill—that is, the vertical-wheeled, geared mill which became the standard water-powered mill until the early nineteenth century when they were finally supplanted by turbines. He strongly argues for the theme of continuity, and demonstrates that while there was a wide array of mechanical options available to the Romans, the Vitruvian wheel was the one that passed to the Middle Ages, virtually unchanged.

While Brooks considers the origins of the vertical watermill, NIALL BRADY similarly offers a longitudinal study of mills—both vertical and horizontal—but does so in the regional context of the catchment basin of the River Liffey around Dublin. He quite effectively looks "beyond design", as his title puts it, demonstrating that analyzing mill sites can begin to get at questions about our paradigms of economic rationale, ownership, and cultural development. The building section then concludes with D. FAIRCHILD RUGGLES' look at another use of water channeled and controlled by society, namely to bring life to gardens throughout the Islamic world. Focusing on existing archaeological examples in Spain and on literary examples from across the Islamic world, she reminds us that literary license often reflects reality more closely than we sometimes admit. Whether the various water-moving or water-moved devices she discusses seem prosaic or fantastic to modern sensibilities, Ruggles shows that they were all conceivable, probable, and based on straight forward hydraulic mechanisms available to Islamic engineers through classical and Arabic sources.

The middle section of the volume deals with mills and water systems and their owners and users. This section more than the others takes on the Lynn White Thesis from both well-trodden and novel angles. In terms of ownership, production, legal status, social function, and social reprobation, the authors in part two help explain why mills and their ilk were so fundamentally important to the Middle Ages. ADAM LUCAS addresses the now seven-decade-old argument about the role of the monastic houses that spread across Europe in the early and high Middle Ages as instigators of industrial milling.[21] Were they also (or just) the vector, or merely along for the ride? Is it only because they had the record-keeping system in place that we even know about it at all? His impressively deep investigation of monastic records of mill ownership shows that the monks were but one of the groups responsible for medieval innovation and diffusion, and also that the various orders did not conform so simply to the role that previous historians such as Marc Bloch and Lynn White have ascribed to them.

This context of this debate is augmented by two related papers on the legal status of mills in the Middle Ages. JANET LOENGARD, considering nuisance lawsuits primarily against watermills, shows how these key parts of the medieval economic system generated a great number of complaints. In her extensive reading of English legal records, she shows that mills reflect many facets of the English medieval conceptions of the ownership and use of land and water, the role of free and unfree tenants, the construction and repair of mills, and the sale of their products. TIM SISTRUNK, on the other hand, considers how the medieval legal system dealt with the new invention of the windmill. Virtually all other situations in medieval law could look back to Roman law precedents for guidance, but here the legal record was of course silent, windmills having appeared only in the twelfth century. The enigmatic wind forced a reappraisal of legal statutes and criteria, and brought to the fore the question of humans, ownership, and natural resources.

Following this legal exploration, two papers explore cases of water from the later Middle Ages, but from separate regions, and explore how these water and milling systems actually functioned (or failed to function) in society. ROBERTA MAGNUSSON considers how late medieval London managed to keep both fresh water flowing to its growing population, and waste water and other materials (hopefully) flowing away from them. In a world with either rudimentary or laissez-faire attitudes towards both hydrology and sanitation, it was no mean feat to do this. London Bridge, for example, posed a contradictory meaning for London: on one hand it was a vital link in the transportation infrastructure (and had also at times had mills under the arches turning on the current and tides),[22] but it also became a hydrological liability as its arches impeded water flow as well as boat traffic. In comparing the water supply systems to the waste disposal systems, Magnusson shows quite clearly where the "reverse salients" in this technological system[23] were: it was much easier to get fresh water to the citizens of London than it was to clear the rivers of their human, animal, and industrial wastes, and the local governmental responses, while well-meaning, simply were not up to the tasks at that period in time. Turning to both the production side and the human element of the story, THOMAS GLICK and LUIS PABLO MARTINEZ explore grain, milling, and millers in the *Huerta* around Valencia in Spain. Considering first the way milling had to occur within the agricultural grain system of the time, these authors show how town and countryside were interlocked in a "wheat-flour-bread" system. But if they did interlock smoothly, the millers could often make the interconnection a bit "rusty" (in both senses of metal rust causing rough functioning, and wheat rust partially poisoning the system). Hinging their tale on Jaume Perfeta, a quintessentially "evil mill owner", Glick and Martinez demonstrate how peasant grain production systems in late medieval Spain (and by implication, elsewhere) functioned as parts of economic, trade, industrial, and social networks.

The volume concludes with three papers about how the Middle Ages perceived mills and their meanings in art and culture. DAVID MARSHALL tackles an enigmatic letter from the 1381 Peasants' Revolt in which a postmill is invoked to rally the commoners to action. The vanes of sails are each personified, and, like Catherine's wheel, follow inexorably one after the other, but in this case they follow out of order. Marshall provides an excellent example of how a commonplace object to a fourteenth-century reader or listener can function both metaphorically and concretely; the metaphors of the sails are important, he argues, but only in knowing how a postmill is built and functions (or may malfunction) can we correctly understand the allegory that exhorted commoners to rebellion. Marshall's is an excellent example of, as he puts it, "the symbolic power of a familiar image to embody the concerns of [an] audience." KIRK AMBROSE then looks at one specific depiction of a mill carved into a column capital at the cathedral church of Vézelay. Long held to be a mystic mill that transformed the word of the Old Testament into the New, Ambrose shows instead that the disjunctive pairings of capitals along the nave suggest that the mill capital should be read actively and encouraged the viewer then as now to contemplative understandings of what grinding grain stood for in society and in Scripture. Finally, concluding the volume is SHANA WORTHEN's "Of Mills and Meaning" which explores numerous examples of mills—primarily windmills—across the Middle Ages, from Icelandic sagas to German engravings, and in art, literature, and travel narratives. She ultimately argues that the transformative nature of the technology must remind us to read the imagery of mills as transformation itself. Worthen shows us that while there are places where mills appear in art and literature simply as reflections of what was actually there in the physical world, they are also there as placeholders for what was there in the symbolic world. Thus, we ought to accurately understand the physical world in order to interpret the symbolic.

The eleven essays in this collection offer a multifaceted look at the fluid technologies of the Middle Ages. There are many opportunities for extending the work done here temporally, geographically, or culturally. We hope, however, that out contributions do inspire readers to explore further.

Notes

[1] Mark Knopfler, "Telegraph Road," *Love Over Gold* (London: Chariscourt, 1982).

[2] Karl A. Wittfogel suggested that civilizations dependent upon large-scale irrigation projects demanded centralized control with monopolized governmental and economic power (and, not coincidentally, a reinforcement of certain religions over others); see Karl August Wittfogel, *Oriental Despotism: a Comparative Study of Total Power* (New Haven: Yale Uni-

versity Press, 1957) and for later appreciations of his work G.L. Ulmen, *The Science of Society: Toward an Understanding of the Life and Work of Karl August Wittfogel* (The Hague: Mouton, 1979).

[3] It should be noted that we have taken a more modest approach than to try to be as broadly encompassing as environmental history can be. For suggestive approaches in this vein that resonate with our work, see Richard C. Hoffmann, "Economic Development and Aquatic Ecosystems in Medieval Europe," *American Historical Review* 101.3 (1996): 630-69 and Evan T. Jones, "River Navigation in Medieval England," *Journal of Historical Geography* 26.1 (2000): 60-75.

[4] When American industry moved to electrical motors to power its factories in the early 20th century, the largest power source electrification displaced was still water, not steam, power; see Louis C. Hunter, *A History of Industrial Power in the United States, 1780-1930*, 2 vols. (Charlottesville: University Press of Virginia, 1979).

[5] Notable popular writings that reinforce this effect include Jean Gimpel, *The Medieval Machine: The Industrial Revolution of the Middle Ages*, 2[d] ed (Aldershot: Wildwood House, 1988) and Frances and Joseph Gies, *Cathedral, Forge, and Waterwheel: Technology and Invention in the Middle Ages* (New York: Harper Perennial, 1995).

[6] Sebastian de Covarrubias Horozco, *Emblemas Morales* (Madrid: L. Sanchez, 1610), century III, no. 55 (p. 255); Arthur Henkel and Albrecht Schöne, *Emblemata. Handbuch zur Sinnbildkunst des XVI. und XVII. Jahrhunderts* (Stuttgart: J.B. Metzlersche Verlagsbuchhandlung, 1976), col. 1429. Many thanks to Thomas Glick, who corrected my poor translation, which was from Henkel and Schöne's German rendering: "Die Güter dieses vergänglichen Lebens, die gleich den Flüssen verströmen, sind Einer auf einem Schöpfrad, welche beim Steigen voll und beim Niedergehen leer sind. Es kann hier keine Seligkeit geben, da alles nur aus Wechsel und Veränderung besteht. Der eine lebt in Gunst, der andere in Ungnade, und schöpft der eine, leert der andere aus."

[7] Ian Blair and Jenny Hall, *Working Water: Roman Technology in Action* (London: Museum of London, 2003). For the *Time Team* special, see http://www.channel4.com/history/timeteam/lond_water_wheel.html.

[8] The literature on medieval milling is extensive, and only a briefest suggestion of resources can be provided here. The standard books are: for watermills, Richard Holt, *The Mills of Medieval England* (Oxford: Oxford University Press, 1988); Richard Bennett, *History of Corn Milling* (New York: B. Franklin, 1964); John Langdon, *Mills in the Medieval Economy: England, 1300-1540* (Oxford: Oxford University Press, 2004); and our own contributor's very recent work, Adam Lucas, *Wind, Water, Work: Ancient and Medieval Milling Technology* (Leiden: Brill, 2006); and for windmills, Edward J. Kealey, *Harvesting the Air: Windmill Pioneers in Twelfth-Century England* (Berkeley: University of California Press, 1987). Some other useful reference materials to enter the subject include: Richard Leslie Hills, *Power from Wind: A History of Windmill Technology* (Cambridge: Cambridge University Press, 1994); Ian Keil, "Building a Post Windmill in 1342," *Transactions of the Newcomen Society 34 (1961–62)*: 151-54; Philip Rahtz and Donald Bullough, "The Parts of an Anglo-Saxon Mill," *Anglo-Saxon England* 6 (1977): 15-37; Timothy E. Powell, "The Disappearance of Horizontal Watermills from Medieval Ireland," *Transactions of the Newcomen Society* 66 (1994-95): 219-24;

and especially Örjan Wikander, "Archaeological Evidence for Early Water-Mills—an Interim Report," *History of Technology* 7 (1985): 151-79.

[9] Miquel Barceló, "The Missing Water-Mill: A Question of Technological Diffusion in the High Middle Ages," in Miquel Barceló and François Sigaut (eds.), *The Making of Feudal Agricultures?*, The Transformation of the Roman World 14 (Leiden: Brill, 2004), pp. 255-314 at 297.

[10] Molinological studies has risen to its own field since World War II, and with great success. Journals such as *International Molinology* from the International Molinological Association and *Old Mill News* from the Society for the Preservation of Old Mills (SPOOM) in North America serve to inform, educate, and advocate about and for old mills. At the same time, mill preservation organizations such as the mills section of the Society for the Preservation of Ancient Buildings (related to the Ancient Monuments Society) in the UK as well as myriad private individuals have done wonders at documenting and preserving—and with some luck in a few cases, rehabilitating—surviving mills around the world. To those groups we all owe a debt of gratitude and offer no competition. For a recent and stunningly attractive book on this topic, see David Larkin, *Mill: The History & Future of Naturally Powered Buildings* (New York: Universe Publishing, 2000).

[11] Lynn White, Jr., "Technology and Invention in the Middle Ages," *Speculum* 15.2 (1940): 141-59 at p. 143.

[12] Philippe Leveau, "The Barbegal Water Mill in its Environment: Archaeology and the Economic and Social History of Antiquity," *Journal of Roman Archaeology* 9 (1996): 137-53; R.H.J. Sellin, "The Large Roman Water Mill at Barbegal," *History of Technology* 8 (1983): 91-109; and, more generally, Steven A. Walton, "Review Essay: the Greeneian reappraisal of the context of medieval technology," *AVISTA Forum Journal* 14 (Fall 2004): 25-27. Kevin Greene has recently adjusted our view of the understanding of the Roman-medieval transition in "Technology and Innovation in Context: the Roman background to mediaeval and later developments," *Journal of Roman Archaeology* 7 (1994): 22-33 and "Technological Innovation and Economic Progress in the Ancient World: M.I. Finley reconsidered," *Economic History Review* 53 (2000): 29-59.

[13] See Robert Cresswell, "Of Mills and Waterwheels: The Hidden Parameters of Technological Choice," in Pierre Lemonnier (ed.), *Technological Choices: Transformation in Material Cultures since the Neolithic* (London: Routledge, 1993), pp. 181-213 on a nearly modern example.

[14] This is not to say that mill diffusion cannot be traced, just that the simple model of a single origin and subsequent unidirectional diffusion cannot; see Barceló, "The Missing Water-Mill" (note 9) for the mill story, as well as William H. McNeill, "Diffusion in History," in P.J. Hugill and B.D. Dickson (eds.), *The Transfer and Transformation of Ideas and Material Culture* (College Station: Texas A&M University Press, 1988), pp. 75-90 for general thoughts on the issue.

[15] See Robert Fox (ed.), *Technological Change: Methods and Themes in the History of Technology*, Studies in the History of Science, Technology and Medicine 1 (New York: Harwood Academic, 1996) for the general study; Terry S. Reynolds, "Medieval Roots of the Industrial Revolution," *Scientific American*, July 1984, pp. 123-30, and his *Stronger than a Hundred Men: A History of the Vertical Water Wheel* (Baltimore: Johns Hopkins University Press, 1988) for

a quintessential story of the "rise and profess" genre; and Colin Rynne, *Technological Change in Anglo-Norman Munster*, Barryscourt Lecture Series 3 (Kinsale: Barryscourt Trust, 1998), which deals quite explicitly with mills in Ireland within this framework.

[16] James Burke and Robert E. Ornstein, *The Axemaker's Gift: A Double-Edged History of Human Culture* (New York: Putnam, 1995), p. 108.

[17] Anonymous, *A Description of Clairvaux* [*c*.1140], quoted from Pauline M. Matarasso, *The Cistercian World: Monastic Writings of the Twelfth Century* (London: Penguin, 1993) in "Critique and Ideal: the Cistercian Renewal," online at http://www.etss.edu/hts/MAPM/info22.htm.

[18] There are a few cases of Roman exaltation of milling; see George Brooks, "The 'Vitruvian Mill' in Roman and Medieval Europe," ch. 1 of this volume. For the "medieval Industrial Revolution" thesis, see notes 5 and 11 above, and E. Ashtor, "The Factors of Technological and Industrial Progress in the Later Middle Ages," *Journal of European Economic History* 18 (1989): 7-36. For an early assessment of "technological takeoff" in the Middle Ages, see Lynn White, Jr., "What Accelerated Technological Progress in the Western Middle Ages?" in *Medieval Religion and Technology: Selected Essays* (Los Angeles: University of California Press, 1986), pp. 273-91. And for a review of what has become of the thesis, see Bert S. Hall, "Lynn White's Medieval Technology and Social Change after Thirty Years," in Fox (ed.), *Technological Change*, pp. 85-101 and Alex Roland, "Once More into the Stirrups: Lynn White jr., *Medieval Technology and Social Change*," *Technology & Culture* 44.3 (2003): 574-85.

[19] These meanings come from Philippo Picinello's *Mundus Symbolicus, in Emblematum Universitate Formatus, Explicatus, et tam Sacris* (Coloniæ Agrippinæ: Herman Demen, 1681), sig. Vu3ᵛ [reproduced in Henkel and Schöne (eds.), *Emblemata* (note 6), col. 2164].

[20] Guillaume de La Perrière, *The Theater of Fine Devices Containing an Hundred Morall Emblemes*, trans. Thomas Combe (London: Richard Field, 1614), emblem lxxxv. The original French version is Guillaume de la Perriere, *Le Theatre des bons engins* (Lyon: J. de Tournes, 1545).

[21] Some other interesting articles not mentioned by Lucas include: F.V. Evans, "Monastic Multinationals: The Cistercians and Other Monks as Engineers," *Transactions of the Newcomen Society* 68 (1996-97): 1-28 and Anna Götlind, *The Messengers of Medieval Technology? Cistercians and Technology in Medieval Scandinavia* (Alingsås, Sweden: Viktoria bokförlag/University of Göteborg, 1990).

[22] Boatmills, often anchored under bridge arches to make use of the swift currents in these narrowings of the river, have been remarkably understudied; a comprehensive study by D. Graef, *Boats Mills in Europe from Early Middle Ages until Modern Times*, is forthcoming in the *Bibliotheca Molinologica* series of the International Molinological Society.

[23] For this concept, see Thomas P. Hughes, "The Evolution of Large Technological Systems," in Wiebe Bijker, Thomas P. Hughes, and Trevor Pinch (eds.), *The Social Construction of Technological Systems* (Cambridge: MIT Press, 1989), pp. 49-82.

The "Vitruvian Mill" in Roman and Medieval Europe

GEORGE BROOKS (VALENCIA COMMUNITY COLLEGE)

The *hydraleta*, or "watermill," described by Marcus Vitruvius Pollio in book ten of *De Architectura* is the ancient world's most significant industrial machine. Also called a "corn mill" or "grist mill," scholars have long referred to it as a "Vitruvian mill" out of respect for the only ancient writer to provide a careful description of its internal components and mechanical operation. Thanks to Vitruvius, technological historians have a clear picture of the West's first major industrial machine near the point of its entry into the Roman world. The machine he describes was not the only type of water-powered mill developed in antiquity, nor was it the only one to spawn a technical tradition, but it is the type that the Romans built throughout their empire, and it was the one which would inspire the most significant technological descendants in the Middle Ages and beyond. The importance of this device cannot be overstated. The watermill was the first widely used machine which harnessed natural forces to do significant work—and thus a reliable and ubiquitous example of the possibilities of such labor-saving devices—and from this machine sprang, through variations of its basic mechanism, the next dozen or so inventions of the medieval mechanical revolution. It was the essential technological component in the confluence of forces that came together during the Middle Ages to trigger the creation of the industrial West. Also surviving in large numbers into the Middle Ages would be Vitruvius' manuscript, although in its medieval life it would have no connection to the millwright tradition it describes. Both mill and manuscript have left sufficient evidence, although admittedly sparse in some places, to trace the technological tradition that led to the Vitruvian mill and follows its path into the medieval world. From the time this technology was established at the dawn of the Roman Empire, it remained in continuous use throughout Roman and medieval Europe.

The Evolution of the Watermill in Antiquity

A variety of water-lifting devices and a few water-powered devices preceded the appearance of the watermill in the first century BCE. The precise place and date of most of these inventions is unknown. Unlike the battles between kings and amongst philosophers, the triumphs of technology rarely attract the attention of the literate few, and so go largely unrecorded. Most of the occasional written references that survive only allow us to place the point in time by which a device was definitely known to Greek or Latin writers. It is always possible that a particular device had been in use for decades or centuries before attracting a comment from an ancient writer, or writings that may have taken note might not have survived. Archeology has made regular and hefty contributions to the study of technology, unearthing many fragments of ancient engineering. This evidence, however, is scattered and much of it comes from late antiquity and so must be used cautiously. Surviving specimens of ancient engineering may not reflect its original appearance, but rather the evolution of the device after centuries of practice and innovation. The few engineer-authors who recorded their careers have left invaluable material regarding their work, but they usually reveal little about the sources of their ideas or the technological conditions of society beyond their own sphere of activity. In a few cases, the intriguing descriptions of mechanical devices in the manuscript of an ancient author are not part of the original work, but additions made by later researchers or scribes with a lively imagination. Being cautious of the often misleading relationship between written records and mechanical devices, it may be safely asserted that the watermill was invented within a two-century period in the late Hellenistic era, bracketed between two collections of evidence: the engineering tradition and treatises from the school at Alexandria in the third century BCE at one end, and the *De Architectura* of Vitruvius, completed about 25 BCE, at the other.

The Ptolemies, who ruled Egypt after the death of Alexander the Great, established and maintained an impressive research center in Alexandria in the third century BCE. The famous library at Alexandria was built to support the study done at this school and many of antiquity's greatest scientist-engineers— Ctesibius, Philo, and Archimedes among them—were active here across the third century. The earliest recorded research into the development of hydraulic machines originated here; but equally significant is that many of the basic devices which were steps toward or components of the watermill are *not* found in the works of these pioneering minds. Given the cosmopolitan nature of the intellectual society gathered at Alexandria, and the many ingenious devices which were invented or utilized here, it is fairly safe to assume that useful or clever machines not found here were not yet invented or just emerging in the Mediterranean or Near East. At the other end of this period, in the first century BCE, a number of written references appear from poets, historians, and engineers concerning water-lifting wheels and true watermills. Finally, as the Roman republic was becoming an empire, the architect-engineer Vitruvius composed his *De Architectura*, which includes detailed descriptions of nearly all the hydraulic technology that appeared in antiquity.

The impressive engineering tradition that emerged from Alexandria in the third century BCE began with Ctesibius, a native of Alexandria and the son of a barber. No known works of Ctesibius survive, but Vitruvius tells us that his books were readily available in his day.[1] We know nothing of his career except that he was affiliated with the research institute at Alexandria where he made ingenious devices to delight his aristocratic patrons. A famous anecdote relates how his aptitude for gadgetry showed early in his youth with the construction of a hidden counterweight device to effortlessly lift and lower a heavy bronze mirror in his father's shop. The accidental sounds produced when the falling counterweight forced air out of its tube-shaped housing inspired the young Ctesibius to explore the potential of pneumatics. He constructed the first pipe organs based on his discovery along with the first keyboards with which to play them. Hydraulic organs, water clocks, and metal springs were among his inventions and he experimented with compressed-air catapults. His most widely used invention was the double-action force pump, known in antiquity as the "Ctesibian machine" [*Ctesibica Machina*],[2] which the Romans applied to the bilging of ships and in fire-extinguishers, as described by Hero of Alexandria in the first century CE. Ctesibius made a wide exploration of the possibilities of suction and compression, inspiring the next generation of engineers who would discover other means of harnessing the forces of water and air.

Philo of Byzantium continued working with these principles during the mid-third century BCE, designing devices that dispensed or retrieved water in ingenious ways, making it appear as if a mechanical bird or other animal were dipping into the basin and drinking the water. Philo studied at Rhodes and Alexandria and may have been a student of Ctesibius whose ideas he seems to have absorbed and expanded. Philo wrote a compendium of mechanical engineering, *Mechanice Syntaxis*, in nine books, presumably as a textbook for researchers at Alexandria, and for posterity.[3] Book IV and parts of VII and VIII exist in Greek copies and deal with various aspects of military engineering: ballistae design, city defense, and siege techniques. Book V, existing only in a medieval Arabic copy,

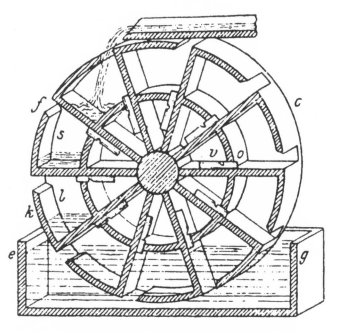

Figure 1: The "Whistling Water Wheel" invented by Philo of Byzantium in Alexandria; from T. Beck, "Philon von Byzanz," *Beiträge zur Geschichte der Technik und Industrie* 2 (1911): 73, fig. 21.

is on pneumatics and contains several descriptions of waterwheels. Although the most complex of these devices are surely medieval Arabic additions to the text, the core material seems to be genuinely Philonian, and one clever device, a little "whistling water wheel", does shed light on the state of water-related technology in Hellenistic Egypt.[4]

The "whistling wheel" of chapter 61 is based on the insight that water escaping from a tube draws air in behind it—the mechanical simulation of a breath of wind. By channeling this artificial breath through a whistle, and devising a means to make this a repetitive action, a mechanical whistler is made. The text describes a hollow wheel made of wood or copper and fitted with two concentric rows of compartments (Fig. 1). The outer row of compartments has openings to the outside circumference designed to catch the intake of a falling stream of water and then release it as the wheel continues to turn. Each inner compartment is sealed tightly with only one small opening between the compartments into which the whistle is fitted. As the filled outer compartments turn, they release their water into a reservoir below while drawing air through the whistle hole,

Figure 2: **A reconstruction of the irrigation compartment wheel (*tympanum*) used in Egypt which seems to have been Philo's inspiration**; rendering by Joshua Chiet.

producing tones. The text also describes two other necessities: a spigot to regulate the stream of water flowing to the machine, and the method for tuning the whistles. The most important technical idea in this wheel is not the pneumatic action of the whistles, which has clear precedence in the works of Ctesibius, but in the harnessing of hydraulic forces to effect constant rotary motion. Music aside, in the turning of the wheel itself we have the essential features of an overshot waterwheel; but the potential of this device as a source of motive power for other machines was not developed by Philo and would not appear again for three centuries. What does emerge from this period are a variety of water-lifting wheels powered by human treading—smaller ones with compartmented bodies at first, followed by much larger wheels with compartments only around the rim. In less than two centuries, this basic mechanism would evolve into hydraulic engines that raised water and ground grain without human toil. A comment made by Philo allows further understanding into the genesis of this machine. The author mentions that the basic design of the wheel is similar "to wheels used for irrigation." This is one of the earliest references to a water-lifting wheel of any kind and implies that, by the mid-third century BCE, Hellenistic Egypt already had some type of irrigation technology in general use which the clever Philo combined with Ctesibian pneumatics to produce his musical innovation.

These "wheels used for irrigation" could only have been compartmented waterwheels, a species of technology that Vitruvius would later call a *tympanum*. This is the simplest type of water-lifting wheel in design, the simplest to construct, and was probably invented many centuries before this mention by Philo. No archeological evidence exists to support this, but a passage in the Hebrew Bible infers the use of water-lifting devices powered by treading in pre-Hellenistic Egypt: "You sowed your seed and watered it with your feet, like a garden of vegetables" [Deut. 11:10-11]. The only machine likely to have been raising water by treading, which leaves out the hand-powered *shaduf*, is a compartment wheel. The Vitruvian *tympanum* is also the closest in design to the wheel described by Philo: each of them has eight compartments (Fig. 2). Philo's insight was to divide each compartment into inner and outer spaces so that Ctesibian pneumatic ideas could be made to work with the turning of the wheel. This accounts for the seeming strangeness that Philo would have invented something as ingenious as the waterwheel only to apply it to something as apparently frivolous as a whistler. He felt no need to apply his device to the improvement of irrigation because this was already well-handled by teams of workers treading such wheels. Philo's little whistling wheel likely tweeted in gardens where irrigation water had been supplied for centuries by much more substantial wheels built and worked by people not in the habit of writing for posterity.[5]

The future of hydraulic technology would stem from an improvement upon the water-lifting compartment wheel that Philo had employed.* The builders of compartment wheels came upon a design limitation when they attempted to adapt them to more ambitious projects: as water fills the hollow compartments the weight of the wheel becomes excessively heavy and difficult to rotate once a

---

* Omitted here is another important line of hydraulic technology, the *Archimedean Screw*, which also emerged from the researches at Alexandria later in the third century BCE. Archimedes made important studies of spirals and may have been inspired to design the *screw* by imagining the eight sections of the compartment wheel extended into spirals, just the type Vitruvius later described. Actual Roman specimens, which were used to bilge ships and drain mines, invariably show only two or three screw threads, indicating that practice with the devices eventually revealed the screw would work with only a few screw threads, and this would mean less cost of construction, maintenance, and repair. This is the only ancient example of water technology to have its inventor's name remembered. This device serviced the Romans until the end of their empire but eventually fell out of use by the end of antiquity, having produced no further technological progeny.

certain size has been reached. Unmentioned in the Alexandrian material, but emerging soon after, is a water-lifting wheel with compartments only around the rim. This approach is far more efficient, as the small compartments which hug the rim allow water to be lifted nearly the entire distance of the wheel's diameter, as opposed to fully compartmented wheels which empty at a hole near the axle and thus raise water only about half the wheel's diameter. It can also be expanded to much larger sizes and still remain at a manageable weight in proportion to the entire wheel. This wheel, called a *rota* by Vitruvius, would become the standard device used by the Romans for all manner of water-lifting needs (Fig. 3a, b). Both the compartment wheel and its improved variation, the wheel with compartmented rim, emerged in the eastern Mediterranean without the name of an inventor becoming attached to them. The original wheel may have been very old indeed, while the improved version probably existed for a century or more without eliciting comment until several innovations based on this wheel appeared in the early first century BCE. These innovations did draw the attention of several ancient writers.

Neither the water-powered water-lifting wheel nor the watermill can be confidently located among the achievements of the third-century Alexandrian engineers, but within about a century both had been invented. In the intervening period, an ingenious adaptation was made to the waterwheel: radiating wooden planks were attached to the circumference of the water-lifting wheel which allowed the impulse of the river to turn it. This technical novelty inspired a smattering of comments from writers over the next half century. Around the middle of the first century BCE, an anonymous poet was astounded at the sight of a water-powered water-lifting wheel which he called, in Greek, an *antlia* [from *antlein*, "to bail or lift water"] and wrote:

> It pours out and scoops up water, discharging on high the stream it carries, and it drinks up a river only to disgorge it. A marvelous achievement! It carries water and is carried along by water. In this fashion a stream is pushed up by a stream, and a new device scoops up the old-fashioned fluid.[6]

This description does not allow us a precise reconstruction for we cannot absolutely determine if this is a compartmented wheel or a wheel with compartments on its rim. Nor can we discern whether this wheel was turned by rounded scoops or broad flat paddles. But what is clear is that by this time the first critical step towards harnessing water power had been taken. Soon afterward this paddlewheel was fitted with gearing enabling it to turn a large millstone (a job usually performed by slaves or draft animals). A few decades later, another poet, Anti-

Figure 3a: **Fragment of Romano-British *rota* showing water-lifting compartments** (in the "Roman Life Room" of the British Museum); photograph by the author.

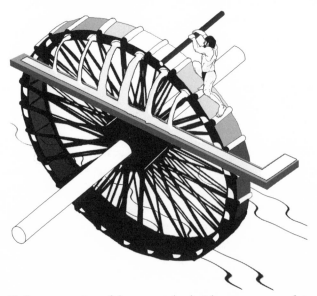

Figure 3b: **Reconstruction of the *rota*, a wheel with compartmented rim operated by treading**; rendering by Joshua Chiet.

pater of Thessalonica, extolled the benefits of this labor-saving device and rhapsodized about the return of a Golden Age, when the Earth gave up her fruits without the grudging labor of humans:

> Rest your mill-turning hands, maidens who grind! Sleep on even
> when the cock's crow announces dawn, for Demeter has reassigned
> to the water nymphs the chores your hands performed. They leap
> against the very edge of the wheel, making the axle spin, which
> with its revolving cogs turns the heavy pair of porous millstones
> from Nisyros. We once again have a taste of the old way of life, if
> we learn to feast on the produce of Demeter without toil.[7]

Writing around 55 BCE, the Roman philosopher-poet Lucretius described the revolutions of the celestial spheres by analogy to a water-powered wheel. A current of air, he theorized, "rotates the sphere on the same principle as we see rivers turning water-wheels by pressure on the scoops."[8] The use of the term "scoops" [*austra*] as opposed to "paddles" [*pinnae*] may indicate that he was referring to a water-lifting wheel [*antlia*] rather than a water-powered mill such as described by Antipater.[9] Another reference to a water-powered device occurs in Strabo's *Geography,* where one is listed among the marvels of a lavish palace captured by Pompey around 65 BCE. Strabo tells us: "It was at Cabeira that the palace of Mithridates was built, and also the [*hydraleta*] and here were the zoological gardens, and, nearby, the hunting grounds, and the mines."[10] Here we have a water-powered device, but it is uncertain whether it was a mill or a water-lifter, as this was a relatively new word when Strabo used it. What is clear from this cluster of remarks from across the first century BCE is that a new form of hydraulic technology had become established in the Mediterranean world.

Vitruvius

We find ourselves on a rare spot of solid ground about 25 BCE thanks to the efforts of Vitruvius and his *De Architectura,* antiquity's only comprehensive text on architecture and engineering. He was first a builder, who spent his days on dusty construction sites, and only secondly did he aspire to the pen, in an attempt to collect and pass on what he had learned in a lifetime amongst bricks and timber. His descriptions of the elements of building are the practical, detailed instructions of a professional foreman and career engineer. He was an artilleryman under Julius Caesar, a job which entailed the construction and maintenance of catapults, *ballistae,* and other elements of military engineering. The association with Caesar later translated into work on behalf of his nephew, Octavian, and Vitruvius seems to be one of many architect-engineers involved in the heyday of the Augustan building programs in Rome. Vitruvius is known to us only through his treatise. He says little about himself or his career, sticking to his synopsis of architecture and eschewing any self-aggrandizement.[11] His sole comment about himself was that he was afflicted with the ills of old age and thus would win the approval of the emperor by the expertise evidenced in his writings. *De Architectura* covers every aspect of the engineer's profession, from determining the site for a city, to polishing the marble on the temples. He explains the properties of all types of wood and stone and the methods for working them. Vitruvius' knowledge ranges from the theories of the philosophers to protecting timber during the winter; and he relates dozens of interesting historical anecdotes that have left their mark on architecture. He dedicated his work to the Emperor Augustus and intended it to be used as a codified manual of civil and military engineering, which it was. Vitruvius also wrote for posterity, ordering his knowledge into ten books and prefacing each with stories and reflections orchestrated around themes significant to the chapter that follows.

Not all modern scholars have appreciated Vitruvius' efforts. In the preface to his translation, Morris H. Morgan says of Vitruvius: "He has all the marks of one unused to composition, to whom writing is a painful task." Morgan, like so many other academics, viewed Vitruvius from the point of view of a classical literary scholar, and condemned his prose as "turgid and pompous rhetoric."* But from the standpoint of the history of science and technology, Vitruvius is particularly valuable precisely because he was not a literary man or a gadget-maker, but a serious builder who took great pains to explain to posterity the principles

---

* Consider carefully the assessment of Vitruvius as a Latin writer, as reported by the late Professor Morgan's student, Albert A. Howard: "Vitruvius was not a great literary personage, ambitious as he was to appear in that character. ... In his hand the measuring-rod was a far mightier implement than the pen. His turgid and pompous rhetoric displays itself in the introductions to the different books, where his exaggerated effort to introduce some semblance of style into his commonplace lectures on the noble principles which should govern the conduct of the architect, or into the prosaic lists of architects and writers on architecture, is everywhere apparent. Even in the more technical portions of his work, a like conscious effort may be detected, and, at the same time, a lack of confidence in his ability to express himself in unmistakable language. He avoids periodic sentences, uses only the simpler subjunctive constructions, repeats the antecedent in relative clauses, and, not infrequently, adopts a formal language closely akin to that of specifications and contracts, the style with which he was, naturally, most familiar. He ends each book with a brief summary, almost a formula, somewhat like a sigh of relief, in which the reader unconsciously shares. At times his *(cont.)*

and practice of ancient architecture and engineering. Historians are especially fortunate to have such a professional as the first author to explain in detail the form and function of the watermill.

De Architectura is immensely important for students of Western technology and engineering. Vitruvius allows us to peer more deeply into the mind of an ancient engineer than is usually possible as we follow the paths from his detailed descriptions of methods and machines to his more generalized conclusions and organizational scheme. His aping of literary conventions, and desire to create a useful reference book, resulted in the recording of many of the writers and authorities upon which Vitruvius depended for his own knowledge. This is uniquely valuable material for what it tells us about the spread of the ideas of ancient writers and about the uses of philosophical ideas in the world beyond the schools. Beginning his work with the education of the architect, Vitruvius advises:

> The architect's expertise is enhanced by many disciplines and various sorts of specialized knowledge; all the works executed using these other skills are evaluated by his seasoned judgment. This expertise is born both of **practice** and of **reasoning**. **Practice** is the constant, repeated exercise of the hands by which the work is brought to completion in whatever medium is required for the proposed design. **Reasoning**, however, is what can demonstrate and explain the proportions of completed works skillfully and systematically. [I.1.1]

This healthy appreciation for a balance of manual and intellectual labor should caution us not to carry the disdain for work expressed by ancient authors too far outside the realm of the *literati* who, after all, are the ones who produced that

---

meaning is ambiguous, not because of grammatical faults, which are comparatively few and unimportant, but because, when he does attempt a periodic sentence, he becomes involved, and finds it difficult to extricate himself" (Howard, preface, pp. iv-v; see also n.17, below).

This harsh condemnation of Vitruvius as a writer is indicative of the problems inherent in the academic treatment of technological writings and in the history of technology in general. The standards of judgment and the methods of weighing evidence employed by most academicians are completely unsuited to the study of pre-modern engineering. Vitruvius was not writing a theoretical treatise, but a lively, informative textbook on building. By Howard's standards, every modern engineering and math text, with their repetitive examples and introductory historical blurbs, deserves to be condemned as "pompous and turgid rhetoric." On the other hand, if we adopt a different aesthetic, as we might for reading folklore or mythology (for how refined do classicists find the language of Homer or Hesiod?), and remind ourselves that we are holding the writings and reviewing the accumulated knowledge of someone who actually *knew* how to build a classical temple, we find ourselves humbled and grateful for the opportunity to learn—despite the difficulties with periodic sentences.

disdain. The literate elite may have disparaged manual labor as something that slaves performed, but it does not follow that those who build have ever despised manual dexterity or been unaware of the theoretical basis of their craft. The philosopher's preference for pure contemplation is a notion that Plutarch may put into the speeches of his literary-historical Archimedes; but Archimedes himself left us the legacy of a prodigious career spent in equal measures of mathematical research and mechanical construction. Such men were not as comfortable with the vocabulary of the natural philosophers, but they were interested in the mathematical and cosmological ideas of their time and surely understood some of them. In addition, this highlighted distinction between "practice" and "reason" (as Ingrid Rowland has done here in her translation, as with "machines" and "engines", below) also represents the medieval tradition, for many surviving manuscripts also highlighted these distinctions with rubrication and marginal annotations. Vitruvius provides a lecture on proportion, geometry, and harmony followed by a discussion of the structure of the cosmos and the elements of astrology. The scholar will always prefer the writings of an Aristotle or Lucretius for these topics, but Vitruvius is one of the few sources that reveals to us the *practical* connections made of this body of theory. The blunt simplicity of Vitruvius' explanations are thus not literary shortcomings, but the natural form of a practical handbook version of the great ideas of the past, edited to show what is actually useful for the builder amidst all the high-flown verbiage.

Vitruvius devoted the last book of his treatise to the principles which govern machines, and here we find, at last, unambiguous descriptions of every type of ancient water-lifting device save one.* The sixteen chapters of book ten can be grouped into five general sections: (1) hoisting machines, (2) the principles of motion and their application to machines, (3) five types of waterwheels and a water screw, (4) three other machines: the pump of Ctesibius, the water organ, and the *hodometer*, (5) seven chapters on catapults, siege engines, and measures of defense. The five waterwheels and his descriptions of machinery are of particular importance to this discussion, but we can also learn something from the arrangement of his material and from occasional authorial comments. Vitruvius' definition of a machine, by which he begins the first chapter, is "a continuous piece of joinery that has outstanding capacities for moving loads. It is moved systemati-

---

* Only the overshot waterwheel is missing from Vitruvius, either because it was not yet in use or not yet developed sufficiently to have been deemed useful to a practical Roman engineer. The first clear evidence of the overshot watermill is in a Christian wall painting in the Roman catacombs dated to the third century CE. Other archaeological, visual, and literary evidence slowly accumulates from this point on.

cally by the revolutions of circles, which the Greeks call *kuklike kinesis*—'circular motion'" [X.1.1]. Here we see the plain description of the builder, followed by the less familiar philosophical underpinnings. Three classes of machines are distinguished: hoisting machines for lifting stones, climbing machines for lifting people up rapidly to inspect the site, and pneumatic machines using compressed air to lift stage props and such. Other devices, such as the waterwheels, fall into a different category—not "machines," but rather "engines."[12]

> The difference between **machines** [*machina*] and **engines** [*organa*] seems to be that machines must be run by many workers, that is, with a great deal of force to have their effect, like ballistae and presses, but engines complete the task at hand with the knowledgeable touch of one skilled workman: the rotations of the scorpion or anisocycles are examples of this. [X.1.3]

In his deliberate choice of terminology, Vitruvius shows that he has considered the fundamental differences between those devices that are merely tools to extend human muscle, and those that are operated by a single person by means of stored energy or by forces of nature. But his method of classification is not fully digested. He distinguishes on the basis of whether it requires many men to operate the device or only a single man. The first class—machines—includes hoisting devices, which are operated by teams of workers, and ballistae, which operate by storing the muscle strength of the men required to torque the ropes; the second class—engines—includes scorpions (large, dart-throwing crossbows) which can be wound and fired by a single man whose muscle energy is stored, as well as watermills, which are powered by a non-human source. He is not strict in his use of terminology, for he later refers to both ballistae and scorpions as engines and in the midst of his description of the watermill—surely a device that belongs to the category of "engines" by the above definition—Vitruvius will still use the word *machina* [X.5.2] which seems to be the common label for all sorts of mechanical devices regardless of their sophistication. After discussing hoisting machines, Vitruvius provides a philosophical primer on the elements of motion before describing the water-lifting wheels. He gives a simple rendering of Aristotelian physics (motion is of two types: circular and rectilinear, both of which are necessary in lifting) followed by a discussion of the lever and a half dozen examples of its application. As an experienced user of such devices, Vitruvius the cost-conscious engineer knew how to assess construction equipment in terms of the labor that would be needed to employ it. Again we see a lifetime of engineering experience offering exhaustive case studies to convey abstract ideas, whose direct, generalized expression is difficult.

Chapter four describes three water-lifting devices powered by a single human. The first he calls a *tympanum* which "does not lift water very high, but it does extract a great quantity very quickly." Vitruvius is the only ancient author to refer to the compartment wheel as a *tympanum*, but it is clearly the same device used in Egyptian agriculture mentioned by Philo. It is also the same compartmented water-lifting wheel that inspired Philo's little whistling device. He treats it as a perfectly standard device for accomplishing low-lift needs: "irrigating gardens or adjusting the level in saltworks" [X.4.1-2]. Although there is no other mention of such wheels between the third century BCE and the time of Vitruvius, the relative simplicity of its design, and its obvious benefits, argue against its having gone out of use, as does the continuing tradition of craftsmanship and engineering which is elsewhere apparent during this period.*

The second water-lifting wheel described is the larger wheel with compartments around the rim. Vitruvius presents this wheel, which he calls simply *rota* [wheel], as a logical extension of the first one. Vitruvius explains:

> If there is a need to lift water higher, the same principle should be adapted as follows: a wheel should be built around an axle, large enough so that it suits the required height. Around the outermost edge of the wheel, square buckets should be attached, sealed with pitch and wax. When the wheel is turned by treaders, the full buckets, lofted to the top, will automatically pour out the water they have raised as they return downward; this they pour into a holding tank. [X.4.3]

It is this second wheel which is well represented in the archaeological record[13] and had probably been in use in Hellenistic Egypt for a century or two before Vitruvius described it. By his time it was already becoming the answer to many of Rome's water-lifting needs: from servicing irrigation, to supplying the baths, to its frequent use in draining mines (Fig. 2). Vitruvius describes the machine without comment, apparently considering it no more intriguing than its smaller compartmented ancestor.

Vitruvius' third machine is the "bucket-wheel", which he presents as a further adaptation of the *rota*. The same means of propulsion by treading is employed, but if the water has to be supplied to a place higher than a wheel can be

---

* It is much easier to imagine the scenario by which no written references to this specific type of technology would have survived or that few would have paid a common machine much notice than it is to imagine the ancient Egyptian farmers losing or abandoning a device upon which their harvest and their lives depended. The reappearance of a steady tradition of such technology two hundred years later indicates an unbroken tradition of waterwheel construction despite its sporadic representation in the literary records.

constructed, "then a double iron chain, wrapped around the axle of the same wheel and cast downward, should be placed at the lowermost surface of the water, with bronze buckets hanging from it that hold a *congius* (about 6 pints or 3.5 liters) each" [X.4.4]. This "bucket-chain" seems to Oleson to have the appearance of a further Hellenistic innovation upon earlier models. It is unclear whether Vitruvius is describing a machine he knew from experience, or if he is relating something from his research into other engineering treatises. His description is brief and fails to address the problem of slippage: the ascending side of the chain with its water-laden buckets outweighs the descending side of empty buckets and would tend to slip without some device to engage the chain more decisively.[14] A sprocket gear would be the obvious solution, but Vitruvius makes no further provisions for how the chain will engage the axle. An installation much like the one Vitruvius describes was in operation in Pompeii during the time he was writing, but that is the only sure example we have from the Roman world until they begin to appear in archaeological remains from the second, third, and fourth centuries CE. It is also noteworthy that Vitruvius has specified only one method of powering the device, by treading a wheel attached to the same axle as the chain wraps around. The *saqiya* gear is not mentioned. The device was surely known by about the time of Vitruvius, since a painting dated to that period—significantly, in Alexandria—depicts two oxen yoked to such a gear. It too may have been an offshoot of late Hellenistic research in Alexandria. The concepts involved in the gearing were not beyond Vitruvius, as is shown by his description of the water-mill which follows. The absence of this device is all the more puzzling since we know he was attempting to write a comprehensive text. One must conclude that the *saqiya* was just emerging at this time and took longer to spread through the ancient world, being eagerly adopted in the drier southern and eastern realms of the Empire, where it was the ideal machine for lifting water from underground wells. Schiøler has carefully traced the subsequent history of these machines among the Muslims who inherited and successfully exploited them throughout their empire.[15]

    In the following chapter, Vitruvius describes the two most progressive machines in his treatise: a water-powered water-lifting wheel, and a true watermill. The first is an undershot waterwheel designed to be turned by the current of a river:

> Wheels [*rotae*] are also made in rivers according to the same methods as those described earlier. Around their edges paddles [*pinnae*] are fixed which, when they are struck by the surge of the river, force the wheel to turn as they proceed forward, and draw-

> ing the water and carrying it up in buckets, these wheels, turned
> by the force of the river itself rather than by workers' treading,
> furnish what is necessary for the job. [X.5.1]

Vitruvius gives no special name for this device. He describes the wheel as yet
another innovation spawned by the compartmented rim wheel, but the results
achieved by attaching radiating boards around the circumference drew little additional comment. In his repeating of the essential benefit of this wheel, that
they are "turned by the force of the river itself rather than by workers' treading,"
we see some of the same amazement that inspired Antipater's poem and Lucretius' analogy. It is likely that these first-century BCE writers were responding to a
machine that was new to their time—such enthusiastic commentaries disappear
by the next century.

Device number five in Vitruvius' arsenal of hydraulic machinery represents
what is arguably the most important achievement in ancient engineering and
the only one which endured into the western Middle Ages: the vertical watermill. Grinding grain into flour to make bread is a labor-intensive chore, and the
Romans met their enormous needs with industrial-sized grinders powered by
draft animals. Such a mill usually consisted of a cone-shaped bedstone with a
large, hourglass-shaped runner stone turned by donkeys, horses, or slaves. Specimens are found in abundance in the ruins of Pompeii, clustered along a couple
of streets within the shops of the bakers (Fig. 4a, b). We learn from these ruins
that bakers did the grinding of the grain, as well as the preparation of the flour
and baking of the bread, all within the cramped quarters of a small kitchen/shop.
Vitruvius does not describe this humble machine, either because it was already a
common device in his day, or because it did not fit his chapter theme of machines
derived from waterwheels. But at some point during the century before he wrote,
the application of waterpower to industrial grinding had taken place and this he
felt was worthy of description. Vitruvius calls them *hydraletae*, a Greek term indicating an Alexandrian origin, and describes the machine as related to the *rota*
discussed above:

> Water mills [*hydraletae*] are turned by the same principle; every
> feature is the same except that on one end of the axle a toothed
> wheel [*tympanum dentatum*] is installed. This, placed on the per-
> pendicular, that is, on its edge, turns at the same rate as the wheel.
> Alongside it, a larger drum, also toothed [*tympanum maius item
> dentatum*], is placed on the horizontal so that the two engage.
> The teeth of the drum that is fixed to the axle, by driving the
> teeth of the horizontal drum, cause the circling of the millstones
> to occur. A hopper overhanging this machine provides the grain

Figure 4a: **Horsemills, sinks, and ovens along the bakers' street, Pompeii;** photograph by the author.

Figure 4b: **Reconstruction of a horsemill in operation;** rendering by Joshua Chiet.

to the millstones and by means of the same rotation the flour is ground. [X.5.2]

This is the so-called "Vitruvian Mill" which features the revolutionary advance of right-angle reduction gearing. Two gears of the same design[16]—cogs radiating perpendicularly from the circumference of the wheel—mesh at a 90° angle and transfer the vertical rotation of the axle to the horizontal plane. The vertical axle is then attached to a millstone which spins atop its partner stone to grind the grain into flour.

There is some controversy regarding the relative sizes of the two gears. Earlier translations of Vitruvius render a larger gear attached to the axle engaging a smaller horizontal gear, which would have the effect of stepping up the speed of the millstones.[17] L.A. Moritz argues that eighteenth-century authors emended the portion of the text in which Vitruvius specifies the gear sizes in light of modern experience with high-speed mills.[18] Moritz' reconstructed size specifications call for a larger horizontal gear to decrease the rate of the millstone's rotation. Recent translators have made this correction and rendered the passage with a larger horizontal gear which would step down the speed of the millstones.[19] (Fig. 5) This corrected rendering accords with the only ancient archeological example for which the gear ratios can be ascertained: the overshot watermill complex built in the Athenian Agora in the fifth century CE. In this case, however, we have a configuration Vitruvius does not mention: an overshot mill fed by a mill race which has the potential to deliver water at high speed to the top of the wheel. The mill Vitruvius describes is an undershot type, turned much more slowly by the natural speed of the river into which the bottom of the wheel dips. It is possible that Vitruvius has conflated two examples: an aqueduct-fed mill with step-down gearing placed in a stream-side setting where undershot mills with step-up gearing could also be found. Medieval undershot mills almost always feature smaller horizontal gears which step up the speed of the millstone's rotation. Regardless, this point in the translation should have little bearing on our conception of the engineer's practice. Once this level of gearing had developed for use in large-scale programs such as the Romans accomplished in water transport and milling, it could not have been missed by them that the speed of the vertical axle driving the millstones, which adjoins the power source through gearing, is directly related to the size of the two gears. Considering the rare but very sophisticated examples of geared mechanisms, like the Antikythera mechanism from *c*.80 BCE,[20] it is not difficult to credit engineers of the Imperial Age with the ability to increase or decrease the speed of millstones at will by the substitution of differently sized gears. Vitruvius makes no mention of the overshot mill, and

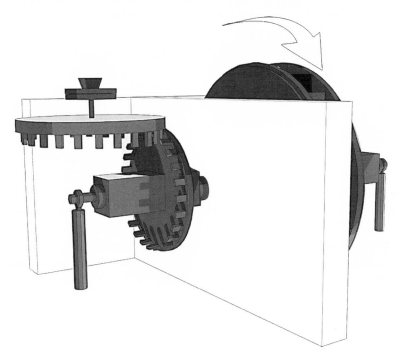

Figure 5: Reconstruction of "Vitruvian Mill" with correct gearing;
rendering by Joshua Chiet.

no evidence of it exists until the third century CE when one appears among the paintings in the Christian catacombs. But it could not have taken long from the invention of the undershot mill for the overshot variety to have emerged.

Once gearing had been developed to allow a vertical waterwheel to turn a millstone on the horizontal plane, and the purpose of turning the wheel had become work other than raising water, this next stage of development was free to happen. We should not make the mistake of imagining ancient mills in the same setting as their medieval successors, which often sat on riverbanks and received the natural impulse of the river or a diverted rivulet. Most of the Roman mills of which we have any knowledge were placed in an urban setting and fed by an aqueduct and so were already attached to an artificial and controllable source of water which as likely as not was already above the mill wheel. In this environment, it could not have taken long for the builders to note the different places that the water can be made to strike the wheel effectively, from above as well as from below, providing a natural inclination towards the development of the overshot watermill. Fortune has left us no clear archaeological evidence to support this; only Antipater's allusion to "water nymphs... [that] leap against the very edge of the wheel" attests to the possible existence of the overshot watermill before the third century CE.

Vitruvius is certainly not the inventor of the gearing, or of the mill, but he deserves to have his name attached to it for being the only ancient writer to describe the technical aspects of this machine clearly—most ancient writers falter at precisely this point. Untold millions of hours of difficult hand milling were replaced by the watermill, the first true piece of labor-saving industrial machinery driven entirely by natural forces. Ancient examples of the *hydraleta* are rare, but it is hugely significant that watermills of precisely this design existed in the thousands during the Middle Ages, descendants of the model described by Vitruvius.

The First Millennium of Watermilling

At first glance, it would seem that the Romans failed to make much use of the watermill. After a flurry of literary comments and Vitruvius' technical description in the first century BCE, an almost complete silence ensues concerning hydraulic power until Late Antiquity. Only the ever-curious Pliny the Elder makes a reference to watermills in use in Italy,[21] but we can adjudge nothing from it other than that watermills were known and apparently no longer as startling as when Antipater encountered one a century before. During the fourth century CE, references to watermills begin to reappear, often in the context of the crises that plagued the last years of the Western Empire. Palladius recommended diverting waste-water from the public baths to drive watermills and thus free up the labor of men and animals.[22] It would seem as if the pressures of labor shortage and the decline in the numbers of slaves imported to Rome gave new impetus to the idea of labor-saving machines, resulting in the proliferation of watermilling only in the twilight of Antiquity.[23] In 537 CE, when the Goths were besieging Rome and taxing the skills of the great general Belisarius, the destruction of the aqueducts supplying water to the mills on the Janiculum Hill threatened mass starvation, indicating that the majority of Roman citizens in the early sixth century ate bread produced from mechanically milled grain. A further technical innovation rescued Rome from its plight: since they still had the services of the Tiber, the mills were suspended between two boats and moored to the river, allowing the current to push the wheels from below.[24] This is the first known instance of a *floatmill*, a device which would reappear under the bridges of many medieval towns during the twelfth and thirteenth centuries. This apparent resurgence in watermill technology was continued in the early Middle Ages according to the testimony of Carolingian documents which abound in references to mills and the rents collected from them. The early medieval period, a time long-dismissed as a "dark age," was widely serviced by hydraulic technology.

Such were the revelations brought forth by Marc Bloch seventy years ago in his highly influential study on the watermill.[25] According to Bloch, after a slow crawl through the ancient world, watermilling suddenly took hold during the decline of the empire and took off in the Middle Ages. The period of explosive growth in the use of watermills, documented by the abundance of mundane charter references concerning construction and repair of the mills, was the Carolingian era. Bloch's careful search through the Carolingian charters turned up a world familiar with watermilling as an everyday activity, where feudal *potentes* constructed, maintained, and enforced the exclusive use of *molens* recorded in charter records too numerous to reproduce here. This explosion in the application of hydraulic technology cannot be tied to dwindling labor conditions as it may have been in the late Roman period, as the reasonably settled *demesnes* of Carolingian lords were amply supplied by a landed peasantry. The rigorous exploitation of watermilling which Bloch saw in the charters was explained to be the product of industrious and efficient lords seeking to better exploit their lands and extract more of the produce of their peasants' labor. There is no mistaking the signs of a vibrant early capitalism in Bloch's analysis, already stimulating the nascent technologies that show promise of increasing production. Medieval achievements in the application of hydraulic machinery seem to have far exceeded the ancient world's most ambitious efforts. Clearly, medieval people were not slow to capitalize on the potential of this technology. But could the ancient Romans really have done so little with so useful a device?

In the seven decades since his study appeared, evidence has been accumulating that questions Bloch's dismissal of ancient watermilling. Archeologists began unearthing Roman mill sites soon after Bloch published, and additional written sources, mostly legal documents, which Bloch did not examine, further sharpen our image of the situation. Watermills may not have attracted the attention of the ancient authors which Bloch had scoured so carefully, but they were attractive to those looking for sources of tax revenue. An edict of Diocletian issued in 301 CE lists four types of mills and their value for tax purposes: hand-mill (250 *denarii*), donkey-mill (1,250 *denarii*), horse-mill with stones (1,500 *denarii*), and water-mill (2,000 *denarii*).[26] An edict of Arcadius and Honorius from 398 CE imposes heavy fines on those who divert water destined for the watermills on the Janiculum upon which Rome depended.[27] Several measures are taken against dishonest millers in an edict of Dynamius around 480 CE, including official weighing machines to be set up on the Janiculum and fixed payment for millers, along with the usual threat of heavy fines. This same book of edicts also pronounces on water rights for mills near Pomona.[28] All of this is in accordance with what we would expect to find given the crisis we know Belisarius will face in the next century. One also notes with some surprise the opportunities for entrepreneurial capitalism in late antiquity, in cooperation with the state (which must grant access to the aqueduct) that allowed the dishonest Janiculum millers to get into trouble—but it is also enlightening to see the forerunners of Chaucer's scoundrel miller already exciting popular disdain in ancient Rome. Moving from legal to religious texts, a Talmudic complaint from as early as the first century CE, against operating watermills on the Sabbath in Roman-occupied Palestine, suggests that the Romans had been at this for some time already.[29] By the testimony of these documents, watermilling was not a desperate stopgap to rectify the labor problems of a declining ancient world, but a regular activity during the five centuries of the Roman Empire and beyond.

Archaeological evidence confirms the opinion derived from legal documents and expands the range of where we know the Romans employed watermill technology. The earliest unambiguous find was unearthed near Pompeii, in Venafro. It consisted of the mill-race and prints of the millstones on the housing wall. Nearby, the perfect impression of a wooden, undershot waterwheel was recovered from the layer of ash left by Mt. Vesuvius in 79 CE. It was a bulky wheel: six and a half feet [2m] in diameter with a three-foot [0.9m] diameter hub with eighteen flat radial spokes connecting hub to rim (Fig. 6). Reynolds commented on the excessively large size of the hub, which he found inefficient due to the needless weight it adds to the wheel.[30] It was, however, a remarkably sturdy wheel and elegant in the design of the tapered paddle-blades that narrow as they approach the hub. Aesthetic reasons aside, this shape increases the striking surface of the paddle extremities without increasing the weight along the entire length of the blades. This wheel, Reynolds agreed, would be capable of very high-speed rotational velocities maintained for prolonged periods. If it were attached to a mill with reduction gearing, like the fifth-century wheel in the Athenian Agora, then this wheel engineered for maximum endurance under high-stress operations may have been the ideal design for this particular application.

The fact that it took the sudden explosion of Mt. Vesuvius with its subsequent tons of protective ash to preserve physical evidence of a first-century wa-

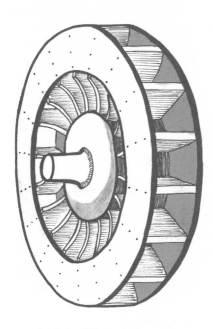

Figure 6: **Model of waterwheel made from ash impression found in Venafro, outside of Pompeii**; redrawn from Charles Singer, *et al.* (eds.), *A History of Technology* (Oxford: Clarendon Press, 1956), II:598, fig. 545 (after C. Reindl, "Ein römisches Wasserrad," *Wasserkraft und Wasserwirtschaft* 34 [1939]: 143).

terwheel should caution us not to assume too much based on the lack of evidence. Roman watermills and other water-lifting devices were constructed almost entirely of wood, which has a very low survival rate over two millennia. What does stand a better chance of survival into the archaeological record are the aqueduct networks, mill-races, sluice-gates, and other apparatus to supply the mill with water, along with the occasional find of the millstones themselves or an iron-spindle. However, since it is the nature of traditional craftsmanship to reuse costly materials whenever possible, we should expect that most of the broken millstones were laid into later foundations, the iron-spindles were reworked into farm tools, and the broken shafts and paddles of the waterwheel were dried and made serviceable as kindling. Given the odds against archaeological survival, the amount of evidence for Roman watermilling is actually quite staggering.

Between the Venafro wheel of the first century and the Athenian Agora mill of the fifth, there is the evidence of a large milling complex in southern Gaul built around 300 CE.[31] What survives from Barbegal are parts of the aqueduct and mill-races which fed eight pairs of waterwheels arranged in descending steps so that the fall of water would impel each pair of wheels in turn as it ran down the channels. The wheels themselves have not survived, but the dimensions of the races and falls, along with lime deposits on the sides of the structure, permit an estimate of wheels which were over seven feet [2.13m] tall and almost two and a half [0.7m] wide. The incrustations indicate that these were probably overshot wheels. The amount of grain that such a milling factory could produce has been estimated at 28 tons per day.[32] This surely would have exceeded the needs of nearby Arles; the complex was probably built to supply the needs of the Roman legion stationed in southern Gaul. Once we accustom ourselves to the notion that the Romans were builders and users of watermills, the complex at Barbegal appears as an agreeable example of the organizational competence one expects of them.

Another batch of evidence comes from England where archaeologists have been active in searching out watermills—both ancient and medieval. Earliest among these finds are the remains of an undershot watermill at Haltwhistle Burn, in northern England, built in the third century. The millhouse was found, its function revealed by several broken millstones, along with the oak-lined mill-race, which diverted water from the river to a trough alongside the house. A few iron nails and flat iron pieces were unearthed, but no remains of the wheel. The dimensions of the trough and its surroundings suggest a size of ten to twelve feet [3.0-3.7m] in diameter and about fourteen inches [36cm] wide.[33] Other archaeo-logical remains show that watermilling was common in Roman Britain. Three mills have been detected along Hadrian's wall, and evidence of watermilling has been found in Lincoln, Chollerford, Willingford, Chedworth Villa, Wollaston Villa, Great Chestorford, and at two locations in Ickham, Kent.[34] All of the evi-dence is dated between the second and fourth centuries CE, with the majority of it clustered in the third century. This was a period of relative peace and stabil-ity in Roman Britain, when towns were developed and the desire to improve the quality of life so far away from the warm Mediterranean must have been deeply felt. The establishment of watermills to service the towns and legion camps built by the Romans would certainly have been a top priority, and this appears to have been a routine task for the engineers who accompanied Roman legions and colo-nists.

We must therefore reconsider certain aspects of Bloch's model of early wa-termilling. Watermills were known throughout the entirety of the Roman Em-pire and treated as common devices which accomplished a basic and necessary task. Those that were connected to an aqueduct-fed water supply were regulated and their revenues were taxed.[35] The last writers to express shock at the sight of a machine lifting its own water or grinding grain without human hands had lived in the first century BCE. And if watermilling were indeed this common during the Roman Empire, then there could not have been a sudden and dramatic in-crease during the Middle Ages. What Bloch had observed was an illusion created by the fragmentary nature of historical evidence and the artificial nature of its analysis.[36] Bloch had searched the ancient authors and found only a handful of references to watermills, in sharp contrast to the numerous references from the Carolingian era. But these two collections of evidence are very unlike each other. The first consists of ancient writers, most belonging to an elite and erudite circle, writing about the concerns of the upper classes: poetry, epic, drama, philosophy, and history. The second, from the Carolingian era, consists of little in the way of refined literature, but is rich in the mundane records of estate administration: deeds, tenants, obligations, rents, and goods—including mills. Estate records from early medieval France and England survive only in pockets, for they are not the type of writing which enjoy affectionate transmission by scribes; but where they do survive they are autograph accounts of anything valuable on the land—like watermills. This class of medieval documents is thus particularly disposed to record any instance of a valuable machine.[37]

In contrast, few of the ancient writers whose works still exist were concerned with such things. It is usually only an architect like Vitruvius, or a naturalist like Pliny, who finds watermills interesting enough to write about. But Vitruvius' occasional references to now-lost engineering treatises, which his readers are advised to consult, clearly indicate that a substantial body of technical writing existed in his day. We must be aware of the lack of range of ancient writing that has survived to us. Few of the authors in the Loeb Classical Library survive in original or even ancient copies, but rather in medieval manuscripts preserved by Christian and Muslim scribes and rediscovered by Renaissance humanists. Our selection of ancient reading material has already undergone a process of pre-selection by the pious *literati* who succeeded the ancients and chose to preserve only those things which they thought useful. The chance survival of unique manuscripts—Frontinus, Vitruvius, Lucretius—reminds us of how much variety from the ancient world has been lost. Manorial records are equally—but differently—fragmentary, owing simply to the ravages of time and human activity on the material artifacts themselves. Centuries of small accidental fires, hungry rats, and the deliberate property damage that accompanies warfare have destroyed the majority of medieval manorial accounts, but where those lucky survivals do exist, they are far more predisposed to mention a watermill than a chance survival of ancient poetry. We simply do not have the records to address the question of ancient watermill use. The one exception for this lack of ancient evidence is the collection of Egyptian papyri, analyzed by Oleson, and which is indeed full of references to the simple water-lifting wheel, and the more primitive *shaduf*, the standard technology in use in Egypt at that time.[38] This point cannot be overemphasized: the paper trails of history, by which we scrutinize and reconstruct the past, are a singularly deformed window through which to view the historical activity of engineering, technology, and craft. The concerns of most of the people who wrote for posterity were far removed from contemporary methods for producing flour. When such common written records do begin to appear, they abound in such references.

The vertical watermill that Vitruvius describes was put to widespread use by the Romans and continued into medieval usage in an unbroken tradition. Despite the persistent image of the early Middle Ages as swarming with barbarian hordes, the invaders from the north did not annihilate the towns of Italy and southern Europe. The authority of Rome and the power of her legions may have been destroyed, but farms, towns, and shipping represent wealth that the northern conquerors were very keen to control and enjoy themselves. Even during the tumult of the transitional age following the decline of the western empire, farming and town life carried on and watermills continued to be essential to both. Gregory of Tours, writing around 575 CE, describes how the stream before the gates of Dijon, in southern France, "turns mill-wheels with marvelous speed."[39] These mills presumably ground grain for the citizens and farmers of the region. Monasteries also provided fertile ground for the proliferation of water-powered technology. Cassiodorus, around 538 CE, was concerned with finding the best place for his monastery, the *Vivarium*, and insisted upon a site with a stream suitable for watermills.[40] Both Cassiodorus and his contemporary Benedict founded experimental religious communities that became the models for Western monasticism. Watermilling technology was an essential component of that model from the beginning.[41] The oldest known monastic blueprint, the St. Gall plan (early ninth century), clearly indicates watermills, and possibly mills with mechanical pounders, as essential components of an integrated hydraulic system that further supplied water to various parts of the monastery.[42] References to watermills in a variety of situations appear sporadically in the early medieval period, and then abundantly in the Carolingian era and beyond. Even without this collection of manorial accounts, the ubiquity of watermills is still clearly indicated by one unique and astounding document: William the Conqueror's account of his English possessions made in 1086, *Domesday Book*. Along with the farms, livestock, rents, and moveable goods that William's clerks recorded were the many watermills that lined the riverbanks in nearly every inhabited region. Scholars differ on the number of watermills indicated by the sometimes vague language—the usually quoted estimate of 5,624 has been recently revised upward to 6,082.[43] It hardly matters. Since we cannot possibly construct a scenario by which Norman engineers rapidly retooled the peasantry (and since no one has argued for an Anglo-Saxon technological revolution), we can only conclude that watermills had been part of the English landscape since the Romans introduced them a millennium earlier. If there is a lingering controversy, it is over the type of watermills indicated in the records.

So far, this discussion has been concerned with the development and proliferation of the vertical watermill, that is, mills with a vertically oriented wheel turning a horizontal axle. There was, however, another type of watermill common primarily in northern Europe. The horizontal watermill involves a ring of angled or spoon-shaped paddles oriented on a horizontal plane and attached to a vertical axis. It is mechanically a simpler machine as it involves no gearing—the impact blades are directly attached to the spindle, which turns the upper grindstone. With no gearing involved, it would have been an easier machine to conceive and construct, although it does require the controlled channeling of water to the paddles. It appears to have been a "barbarian invention," as Lynn White put it, and archeological finds are concentrated in the north of Europe for the ancient and medieval periods.[44] Because of this, it is often called a "Norse Mill," although there is no evidence that specifically Nordic people had anything to do with its development. Horizontal mills are agreed to be the type indicated in the *Senchus Mor,* the codification of Irish law, and were the subject of legal disputes.[45] Another horizontal mill, dated to the eighth century, has been excavated at Tamworth, a Mercian urban center in Anglo-Saxon England.[46] Both types of mills were known in early medieval England, and many of the *Domesday* mills may have been of the horizontal type. Regardless of the percentages involved, it can only increase our appreciation for early medieval technological prowess that they employed several types of mills and assuredly understood the advantages of each type under various circumstances. Because of their relative simplicity of construction, the appearance of small horizontal mills across the north of medieval Europe may also represent the activities of local craftsmen. The future of watermilling would belong to the more powerful and versatile vertical mill, and these would be owned by lords or organizations of merchant investors who were capable of supplying the capital for construction. Further, as Holt argues, the disappearance of horizontal mills seems to have been the result of more ambitious efforts to exploit water power.[47] The simple horizontal mill has little room for improvement and is a far less powerful machine than the vertical mill. Population growth and the increase in administrative consolidation and perhaps efficiency after the Conquest directed most investments in hydraulic technology towards the vertical type; but the simple "Norse mill" would continue in use in more remote and mountainous areas, among people of simpler means.

The technological relationship between horizontal and vertical watermills has been a source of debate and frustration for some scholars. Lynn White notes the simultaneous appearance of horizontal mills in Denmark and China around the time of Christ and speculates a point of origin somewhere between.[48] This is certainly possible, but his statement that "doubtless the earliest water-wheels were horizontal" cannot be supported based solely on the simpler nature of the device. The process of invention stands in a complex relationship to social and economic conditions and usually grows from prior technology. Ancient watermills developed from water-lifting wheels, which, obviously, were vertical. Horizontal mills may perform the same task and be powered by the same force as vertical wheels, but they are mechanically different devices. There is no reason to think that the one should have led to the other, or that the development of any particular line of technology must include each possible variant in its development, or move inexorably from less complex to more complex. It is only in retrospect, having gathered centuries of various types of machines for performing some task, that we 'organize' these scattered specimens into an artificially coherent family tree of devices. It is valuable to note that nowhere in the writings of the Alexandrian engineers, nor in Vitruvius, do we find mention of a horizontal watermill.

An important improvement in the vertical watermill occurred in the design of the gears, but we cannot say with certainty whether it was a Roman or medieval innovation. Vitruvius described two gears of different sizes but of the same type: "drums with teeth" engaging at a 90° angle. It is an important *terminus a quo* that Vitruvius' mill is geared with two crown-gears rather than a crown-gear and a lantern pinion.[*] His design is functional, but not the most problem-free of choices. It is difficult to mount two crown-gears to engage at a right angle under high-stress operating conditions and maintain the integrity of the machine. With time, the wheels slowly repel each other and the wear on the cogs causes deformities, which further impinge upon their ability to meet squarely as the gears are turned. A much surer method involves the use of crown-gear and lantern pinion. The lantern pinion, also called a *rundle-wheel*, or simply a *rundle*, consists of two disks of wood connected by a ring of dowels around the rims, resulting in a gear that looks something like a bird-cage. The teeth of the

---

[*] Only Landels seems to have taken note of this aspect of the gearing in the Vitruvian mill. Most scholars, following Beck's reconstruction, have pictured the horizontal gear, which turns the millstones, as a large flat lantern pinion.

crown-gear engage the spaces between the dowels of the lantern pinion and accomplish the same job as the earlier gearing, but with much less risk of bowing and slippage as each engaged dowel of the lantern pinion is supported on both ends. The lantern pinion can also be made in varied sizes, so the advantage of reduction gearing is not lost. We cannot know when this important innovation came in—it is not described in Vitruvius (despite inaccurate reconstructions to the contrary), but the lantern pinion is integral to the efficient operation of the *saqiya*—the geared machine which allows a bucket chain to be lifted by a yoked beast pushing a beam in a circular path around it. The enormous weight of long chains of buckets being pulled from underground wells demanded a more reliable gear for the lifting mechanism. It is likely that *saqiya* builders would have felt the necessity to improve the capabilities of gearing and invent the lantern pinion.* *De Architectura* was being written in Italy while these very developments were taking place in the dry regions around Egypt, just beyond the range of Vitruvius' research. Vitruvius must not have known of the lantern pinion, or its role in the *saqiya*, since he would surely have reported on a useful new gear had he known of it. By the twelfth century, the lantern pinion is described quite clearly in illustrations.

It will be more than a thousand years after Vitruvius' time that we are again given a glimpse into the internal gearing of the watermill. But the mechanical design of medieval watermills can be understood with surprising accuracy based on manuscript illustrations and other decorative arts beginning in the twelfth century. The most unambiguous image of a watermill appears in the twelfth-century *Hortus Deliciarum* of Herrad von Landsberg (Fig. 7a). The drawings in this text are done in a clear, linear hand by an illuminator who was undoubtedly fascinated with technology. Although the text is purely religious, the illustrator managed to include carefully executed details of a watermill (as well as a wine-press, a wheeled plow harnessed to two oxen, boxing puppets, and an allegorical figure of fortune "cranking" her wheel of fate). The watermill, clearly of the undershot variety, is turned by a large, spoked waterwheel with a ring of flat paddles attached on both sides by rims that are affixed to the central spokes. This drawing is often called a "Vitruvian mill" because of its supposed faithfulness

---

*   The Alexandrian illustration of a *saqiya* (or, more specifically, a *tabut*, since it is a bucket-wheel rather than a bucket-chain which the oxen lumber around) does not show what type of gear is involved, but the cramped quarters of the room and the closeness of the vertical shaft to the waterwheel both favor a small lantern pinion. But, as with all artistic renderings of ancient technology, we can never be sure what is observation and what is artistic license or the result of the artist's ignorance of technical matters.

Figure 7: **The "Vitruvian Mill" in the High Middle Ages.** Note the consistency of design and relative proportions of crown gear/lantern pinion arrangement.

a) [above] Twelfth-century image in *Hortus Deliciarum* of Herrad von Landsberg (above); redrawn from Charles Singer, *et al.* (eds.), *A History of Technology* (Oxford: Clarendon Press, 1956), II:648, fig. 590;

b) [above right] Thirteenth-century depiction on Spanish reliquary; redrawn from Singer, II:648, fig. 591 (after W. W. Cook and J. F. Ricard, *Ars Hispaniae* [Madrid: Editorial Plus Ultra, 1950], VI: fig. 261);

c) [right] Thirteenth-century depiction in English manuscript; Bodleian Library, MS 764, fol. 44r reproduced in Nigel Saul (ed.), *The Oxford Illustrated History of Medieval England* (Oxford: Oxford University Press, 1997), p. 164, reproduced by permission of Oxford University Press.

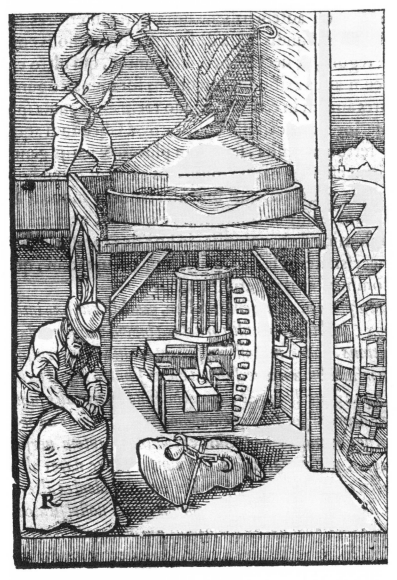

Figure 8: Sixteenth-century **cornmill**; from Vitruvius Pollio, *M. Vitrvvii Pollionis De architectvra libri decem / cvm commentariis Danielis Barbari* (Venetiis: Franciscum Franciscium Senensem, & Ioan. Crugher Germanum, 1567), p. 438; **woodcut by** Johann Chrieger after an anonymous Florentine artist (*c.*1550); Reproduced with the permission of the Special Collections Library, the Pennsylvania State University Libraries.

to the design described by the Roman architect. It is even possible that the pious nuns possessed a copy of Vitruvius to which they could have compared their monastery's mill. If the nuns had compared text and machine closely, they would have found a critical divergence from the Vitruvian model formed by centuries of medieval experience and craftsmanship. The lantern pinion, which Vitruvius does not describe, has replaced one of his crown-gears; and the gearing ratio has been reversed from standard Roman step-down gearing (suitable for aqueduct fed mills) to the common medieval step-up gearing (suitable for river mills). The scattering of illustrations of medieval watermills, which clearly depict the gearing, show a remarkable consistency in design. A vertical undershot watermill, depicted on a Spanish reliquary of the thirteenth century (Fig. 7b), reveals the same type of gearing and with the same relative proportions as the mill in the *Hortus Deliciarum*. An English manuscript, also from the thirteenth century (Fig. 7c), indicates the same preference in mills across the Channel. Thus, three separate illustrations made in three separate countries and in three separate media, but within 150 years of one another, provide identical testimony to the state of watermill gearing in the High Middle Ages.

Renaissance illustrations of watermills in the works of Francesco di Giorgio are more elaborate, but have not abandoned this basic gear which we still find in use in hydraulic engineering illustrations of the mid-sixteenth century.[49] (Fig. 8) We have no ancient or early medieval evidence specifically indicating the innovation of the crown-gear/lantern pinion arrangement. It can only be said with absolute certainty that it developed somewhere in the twelve centuries between Vitruvius and the *Hortus* manuscript. But we have little reason to imagine that the later Roman or early medieval craftsmen would have been incapable of making this mechanical improvement. The stresses on the horizontal gear, turned for hours at a high velocity, would have been the motivation to shore up the design by affixing a second, stabilizing disk to the free ends of the teeth. The appearance of this adaptation in countries from Spain to England in the later centuries of the Middle Ages suggests that it had long ago become the standard technique.

Conclusion

The fortunate survival of multiple detailed images of watermill gearing from the later Middle Ages, together with the roughly one hundred surviving medieval copies of the Vitruvian manuscript, allow us to speculate on the relationship between Vitruvius and the machines named for him. Medieval watermills are

"Vitruvian" only in the sense that they are the descendants of a machine, and of a technical tradition, which were known to Vitruvius. The *hydraleta* he described in *De Architectura* stood at the beginning of a hydraulic engineering tradition that continued unbroken through the Middle Ages and beyond. The several clear images of watermills and their gears that cluster around the medieval renaissance are reflections of the state of the machine more than a millennium later. But while the "Vitruvian mill" has been updated, the manuscript of Vitruvius has not. Despite the several chapters on machinery, *De Architectura* did not serve as a textbook on mechanics in the way that the works of Philo of Byzantium did among medieval Muslim engineers. The lack of additions, accretions, and updates in the mechanical and engineering sections of Vitruvius—the lack of a "pseudo-Vitruvian" tradition—indicates the meager attention these chapters received. Vitruvius was valued by medieval readers, but primarily for his discussion of the application of Pythagorean geometry to architectural design.[50] It is clear that those who did the copying were not part of the craft tradition that included watermills; neither were the builders and maintainers of watermills using Vitruvius as their guide.

The watermill had been derived from the application by ancient engineers of two mechanical principles which had been learned independently of each other: (1) the power-generating capabilities of a water-lifting wheel outfitted with extended blades to harness the impulse of flowing water; and (2) the ability of gearing to change the speed and direction of rotary motion: both its rotational direction and its planar orientation. These two insights—power-wheel and gearing—were joined in the anonymous invention of the watermill, somewhere between the late third and early first century BCE, triggering in Europe and the Mediterranean region the vast mechanization of the most arduous aspect of bread production. For the next thousand years, watermills performed the chore of grinding across the European continent, with most of the further innovation involving variant means of supplying and harnessing the flow of water that powered them, and in developing more efficient gear designs. The early medieval period can probably boast a larger number and wider range of watermills and watermilling activity than the preceding Roman era, but this may only be the result of having had many more centuries to build them, and not necessarily because they were possessed of a more progressive attitude towards machinery than their predecessors had been.

Watermills continued to be used in many parts of Europe, despite its fragmentation into smaller kingdoms after Roman hegemony dwindled in the fifth century. Legionary camps and Roman settlement towns scattered around the northern edge of the empire were regularly serviced by watermills which found themselves, in the centuries following Rome, in the middle of a burgeoning medieval Europe. The hundreds, if not thousands, of watermills built by the Romans passed into medieval ownership and were maintained by generations of anonymous carpenters and millers throughout the medieval period in an unbroken tradition. Watermills, a legacy from Antiquity as valuable as any philosophy or literature, have been part of the landscape of Western Europe since it was held by the Romans—it is only modern historians who have had to rediscover them.

Notes

[1] Marcus Vitruvius Pollio, *De Architectura,* trans. and ed. by Ingrid D. Rowland and Thomas Noble Howe (Cambridge: Cambridge University Press, 1999): "Those who are taken with his [Ctesibius'] cleverness can find the remaining machines, namely those inspired not by necessity but only by a wish to delight, in the treatise of Ctesibius himself" [X.7.5]. All further references to Vitruvius are from the Rowland text. It would seem that, aside from the obvious usefulness of the force pump which Vitruvius has just described, Ctesibius' book of machines was a text on the construction of fine technology, automata and musical instruments. It was not regarded as a manual of practical engineering such as Vitruvius was writing.

[2] Several dozen of these devices have been unearthed by archaeologists: John Peter Oleson, *Greek and Roman Water-Lifting Devices: The History of a Technology* (Toronto: University of Toronto Press, 1984), figs. 43, 46, 143, and 144. The highly organized Romans put these pump-driven fire-extinguishers or "siphons" to regular use in the capital city, as evidenced by the regular mention of *siphonatores* among the corps of firemen: John W. Humphrey, John P. Oleson, and Andrew N. Sherwood, *Greek and Roman Technology: A Sourcebook: Annotated Translations of Greek and Latin Texts and Documents* (London: Routledge, 1998), p. 320.

[3] Philo was one of a dozen authors on mechanical engineering that Vitruvius lists in his "reference section" to his book on, of all things, wall paintings: "those who have written about machines, like Diades, Archytas, Archimedes, Ctesibios, Nymphodorus, Philo of Byzantium, Diphilos, Democles, Charias, Polyidos, Pyrrhos, and Agesistratos" [VII.intro.14].

[4] See Oleson, *Greek and Roman Water-Lifting Devices,* and Humphrey *et al., Greek and Roman Technology,* for the complete literary, papyrological, visual, and archaeological analysis of the evidence concerning the origins and use of ancient hydraulic technology. All quotes from the engineers of the Alexandrian school are taken from the Oleson text.

[5] There is another and much more complex water-lifting wheel described in Chapter 65 of the *Pneumatica* which was the focus of much twentieth-century debate. The device employed scoops which received the impulse of a channel of water, a bucket chain, and some type of triangular cog. Bernard Carra de Vaux translated Philo into French and, accepting the text as genuine, made a peculiar reconstruction of the device ("Le livre des appareils pneumatiques et des machines hydrauliques de Philon de Byzance d'après les versions arabes d'Oxford et de Constantinople," *Académie des Inscriptions et des Belles Lettres: Notices et extraits des mss. de*

la Bibliothèque nationale, Paris 38 [1903]: 27-235). Earlier studies in the history of engineering, such as the widely read A.P. Usher, *A History of Mechanical Inventions* (1954; New York: Dover, 1988), reprinted this reconstruction and continued to attribute the invention of water-powered devices to Philo. Recent scholarship has been more skeptical. A.G. Drachmann, *The Mechanical Technology of Greek and Roman Antiquity* (Madison: University of Wisconsin Press, 1963); Thorkild Schiøler, *Roman and Islamic Water-Lifting Devices* (Odense: Odense University Press, 1973); Terry S. Reynolds, *Stronger than a Hundred Men: A History of the Vertical Water Wheel* (Baltimore: The Johns Hopkins University Press, 1983); and Oleson, *Greek and Roman Water-Lifting Devices*, all suspect, for different reasons, that these are later Arabic interpolations. Because the description exists only in Arabic editions, and features suspiciously complex gearing awkwardly and inefficiently applied to its task, it seems likely that it is a medieval Arabic experiment attempting to apply the technologies of different machines to a novel purpose. A more mechanically plausible reconstruction of this odd device was made by T. Beck (1911) and is reprinted in Oleson, *Greek and Roman Water-Lifting Devices*, fig. 24.

[6] *Latin Anthology* 284 [quoted in Humphrey *et al.*, *Greek and Roman Technology*, p. 31].

[7] *Greek Anthology* 9.418 [*ibid.*].

[8] Lucretius, *De Rerum Natura*, trans. R.E. Latham (London: Penguin Books, 1951), 5.517. Lucretius is thus the first of many natural philosophers who would expound a non-mystical, "mechanistic" view of the cosmos by analogy to an automated machine. A millennium and a half later, the medieval European mechanical clock would become the metaphor of choice.

[9] Humphrey *et al.*, *Greek and Roman Technology*, p. 30. Steven Walton suggests that this term could also indicate the scoop-shaped paddles of a horizontal wheel with directed jet, or "Norse mill," to be discussed below, since it and the cosmos both rotate about a *vertical* axis.

[10] Quoted in Reynolds, *Stronger Than a Hundred Men*, p. 16.

[11] Vitruvius' only reference to his own architectural commissions occurs in Book 5 where, as an example of a properly proportioned basilica, he mentions the one he designed and supervised the construction of at Fano [V.1.6-10].

[12] I have retained Morgan's rendering of *organa* as "engine" rather than Rowland's rendering of "instrument" for this passage; it is otherwise Rowland's translation.

[13] Wheels with compartmented rims have been unearthed in 15 sites around the Western Roman Empire: 6 in Spain and Portugal, 5 in Romania, 2 in Germany (possibly), 1 in Britain, and one elaborate complex of wheels in Ostia, Italy. The Ostian complex supplied water for the baths while all the rest were involved in dewatering mines. Nearly all of the wheels were close to a standard diameter of 15 ft. (4.6m). See Oleson, *Greek and Roman Water-Lifting Devices* (note 2), p. 344.

[14] J.G. Landels, *Engineering in the Ancient World* (Berkeley: University of California Press, 1978), pp. 71-75, takes up the problem of slippage.

[15] Thorkild Schiøler, *Roman and Islamic Water-Lifting Devices*, p. 152, fig. 108 shows an image of the Alexandrian *saqiya* mentioned above.

[16] Note that although the translator has used "wheel" for the first gear and "drum" for the second, Vitruvius makes no actual distinction—they are both called *tympanum dentatum*.

[17] See the earlier translation of Vitruvius: *The Ten Books On Architecture*, trans. by Morris Hickey Morgan (1914; New York: Dover Books, 1960), X.5.2.

[18] L.A. Moritz, "Vitruvius' Water Mill," *Classical Review* 70 (1956): 193-96.

[19] See the Rowland translation of 1999 (note 1). The accompanying images by Thomas Noble Howe show two versions: a "Vitruvian" mill and the "more common practice," p. 303.

[20] Derek J. de Solla Price, "Gears from the Greeks: The Antikythera Mechanism—A Calendar Computer from ca. 80 B.C.", *Transactions of the American Philosophical Society* 64, pt. 7 (1974).

[21] Pliny, *Historia Naturalis* 18.23.97: "The greater part of Italy uses a simple pestle, also wheels that water turns, and the millstone besides" [quoted in Oleson, *Greek and Roman Water-Lifting Devices* (note 2), p. 86].

[22] Palladius, *Opus Agriculturae*, 1.41 [quoted in Humphrey *et al.*, *Greek and Roman Technology* (note 2), p. 33].

[23] The classic account of the labor-machinery question is M.I. Finley, "Technical Innovation and Economic Progress in the Ancient World," *Economic History Review* 2nd series, 18 (1965): 29-45. It has recently been astutely questioned by Kevin Greene, "Technological Innovation and Economic Progress in the Ancient World: M.I. Finley reconsidered," *Economic History Review* 53.1 (2000): 29-59.

[24] Procopius, *Gothic Wars* 5.19ff [quoted in Oleson, *Greek and Roman Water-Lifting Devices*, p. 86].

[25] Marc Bloch, "Avènement et conquêtes du moulin à eau," *Annales d'histoire économique et sociale* 7 (1935): 538-63.

[26] Diocletian, *Edictum de pretiis* 15.56a-59 [quoted in Oleson, *Greek and Roman Water-Lifting Devices*, p. 42].

[27] *Codex Theodosianus* 14.15.4 [quoted in K.D. White, *Greek and Roman Technology* (London: Thames&Hudson, 1984), p. 199].

[28] *Ibid.*

[29] Saul Lieberman (ed.), *Tosefta Sabbath* I.23 (New York, 1962), p. 6, cited by Bradford B. Blaine, "The Application of Water Power to Industry in the Middle Ages" (Ph.D. dissertation, University of California, Los Angeles, 1966), p. 39 [quoted in Reynolds, *Stronger than a Hundred Men* (note 5), p. 30, n. 51].

[30] Reynolds, *Stronger than a Hundred Men*, pp. 43-44. Steven Walton notes that the massive hub could also provide some inertial advantage to smooth out irregular water flow.

[31] The Barbegal complex was excavated by Benoit in 1940. See Reynolds, *Stronger than a Hundred Men*, pp. 38-41; A. Trevor Hodge, "A Roman Factory," *Scientific American* 263.11 (November 1990): 106-11; Philippe Leveau, "The Barbegal Water Mill in its Environment: Archeology and the Economic and Social History of Antiquity," *Journal of Roman Archeology* 9 (1996): 137-53.

[32] Sagui's estimate, quoted in Reynolds, *Stronger than a Hundred Men*, p. 40.

[33] Excavated by F. Gerald Simpson in 1907-08, and quoted in Reynolds, *Stronger than a Hundred Men*, p. 36.

[34] White, *Greek and Roman Technology* (note 27), pp. 200-01.

[35] Frontinus gives us evidence aplenty that water rights to the aqueduct were zealously controlled by state administrators: Sextus Julius Frontinus, *The Stratagems, and the Aqueducts of Rome*, trans. by C.E. Bennett (Cambridge: Harvard University Press, 1961).

[36] There is a lucid discussion of Bloch's analysis and the nature of the evidence used in Paolo Squatriti, "'Advent and Conquests' of the Water Mill in Italy," in E.B. Smith and M. Wolfe (eds.), *Technology and Resource Use in Medieval Europe: Cathedrals, Mills and Mines* (Aldershot: Ashgate, 1997).

[37] See Adam Lucas, "The Role of Monasteries in the Development of Medieval Milling," ch. 2 in this volume.

[38] Oleson, *Greek and Roman Water-Lifting Devices* (note 2).

[39] Gregory of Tours, *Historiae Ecclesiasticae Francorum* 3.19 [quoted in Richard Bennett and John Elton, *History of Corn Milling* (1898-1904; New York: B. Franklin, 1964), IV:71].

[40] *Ibid.*, IV:199 and Örjan Wikander (ed.), *Handbook of Ancient Water Technology* (Leiden: Brill, 2000), pp. 659-60. White, *Greek and Roman Technology* (note 27), also points out a comment in Cassiodorus' other writings, cited by Wikander (ed.), *Handbook*, p. 400, n. 123, but missed by other scholars, in which he cites the number of watermills still operating in Rome as evidence of the large population still living there. Belisarius' famous rescue of Rome from starvation by the innovation of the float mill happened only a few decades later.

[41] There is evidence that a watermill was one of the first things constructed by St. Columban at Bobbio in the early 7th century. Gregory of Tours tells us of a monastic watermill at Loches around this time, *Vitae patrum* 18.2 [quoted in Reynolds, *Stronger than a Hundred Men* (note 5), p. 49].

[42] Walter Horn and Ernest Born (eds.), *The Plan of St. Gall*, (Berkeley: University of California Press, 1979).

[43] The earlier estimate is from Margaret Hodgen, "Domesday water mills" (1939) and the latter by Sir Henry Darby, *Domesday England* (1977), both quoted in Richard Holt, *The Mills of Medieval England* (Oxford, 1988), pp. 7-8. See also John Langdon, *Mills in the Medieval Economy: England, 1300-1540* (Oxford: Oxford University Press, 2004), pp. 9-15.

[44] Lynn White, Jr., *Medieval Technology and Social Change* (London: Oxford University Press, 1962), p. 81. Two horizontal wheels have been discerned in excavations in Jutland from around the time of Christ. Axel Steensberg, *Farms and Mills in Denmark during Two Thousand Years* (1952) [reported in Reynolds, *Stronger than a Hundred Men*, p. 18, n.24].

[45] Donald Hill, *A History of Engineering in Classical and Medieval Times* (London: Routledge, 1984), p. 159; Reynolds, *Stronger than a Hundred Men* (note 5), pp. 104-05.

[46] Philip Rhatz and Robert Meeson, *An Anglo-Saxon Watermill at Tamworth: Excavations in the Bolebridge Street area of Tamworth, Staffordshire in 1971 and 1978*, CBA Research Report 83 (York: Council for British Archaeology, 1992).

[47] Holt, *Mills of Medieval England*, ch. 8, "Mill Technology and Innovation," discusses the reasons for the replacement of the horizontal mill with the vertical type.

[48] White, *Medieval Technology and Social Change*, p. 81.

[49] The cornmill in figure 8 is a woodcut based directly on a drawing by an anonymous Florentine artist, *c*.1550 (Codex Palatine 1077, fol. 128r) attributed to the school of Francesco

di Giorgio Martini; see Gustina Scaglia, *Francesco di Giorgio: Checklist and History of Manuscripts and Drawings* (Bethlehem, PA: Lehigh University Press, 1992), p. 77, fig. 23.

[50] The marginal drawings found in medieval copies of Vitruvius are often on geometrical subjects such as Pythagorean triangles or the secret method of "doubling the square," known as *quadrature* to medieval monks and builders, as well as demonstrate a fascination with his "diagram of the winds." Renaissance inscriptions lean towards stylistic elements such as column and capital designs. See the careful notes in Carol Herselle Krinsky, "Seventy-Eight Vitruvius Manuscripts," *Journal of the Warburg and Courtauld Institutes* 30 (1967): 36-70.

Mills in Medieval Ireland: Looking Beyond Design

Niall Brady (The Discovery Programme, Dublin)

The presence of Ireland in any discussion on medieval milling is well established.[1] A substantial body of archaeological and documentary evidence survives and seventh-century examples of both horizontal and vertical wheeled watermills are known from there.[2] Attention has focussed on issues relating to mill design and on celebrating the fact that such early sites survive.[3] There has, however, been little discussion of other issues or on mills during the later medieval period. Yet a study of mill sites in medieval Ireland presents the opportunity to look beyond the essential issues that have captivated previous researchers. The mill also represents a touchstone to wider issues relating to the development of the agrarian economy. In discussing the period before 1100, it is possible to argue for a revision of our common understanding that the economy operated at a subsistence level; the character of early mill sites does not sit comfortably within this context. In considering milling in the greater Dublin area after 1100, it is increasingly possible to describe patterns of mill construction, mill ownership, and mill value in the region that served as the hinterland to the medieval capital city.

Mill Design in Medieval Ireland

The study of medieval mill sites in Ireland has attracted scholars since the 1800s when various discoveries were reported in the national archaeological journals. In 1853, the first volume of what was to become the *Journal of the Royal Society of Antiquaries of Ireland* included an anonymous piece that brought together information from a range of sites that had been uncovered during agricultural works in counties Laois, Kilkenny, and Cork.[4] The paper sought to confirm the contexts of discovery as mill sites and argued that the mills were early medieval in date (*c.*500-1100 AD) on the basis of their proximity to ringforts, enclosed settlements of the period. Such a dating context was supported by the body of references to mills in the early law tracts from the same period, and this evidence was used to refute an eighteenth-century view that Ireland lacked the apparatus of milling until the arrival of the Anglo-Normans in 1169. Further descriptions of discoveries were made in the 1850s and the early 1900s, but it was not until 1953 that a definitive account on the horizontal watermill in Ireland was presented by A.T. Lucas.[5]

Working from the National Museum of Ireland in Dublin, Lucas wrote a paper that set out the parameters of mill studies for the next five decades. He described the various discoveries of mills up to 1952, and focussed on the discovery of the near-intact basal remains of a watermill in the Irish midlands at Morrett, Co. Laois. His interest was in the complexity of construction, and Lucas argued that it was most important to record each site in detail so that one could appreciate how the mill operated. His work contributed to the study of early medieval milling in general, and his paper is recognized as taking the understanding of watermills further than Curwen's broader essay of 1944.[6] In discussing the larger European progression of watermill design, Barceló has commented that Lucas was the first to be interested in the details of mill construction to the extent that differences in paddle blade shape and form could reveal simple or more complex mill designs. His awareness of the associated features of mill ponds, mill races, and mill dams also drew attention to the larger landscape context of milling.

The application of dendrochronology, or tree-ring dating, in the 1970s transformed the study of milling because it permitted the close dating of individual sites. With a master sequence of oak in Ireland developed at the Palaeoecology Centre of the Queen's University Belfast, supposition and the testing of supporting evidence then allowed clear chronological contexts for these sites. The early date of various mill sites was confirmed.[7] Colin Rynne, in turn, has continued the focus on mill design and has contributed a number of important insights. The recognition in the archaeological record of the vertical watermill as well as the horizontal watermill was perhaps his first important observation. Building on the work of Edward Fahy, who questioned the engineering details of the mill highlighted by Lucas at Morrett, Rynne noted the lack of any obvious mechanism to jet water vertically from a height as might be expected in a horizontal mill.[8] In its place, the penstock was positioned at the same level as the trough where the water could be introduced on a horizontal trajectory to a driving wheel. This arrangement is entirely in keeping with vertical mills, and Rynne has redefined Morrett as the remains of a vertical undershot mill.[9] The site was also securely dated by dendrochronology to 770.[10] Rynne highlighted a still earlier vertical watermill that came to light as part of a rescue excavation in 1977-1978

Little Island Mill Complex

Figure 1: **Little Island, Co. Cork, site location based on Ordnance Survey mapping.** Source: The Discovery Programme.
Note that the location of the mill is some distance inland of the shoreline. This feature is apparent at other tidal mill sites in Ireland, and may suggest a conscious attempt to minimize exposure to storm-filled seas.

in Cork Harbour on reclaimed land at Little Island, and dated to *c.*630.[11] (Fig. 1) The Little Island milling complex was tidal and produced the remains of a horizontal watermill from the same period. It appears that the horizontal mill was designed to power two mill wheels simultaneously, and it is likely that both the vertical and the horizontal watermills were operated at the same time. Such levels of competency are reflected in other watermill sites across the country and suggest the presence of regional variation in milling types at an early date.[12]

Historians have produced further insight, concentrating on the references to mills in the early Irish law tracts—vernacular law codes that have come down to us as "sacred texts"—which were in turn glossed and commented on at a later date. Gearóid Mac Eoin, for example, has highlighted the Old Irish law tract on Distraint, *De ceithri slichtaib Athgabála*—On the four divisions of distraint (also cited as *Di Chetharshlicht Athgabála*)—which lists the parts that served a horizontal watermill, and has presented them as further evidence for the presence of such mills in the early seventh century and possibly earlier:[13]

Im ocht mbullu ara-fognat muilenn: (1) Topur (2), tuidin (3), tir linde (4), lia (5), mol (6), indeoin (7), ermtiu[d] (8), orcel (9), milaire (10), cup (11), comla (12).

Together with the eight parts that serve a mill: (1) The water source (2), the mill race (3), the land of the pond (4), the upper stone (5), the shaft (6), the lower stone (7), the point of the shaft (8), the chute (9), the pivot stone (10), the hopper (11), the sluicegate (12).

The casual discovery of mill sites by archaeologists across the country continues to build on these essential foundations and to confirm the presence of both horizontal wheeled watermills and vertical undershot watermills throughout the early medieval period.

In 1999, archaeologists studying the intertidal foreshore of Strangford Lough, Co. Down, at the opposite end of the country from Cork, made another early discovery.[14] What began as the excavation of a kelp-strewn stone embankment thought to be a fish trap on the foreshore below the monastic site of Nendrum quickly turned into the excavation of a tidal mill complex. A series of sea walls defining a series of mill ponds emerged. At the head of the primary embankment, excavators focussed their attention on the ruins of up to three consecutive mills. The mills were all horizontal types, and the latest design included a stone wheelhouse. Dating of the large collection of timbers from the various mills and associated features indicates that the mill pond for the first mill was built in 619-621 and enclosed a surface area of 6500m². The third and final mill retained timbers dated to 788 and a large intact sandstone flume measuring 3.41m long and 98cm wide. A preliminary account of the excavation suggests an energy output of 1,750-2,250 kWh per annum. It is hoped that the quality of information which survives at Nendrum will in time allow the excavators to consider the volumes of grain that could be processed at the mill site during its period of use.

There have been two other recent discoveries, and both are currently in the process of being analyzed. The first new discovery is another series of horizontal mills associated with a monastic complex.[15] The discovery was made at Raystown, Co. Meath, as part of a national roads scheme project. The excavator has uncovered the remains of six horizontal watermills and associated mill races within a site that includes five corn-drying kilns, bowl furnaces, and the remains of other work activity, as well as burials. It is thought that a pair of mills was in continuous use and that a new watermill was built when the existing mill went out of use. The date range may extend from the sixth to the twelfth centuries. Without doubt, the nature of the evidence at Raystown bespeaks an elaborate and long-term commitment to the processing of cereal grains in early medieval Ireland. The second recent discovery is that of a vertical undershot watermill that appears to have been a tidal mill as well. The mill was identified during another road-building scheme, this time at Killoteran, Co. Waterford.[16] The interest attached to the site is heightened by the dates that are emerging. Carbon-14 determinations indicate that the mill was used between the fourth and seventh centuries, which makes it the earliest mill site discovered so far in Ireland.[17] The present finding calls to mind a useful essay on early Irish agriculture written in 1944, which noted that the Old Irish word for watermill—*muilenn*—was a Latin borrowing from *molina*.[18] In noting this, Michael Duignan highlighted the Romano-British world in the third-fourth centuries as the obvious source area for milling practices in medieval Ireland. Sixty years on, if the radiocarbon dating proves to be accurate, it appears that archaeologists have been able to discover substantial supporting evidence, and in doing so have dramatically exposed what has been a rather invisible period in the country's archaeological record.

If it is the case that watermills in early medieval Ireland have attracted considerable attention, it is equally the case that mills in the later medieval period have not. The body of archaeological data for milling in the period after 1100 is less substantial. Although references to specific mills are more plentiful, fewer sites have been identified on the ground, and still fewer excavated. Nevertheless both the horizontal wheeled watermill and the vertical undershot watermill continued in use. The windmill is mentioned from the late thirteenth century, but references are few.[19] The use of fulling mills is recorded at Clones, Co. Monaghan, in 1211-12, and in Youghal, Co. Cork, in the late 1270s.[20] A water-powered forge has been identified in a thirteenth- or fourteenth-century context in Cork city.[21] The sense of a more diversified application of mechanical power is clear, if a little less visible and somewhat later than the pattern in neighbouring Britain. It is not until the more widespread and numerous sources of the seventeenth century that reference to industrial mills, such as fulling mills (also known as Tuck mills at this time in Ireland), becomes in any sense a common occurrence.

The remains of later medieval mills do not survive above ground, and the excavated examples have been exclusively at watermill sites or on mill-races. It is still the case that only the basal working levels of a mill-site survive for examination; namely, the timberworks associated with troughs, sluices, dams, penstocks, and occasionally the wheelhouse. The most recent archaeological work published is that of Colin Rynne, reporting on a city excavation site at Patrick Street in Dublin which unearthed a vertical undershot waterwheel.[22] Its earliest identified level has been dated to the mid-thirteenth century and it was extensively rebuilt in the later fourteenth century, when it was accompanied by substantial stone revetments to the inlet and outlet channels which were part of a process of canalization on the underlying river. The archaeologists believed that the excavated mill lasted in use until the early seventeenth century when we know Forde's mill occupied the west side of the street, and may well have had a still earlier ancestry on the basis that the millstreams are thought to have been in existence from the late twelfth century.[23]

A sense of the historical development of the mill and its associated water courses is provided by the records that survive for a neighbouring mill associated with St. Patrick's Cathedral which, in their own way, reveal the sometimes intermittent or discontinuous use of such sites in Ireland. In 1326, the Shyreclap Mill generated an annual rent of 70s, and in 1371 Abbot Thomas Minot demised in farm (*i.e.*, leased)

> to John [Pasvaund, citizen of Dublin] the site of the mill ... now altogether thrown down and void, to rebuild a mill there at his own expense ... to have and to hold the said site and mill when rebuilt, with the ancient mill-course and current, ingress and egress (for all going to the mill and willing to grind there) by a certain bridge over the water-course beside the mill on the south: for 60 years, without rent for two years ... in consideration of his outlay; and after ...[that] at 20s a year ... Lest the water-course should be impeded the archbishop grants John custody of the pond, stone bridge and "flodrates" during the term.[24]

If the mills on Patrick Street are representative of later medieval milling in general, then the substantive contribution which these sites have to make relates to the context they occupy. The urban location is new, while the upgrading and canalization of watercourses and associated features of an active river channel reveals a scale and organization of production that has not been so apparent previously. There are comparisons to be made with the development of hydro-technology in medieval London, but on a more modest scale.[25] In the third section of this paper, an attempt will be made to look beyond the isolated instance of the later mills to consider the broader patterns they form on a regional scale. In the meantime it is appropriate to consider the wider context of milling in the period before the twelfth century.

The Distribution and Dating of Mills in Early Medieval Ireland

The distribution of archaeologically attested early medieval mill sites is based on a range of sources that includes fifty-five sites identified by the National Museum of Ireland in an unpublished catalogue compiled by A.T. Lucas and Brendán Ó Ríordáin in 1970 (Fig. 2). Many of these sites form the baseline data to Rynne's work, and his survey of milling published in 2000 serves as a check and re-affirmation of this information. The distribution also includes the more recent discoveries. The map represents locations where indisputable structural remains have been identified and reasonably well dated, be they intact mill wheels, base-plates, flumes, paddles, mill races, dams, or parts thereof.[26] The isolated occurrences of millstones have not been included as they are less readily datable and are prone to be more mobile, with the result that the find-place may not necessarily be where the millstone was originally used.[27] Mill sites that are attested to exclusively in the historical record are not included in Figure 2 either, as the problems associated with geo-referencing placenames and dating such notices from early medieval sources represent a significant challenge in their own right, and one that lies beyond the scope of the present paper.

Perhaps the most apparent feature of the distribution is the extent to which the spread of sites is not an even one across the country. The contemporary settlements of the period, the earthen or stone enclosures known as ringforts, are found across the country, and apart from the west and northwest in counties Galway, northern Mayo, and Donegal, it is difficult to identify large areas where such sites are poorly represented.[28] In contrast, the concentration of mills in the east and south of Ireland is quite clear, and this must suggest the primary areas of active arable cultivation in the early medieval period. The distribution of mills is also focussed in areas of the more fertile soil groups which supports this observation.[29] There are locations where mills occur on what is today bogland, but in such instances the wet ground is localized and may be related to the need for access to water sources for the particular mill. It would be incorrect to assume that the mills are located on the only good arable land in the country. There are tracts of cultivable soils in the very southeast and elsewhere where few mills have been identified. It is perhaps more accurate to note that there are few mills located in areas where poor soil cover predominates. To balance this picture, it should be not be forgotten that hand querns are a typical occurrence on any early medieval site across the country, and therefore the distribution of mills is not an indica-

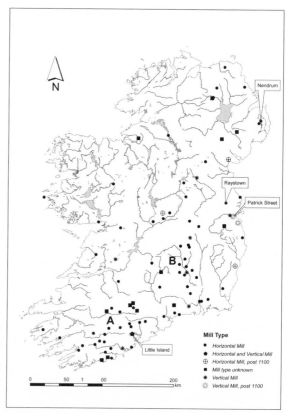

Figure 2: **The Distribution of Early Medieval and Dated Mills in Ireland.** Source: The Discovery Programme. The letters A and B refer to concentrations of mill sites discussed in the text.

Mill Type

- Horizontal Mill
- Horizontal and Vertical Mill
- ⊕ Horizontal Mill, post 1100
- ■ Mill type unknown
- ✳ Vertical Mill
- ❀ Vertical Mill, post 1100

tion of the limits of arable cultivation, but rather highlights where cultivation and processing was most intense.[30]

The early mill sites are generally not built on specific river channels. While there are exceptions, most sites were removed from the main channel and are situated on or adjacent to lesser streams that would in turn flow into a larger river. It is also clear that the mill distribution has two focal areas. Twenty-seven sites are located in Co. Cork alone, in the south of the country (Fig. 2, area A). These tend to be situated along the main river valleys oriented east-west, and along the coast. The second focal point occurs along the River Nore to the east, where twelve sites are found within the river's catchment area in Co. Kilkenny (Fig. 2, area B). The majority of the remaining sites lie in the midland counties and the northeast of the country.

The bulk of the sites that survive are horizontal watermills. Vertical wheeled mills are fewer in number (nine out of a total of ninety-seven) but appear to have become more numerous in the later middle ages. As the example from Patrick Street in Dublin suggests, these mills are associated with more robust and elaborate contexts.

It would be worthwhile to compare the distribution of mills with other aspects of agrarian technology, but this is an aspiration for future study since such work is in its infancy. The case of the plough was addressed several years ago, and while it is possible to generate a distribution of surviving plough irons (iron shares and coulters), the use of the plough proper is witnessed only from the tenth century, before which the evidence suggests that the ard, or scratch plough, predominated.[31] Any comparison with the distribution of mills must also take into account chronological distinctions. Indeed, the distribution of plough irons lies in the northeast and north-central area of the country. It does not echo the southern and southeastern focus of mill sites, and is more in keeping with the distribution of early Viking Age finds and burials.[32] This tends to confirm an origin for the plough in Ireland as a Viking Age phenomenon, but it adds little to the issue of the mill. Further comparative spatial analyses are needed, and at present the mill stands in relative isolation.

The number of mill sites that now exist, however, have begun to provide a critical mass of information that has uses for dating considerations. Of the ninety-seven mills, forty-three sites can be clearly dated (Table 1). Figure 3 simplifies the raw data of Table 1 by showing the chronological spread of sites between the earliest occurrence in what appears to be a fourth-century context, and the latest closely dated site in the thirteenth century. The picture emphasises the chronological distribution apparent in the initial published list of dendrochronologically-dated mills (1982), but it also fills in several of the blank areas and serves to convey a sense of continual construction throughout much of the early period.[33] The renewed building in the seventh century may be associated with what has been argued from written sources to be an era of great agricultural development during the seventh and eighth centuries, when much of the fertile land began to be partitioned among holders and fenced off for the first time.[34] This is in keeping with other indicators, such as pollen research and the study of animal bone assemblages, which suggest a progressive rise in population and a developing agricultural base from the fifth century, if not earlier, that was sustained throughout the early medieval period.[35] What remains striking is the number of sites that belong to the late eighth and early ninth centuries, and the discoveries since 1982 have tended to emphasise this concentration further. The hundred-year block accounts for nineteen of the forty-three sites, and thirteen mills were constructed in the period 800-849 alone. This is the period when the Anglo-Saxon mill at

Table 1: **Dated watermill sites in Ireland, based on dendrochronology (†), C-14, and other dating methods.** Source: Palaeoecology Centre, QUB (†), *et al.*

Site Name	Estimated Felling Date / Date of Construction
Killoteran, Co. Waterford	1530 +/- 60 BP - 2 Sigma, Cal AD 410-650
	1510 +/- 60 BP - 2 Sigma, Cal AD 340 to 600
Nendrum, Co. Down, earliest	AD 619 †
Little Island, Co. Cork	AD 630 †
Ballykilleen, Co. Offaly	AD 636 ± 9 years †
Ballygormill South, Co. Laois	AD 719 ± 9 years or later †
Ballinderry, Co. Derry	AD 744 ± 9 years †
Newcastle Upper, Co. Wicklow	AD 744 ± 9 years or later †
Morett, Co. Laois	AD 770 †
Drumard, Co. Derry	AD 782 †
Ardcloyne, Co. Cork	AD 787 ± 9 years or later †
Nendrum, Co. Down, latest	AD 788 †
Ballyrafton, Co. Kilkenny	AD 794 ± 9 years †
Crushyriree, Co. Cork	AD 799 ± 9 years †
Deer Park Farms, Co. Antrim	8th century
Moycraig, Co. Antrim	8th century
Knocknagranshy, Co. Limerick	8th-9th centuries
Cloghbally Upper, Co. Cavan	AD 803 ± 9 years or later †
Mullantine, Co. Kildare	AD 804 ± 9 years or later †
Cloongowna, Co. Clare	AD 808 ± 9 years †
Boherduff, Co. Galway	AD 810 ± 9 years †
Maghnavery, Co. Armagh	AD 810 ± 9 years †
Ballygeardra, Co. Kilkenny	AD 811 ± 9 years †
Ardnagross, Co. Westmeath	AD 812 ± 9 years †
Rasharkin, Co. Antrim	AD 822 †
Killphillibeen, Co. Cork	c. AD 827 †
Ballynoe, Co. Cork	AD 827 ± 9 years †
Cloontycarthy, Co. Cork	AD 833 †
Ballydowne West, Co. Waterford	AD 841 ± 9 years †
Keelaraheen, Co. Cork	AD 843 †
Coolboy, Co. Wexford	AD 873 ± 9 years †
Farranmareen, Co. Cork	AD 873 ± 9 years †
Lowesgreen, Co. Tipperary	AD 890 ± 9 years †
Brabstown, Co. Kilkenny	AD 913 ± 9 years †
Clonlea, Co. Clare	AD 914 ± 9 years †
Newtown, Co. Tipperary	AD 914 ± 9 years or later †
Ballyroe, Co. Wexford	AD 916 ± 9 years †
Rossorry, Co. Fermanagh	AD 926 ± 9 years †
Knocknacarragh, Co. Galway	AD 973 ± 9 years or later †
Carrickmines Great, Co. Dublin	AD 1123 ± 9 years or later †
Clonlonan, Co. Westmeath	AD 1149 ± 9 years or later †
Corcannon, Co. Wexford	AD 1228 ± 9 years †
Ballymascanlan, Co. Louth	AD 1243 ± 9 years †
Patrick Street, Co. Dublin	13th and 14th century

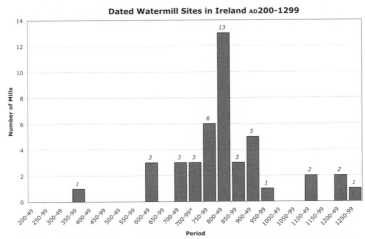

Figure 3: **Chart showing progression of mill construction in medieval Ireland.** Source: Palaeoecology Centre, QUB, et al. Sites that cannot be tied to within a 50-year period are not included. The very early site indicated in the fourth century (Killoteran) may be revised with further analysis of the more fully excavated findings.

Tamworth was built.[36] In Ireland, it is a time of realization for dynastic ambition, be that by secular or monastic interests.[37] It is also the period of the so-called "Golden Age" of largely ecclesiastical art, when the Derrynaflan and Ardagh liturgical chalices were made and other great works produced. It is worth noting that the distribution of mill sites along the Nore valley extends westwards into County Tipperary (Fig. 2, area B), and falls within a regional concentration of high status metalwork in the South Midlands-North Munster zone that has been identified as an especially rich location which could support such prestige work.[38] The mill sites may well inform this discussion by suggesting key areas of production at the local level. In contrast, the absence of construction that follows in the eleventh century is more difficult to understand given the changes then wrought across the island, while the twelfth- and thirteenth-century sites reflect the development sparked first by the coming of the continental orders in 1142 with the establishment of the Cistercian foundation of Mellifont, Co. Louth, and then by the Anglo-Norman colonization from 1169.

The distributional focus on the south and east of the country presents a strong indication of the heartlands of arable husbandry in this period, while the concentration of building in the late eighth and early ninth centuries mirrors broader patterns of social development that are represented widely as the so-called "Golden Age" of early Ireland. There are significant limitations inherent in this discussion, and at a fundamental level the need for further research on agrarian matters is essential to broaden the scope of enquiry in a manner that retains the focus on the production and processing of food. The degree to which there is a meaningful discussion on the nature of the early Irish economy is also central to this theme. The great historian of the early law tracts, Daniel Binchy, famously characterized early Irish society as "tribal, rural, hierarchical and familiar."[39] It is a view that is largely discarded today, but some individuals still support the thesis.[40] More discrete research reveals that the growth of monastic settlements in the seventh and eighth centuries would have encouraged development, and the trading apparatus of the Hiberno-Norse port towns developing from the mid-ninth century in turn forced a still more significant pace of change.[41] Mainstream historians from the later period, for their part, accept that an important agrarian base had developed in Ireland by the tenth century and that the newcomers of the twelfth century developed the existing situation rather than contributed any revolutionary change.[42] The evidence from the early mill sites indicates the presence of an active and vibrant economic structure much earlier in the early medieval period than the tenth century, and this aspect should prompt us to reconsider our understanding of the economic dynamic at work throughout the early medieval period.

Mills and Economy in Early Medieval Ireland

In 1953, Lucas stated at the outset of his discussion on mills that it was "necessary to avoid falling into the error of overestimating their importance and to remember that... a large proportion of the meal and flour for domestic consumption was produced... by means of querns and mortars of various kinds."[43] Lucas had a great affection for ethnology and this may have influenced his tendency to downplay the contribution of technologically advanced systems of production. His sentiment was echoed by Mike Baillie in 1975 when reporting on the first mill to be securely dated by dendrochronology. In Baillie's view, the horizontal mill was the "simplest possible mechanical adaptation of the hand-operated rotary quern. Its major advantage was not seen as a speeding up of the grinding process but as removal of the drudgery associated with manual operation."[44] In contrast, the contemporary written sources suggest a different view. The Old Irish law tracts, which are concerned with how society should exist, not only include a list of the parts of a mill noted above but also recognized mill ownership as an attribute of status. While a mill could be owned cooperatively, the tract on status, *Críth Gablach*, observed that not every freeman was entitled to own his own mill; this was a right reserved for the prosperous commoners and the lords above them.[45] There is a sense of mill ownership as something that required significant capital. Fergus Kelly's close study of the law tracts has noted that the watermill was undoubtedly the most complex piece of technology regularly encountered by an early Irish farmer.[46] Colin Rynne has developed this further by highlighting the fact that the millwright was accorded the lowest rank of nobility.[47] Nevertheless, in terms of assessing the productive capacity of the early mill sites in Ireland, Rynne seems reluctant to appreciate their full potential. Writing in 1990, he was content to note that the nature of the milling reflected an ability to process larger amounts of grain more efficiently and, perhaps, a more broad-based distributive network for cereals.[48] Yet he has not developed this important line of enquiry. Three sites will serve to illustrate the presence of an energetic economic dynamic.

The mill complex at Nendrum, Co. Down, stands out as being different. It is situated on the foreshore below what historians celebrate as one of the most complete examples of an early Irish monastery, where previous excavation, if poorly conducted and reported, has nevertheless shown evidence for occupation and industrial activity and a wide range of locally produced as well as imported artefacts.[49] The more recent excavation programme focussed on the mill site and revealed different phases of mill construction, suggesting the effort expended to construct the associated millponds within the tidal regime. The results further indicate a large-scale and organized construction and maintenance programme that must have satisfied the needs of the large monastic community, if not exceeded them. It remains possible that the mill ponds served a dual function by acting as fish traps as well. The cumulative impression provided by the archaeological data suggests that this was a zone of developed exploitation and production. As noted above, the quality of the information retrieved has also permitted some initial calculations to be made of the potential energy available for milling.[50] When this aspect is developed more fully, it could reveal the extent of milling that was possible over the two centuries of use. Such information may then be used to consider the mill's catchment area. Nendrum lies at the centre of its own small estate whose later boundaries have been charted.[51] It is also within a larger area of good soil cover which would have been suitable for arable cultivation.[52] The sources required to construct the larger context of the Nendrum mill complex therefore appear to exist, and it is hoped that the excavators will be able to develop such lines of enquiry.

The location of Nendrum on the northwest shore of Strangford Lough is in an area that was intensively exploited by large-scale concerns throughout the period. This is evident in the presence of five wooden fish traps that have been discovered close to one another on the eastern shore and dated to between the late seventh and the late twelfth centuries, below what would become in 1193 the Cistercian foundation and fishery of Greyabbey (some 7.2km away, across open water from Nendrum).[53] The early sources are unclear about who operated the fish traps, but it is evident that these lands were part of the monastic estate of Moville, a major concern in the area. Indeed, it may also be that Nendrum was a dependency of the larger bishopric of Armagh and owed her tribute. If this was the case, an argument could be made to suggest that Nendrum served as a specialist centre to provide grain to support the population in Armagh.[54] It is increasingly difficult to see this rural landscape in the northeast of the country as one of quiet dispersed settlement. In contrast, the image is of a busy landscape where large-scale production and therefore trade was dominant.

Charles Doherty has considered the economic context of early Irish society in this period, and in particular that of the Church.[55] He has argued that the larger monasteries exercised control over great estates that are believed to have been organized in a similar way to monastic estates on the continent and to secular estates in Ireland.[56] As secular settlement burgeoned on the fringes of the main enclosures, the monasteries began to act as centres of exchange. The business of feeding and clothing the immediate community as well as those outside the monastery became a busy one, and the adoption by monasteries from the eighth century of the tribal *óenach*, or market, suggests that that level of exchange existed. The *óenach* was a regular feature by the tenth century.[57] Some years ago, John Bradley urged caution against idealizing this early medieval past in terms of the present free market economic paradigm.[58] We should be sensitive to the powerful influence of religion in this society, and therefore cautious not to push the degree of economic maturity too far. Yet it is increasingly difficult to be satisfied with a model of simple exchange, and Bradley now recognizes this in light of the recent archaeological discoveries; the archaeological data are forcing the issue.[59] One of the two new mill sites may represent an outlying production centre that could have serviced a larger monastery. Although its excavation has only been completed, the contexts of the mills at Raystown, Co. Meath, already suggest that this was an elaborate agricultural centre. In addition to the series of six watermills, the remains of five corn-drying kilns, along with bowl furnaces, hearths, and multiple ditches are being exposed within an oblong enclosure measuring approximately 200m by 270m, and which the excavator considers may have been some form of monastic farm. The sense to which it was a centre for large-scale production is difficult to ignore.

A third site that fits this picture of intensive productive capacity is the watermill complex at Little Island, Co. Cork. What is striking in this case is the fact that both the vertical wheeled mill and the horizontal mill appear to have coexisted in the early seventh century. Bearing in mind that the horizontal mill had two flumes, it was therefore possible that the mill complex could have driven three millstones simultaneously. Such a situation would represent large-scale production, and should be recognized as such.[60] Little Island and Nendrum have another feature in common: both sites were tidal mills. Tidal mills represent construction programmes often in exposed locations where the harsh conditions of the sea would have required sturdy building and constant maintenance. Records that document the costs of mills are not available for this period in Ireland, but a later example from England may serve as illustration from the end of the thirteenth century.[61] Henry of Eastry, Prior of Christ Church, Canterbury, was prepared to invest £143 13s to replace a tidal mill on the Isle of Thanet in Kent that had been destroyed in 1290. The mill achieved an annual rent of 25 quarters of wheat, but was destroyed once again in 1316 by floods. The prior was committed to the mill and spent another £74 13s 4d in its relocation and rebuilding. However, the mill was destroyed once again in 1326 by high tides. At this stage Henry had had enough. He abandoned the tidal location thirty-six years after his first recorded rebuild, and built a windmill as a replacement for a mere £12 19s. The prior's story begs a question of justification that can be applied to other tidal mills: why were patrons willing to invest so heavily in a tidal location? Was it not simpler to divert watercourses on land in a more protected environment where there was no exposure to storms and raging seas, and consequently the risk of destruction was far less?

In an Irish context, the early law tract known as *Coibnes Uisci Thairidne*— The Kinship of Conducted Water—provides some insight. While focussing on milling, the seventh-century tract is concerned with the rules for conducting water across neighbours' lands to power a mill. It states:[62]

> Dligid cach comaithech diarailiu tuididin usci thairidne tara c[h]rich
> I neoch ma fo-creth(th)er a fhoch[h]raic téchta[i]; ro[-ch] suidiged
> a fochraic-side for séo(i)t deich screpul dar cach m(b)ru[i]g do-tæt.
> Neoch mad e(a) t[h]am, ceni gaba acht lethgabail de, di-renar in
> chruth-so. Mad ainmín immurgu is let[h]sét inna lóg-side. Alaliu is
> lá cach(a) tire do-tét dlega(i)r aire.

> Each neighbour is entitled from the other to [be allowed to] conduct
> a mill-race across his land if it be paid for with its proper fee; and the
> fee for this has been fixed at a sét worth ten scruples for every stead to
> which it comes. If it be arable land, though it (the mill-race) occupy
> but half a pace(?), it is paid for in this wise. If, however, it be rough
> land, a half-sét is the fee for that. Alternatively a day [at the mill] for
> each parcel of land to which it comes is due for it.

Although the law tracts are notoriously idealistic insofar as they attempt to convey a sense of society as defined by jurists, it is generally accepted that they retain useful indicators of everyday life. In the present context, *Coibnes Uisci Thairidne* is less concerned with the mill per se than it is with the claim that neighbours could have on a mill. While a mill owner had the right to cut a mill-race across a neighbour's lands, he was obliged to pay such landowners an appropriate fee in compensation. This would detract from the profitability of a mill. An ideal solution would be to locate the mill in a location where no one else would be able to claim a part of the mill's profit. Failing access to watercourses on one's own lands, tidal locations would have suited this purpose. The construction of mill ponds along the intertidal foreshore would have used the filling tide to guarantee sufficient headwaters to power a mill on a daily cycle at no "rental" cost to the mill-owner.[63] The presence of the mills at Nendrum and Little Island testify to a commitment to build in these locations. The continued construction of three generations of mill at Nendrum is further testimony to the long-term nature of such a commitment, and echoes the devotion that Henry of Eastry was to give to his tidal mill in Kent.[64]

There are indications of tidal mills elsewhere in Ireland, with seven known sites including Little Island and Nendrum.[65] (Fig. 2) It is perhaps worth noting that not all sites are located on harsh exposed locations. For its part, the Nendrum mill is located in a sheltered part of the Lough, while both of the other excavated mill sites, at Little Island and Killoteran, are situated at a remove from the active shoreline (Fig. 1). This pattern of location suggests the desire to use the tidal waters while at the same time protect the investment in mill structure and components as much as possible. If the decision was informed by a desire to capitalize on the profitability of the mill, as I have suggested, the implications for our understanding of the early Irish economy are significant. Such a rationale does not sit comfortably with the subsistence-based structure prior to the eighth century proposed by Binchy in the 1950s. Nor does it suit the view of a changing economic force during the 700s that was limited to internal or small-scale networks to serve the specific needs of monastic communities. Instead the tidal mill may present a glimpse of a rational economic mind that was concerned with profit from an early date.[66] There is no problem in recognizing the existence of a market economy in the later medieval period, but the situation is different for the earlier period. Clearly more research is required, both on mill sites and on other aspects of the early economy.[67] Perhaps too, scholars have to be more open-minded about the economic aspirations of the Irish during the first millennium A.D. The purpose here is merely to raise the possibilities associated with watermills, and it is hoped that this will provoke an interest that extends beyond the existing focus which has been exclusively on mill design.

Mills in Later Medieval Ireland

In contrast to the period before 1100 where documentary references to mills are generalized, there are frequent and direct references to specific mills in the later medieval period, thanks largely to the survival of manorial extents. The identification of these more numerous sites on the ground is problematical, however, as relatively few have been located. It is not clear why this is so, although one possibility is that the sites of later mills were continually developed during the seventeenth and eighteenth centuries, and large industrial mills were built on the same sites as the medieval mills which essentially erased them from view. The excavated watermill at Patrick Street in Dublin does suggest a scale of construction that was not apparent previously, as well as perhaps a tendency for late sites to be positioned closer to active channels than had been the case before. The discovery of further late sites will help to qualify the implications that such structural aspects suggest. Meanwhile it is possible to consider a broader perspective on later mill sites by looking at the references to mills that occur within a 30km study area around Dublin, the medieval capital city.[68]

The landscape of the study area is dominated by the broad, low-lying floodplain of the River Liffey which empties into the Irish Sea at Dublin and extends westwards through north County Kildare before turning south to its point of origin in the Wicklow Mountains. The same rolling flat land occurs to the north, and if the study area was extended in this direction it would encounter the river valley and floodplain of the Boyne. This is rich agricultural land even today, and where the modern metropolis has not already extended onto the good tillage and pasture lands, market gardening and crop husbandry are favoured over stock-rearing and dairying. In contrast, the mountainous south is given over largely to sheep. That this was intensively settled in the later middle ages is not in doubt; the survival of castles, churches, and other standing structures from the period

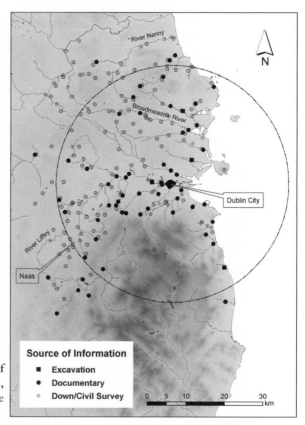

Figure 4: Distribution of Mills in the Dublin region, *c*.1100-1650. Source: The Discovery Programme.

form a dense distribution across the area, with the majority of the land held by the Church in its many and diverse estates.[69]

One hundred thirty-five references to mills have been assembled from the body of sources available for the Dublin area between *c*.1180 and 1550, and a further block of information exists in the seventeenth-century Down and Civil Surveys.[70] Documentary references to mills in the earlier period come partly from extents which survive in two groups; those from the period 1250-1350, and those from the period of the Dissolution in 1540. Other references come from a variety of administrative, judicial, and ecclesiastical sources. In common with what Richard Holt has described for England, the sources in the Dublin area do not reveal details of a mill's construction, and this situation reinforces the importance of archaeological discoveries such as those at Patrick Street.[71] More typically, the documentary information refers to the granting of lands for mills;

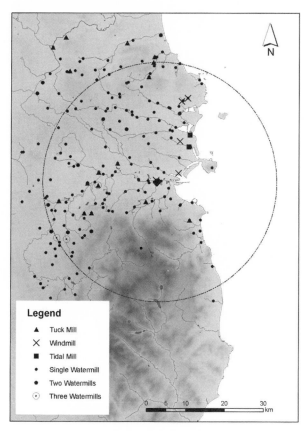

Figure 5: **Types of Mill in the Dublin region,** *c.***1100-1650.** Source: The Discovery Programme.

the leasing of mills; the value of a mill as a manorial component or at the time of the miller's death; and the fate wrought on mills by natural elements. Two new mills, for example, were erected for the King in 1248 near Dublin Castle, while in 1302 the King's mills below Dublin Castle were knocked down in a flood.[72] In neither instance do the sources reveal the sums of monies involved in the construction, income, or repair of these mills. In another example, we see something of the property disputes of which mills fell foul: in 1303, a fishing net attached to the bridge in Dublin was removed by the Prior of Kilmainham, and Dubliners destroyed the prior's mill in retaliation.[73] In yet another, we glimpse the interior of a mill: in 1310, at Castlemartin, Co. Kildare, to the southwest of the city, the death of the miller was reported as an accident in the workplace when the upper millstone broke into three parts and one part struck him as he "prepared the mill

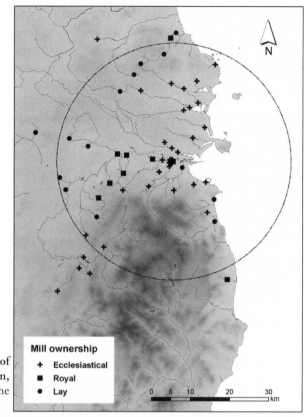

Figure 6: Ownership of
Mills in the Dublin region,
c.1250-1540. Source: The
Discovery Programme.

Mill ownership

+ Ecclesiastical
■ Royal
● Lay

for milling." Value of the upper millstone, the inner and outer wheel and iron of
the said mill, was stated as 7s.[74]

The distribution of mills from archaeological and historical sources is indicated on Figure 4, and includes sites recorded in the seventeenth-century surveys. A note should be made on the actual location of these sites. Where a site
has not been validated by excavation or field survey (and there have been very few
instances where this is possible), the location is based on a combination of attributes that include townland name, reference to the mill being close to or powered by a named stream, and the type of mill where this is recorded. It cannot
be stated that the locations are precisely identified, but the approach indicates
the general location within a deviation of c. 100m, which is more than adequate
for the present level of enquiry. The map shows that mills were not built in any
numbers in the Wicklow Mountains to the south, where high altitude and mar-

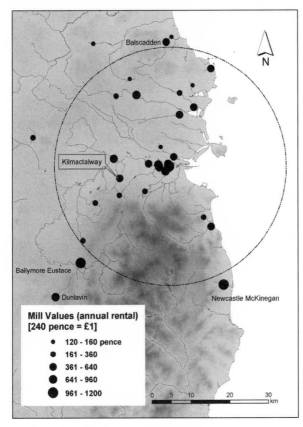

Figure 7: **Value of Mills in the Dublin region,** c.1250-1540. Source: The Discovery Programme.

ginal land predominates.[75] Instead, the distribution follows centres of population. Mills are concentrated on the coastal area, in Dublin city itself, and along the main river valleys which include the Liffey to the west and southwest of the city, and the Broadmeadow, Delvin, and Nanny rivers to the north. The map also suggests a sense of development through time. It will be noted from Figure 2 that few early medieval sites are identified within the study area. This pattern was to change, and by the mid-1200s and on to the mid-1500s significant numbers of mills were constructed. The mills are distributed along the coastal zone particularly to the north of the city, in the city itself, and along the River Liffey valley. By the mid-1600s there were still greater numbers of mills, with an intensification of building in the focal areas, and an extension to the lesser river systems to the north and west of the city itself.

If this is a crude indicator, it nevertheless gives the impression of continuous development throughout the period. Figure 5, in turn, attempts to show the variety of mills in use. The task is often frustrated by the lack of concern to distinguish the type of mill in the sources, other than to indicate whether it was water-powered or not. Consequently, most of the sites are simply referred to as watermills. This is especially frustrating when considering the coastal sites, ten of which could well have operated as tidal mills but only two are identified as such. The records do however distinguish between water power and wind power. The earliest reference to windmills in Ireland is in 1281, and the first example in the Dublin area is in the extent of the lands of William de Vescey at Kildare in 1297, where he had "a windmill worth 26s 8d a year."[76] The next reference occurs in 1330 when Holy Trinity Priory leased land to William de Boseworth in Ostmantown Green, "where Holy Trinity had a windmill."[77] If the Dublin area is representative of the national picture, windmills never became a competitive rival to water power, since there are only six instances identified in our survey. Aside of the two already cited, the other four sites are located close to the coastal zone presumably to avail of the wind off the sea, and they appear as late sites, recorded for the first time in seventeenth-century surveys. Equally, the first reference to tuck (fulling) mills is late, and the distribution of these sites is concentrated on the Liffey valley area and also on the catchments of the rivers Broadmeadow, Delvin, and Nanny in the north of the study area. The distribution may indicate where industrial development was beginning to take hold at the end of the middle ages.

The pattern of mill ownership is shown on Figure 6, and this map is restricted to the period up to 1540. As the dominant landowner, it is little surprise to see the Church as the primary mill owner as well, and the concentration of sites within and immediately surrounding the city reflects the presence of the ecclesiastical houses in the city. The outlying loose concentration in the southwest highlights the town of Naas, where the mills would have serviced that town's needs. For its part, the Crown owned several mills, and with the exception of the King's Mills in Dublin Castle referred to above, the royal mills are located on royal manors at some distance from the city. There is a clear concentration of the royal mills in the middle section of the Liffey valley, in the areas where tuck mills were to become popular somewhat later, and there are two other mills that lie just outside the 30km radius, at Balscadden in the north (which also developed as a tuck mill by the mid-1600s) and Newcastle McKenegan in the southeast. Lay mill sites also developed that were owned by neither institution. There are similar numbers of lay mills and royal mills (ten and nine respectively) and these are also located away from the city itself. However, the majority of lay mills are situated in an outer belt that lies at a remove far from the central zone. These outer mill sites are also distributed in a relatively even manner which may indicate that the produce was consumed locally rather than in the city and its markets.

The wider project from which this preliminary data is taken will be considering mills in greater detail, as it examines the nature and extent of milling at particular sites within the context of supplying the capital city with its needs for consumption and trade. Figure 7 shows the value of mills as represented in 1250-1350 and at the Dissolution.[78] In general what is being valued in the extent is the yearly profit accruing to the owner from the mill. This would represent the value of sales from grain levied as toll from tenants using the mill (referred to as multure) if the mill is under the lord's direct management. Alternatively it would represent the "farm" or rent of the mill if it is being leased out. The value given therefore represents the productive capacity of the mill rather than the inherent value of the structure, machinery, and other equipment (on occasion, the annual yield of eels from the mill pond is also part of the calculation). Frequently the value of the mill is said to be "less" the cost of repairs and maintenance, and sometimes it is said to be "over and above" the cost of upkeep. When a mill was leased out the lessee was usually in charge of maintenance. On occasion the terms of the lease included a remission of the first year's rent in order to allow the lessee to make necessary repairs and sometimes even rebuild the mill. In 1373 when Archbishop Minot of Dublin granted Thomas FitzEustace the mill of Ballymore Eustace, the lease required FitzEustace to keep the mill "styff and staunch" at his own expense.[79] The value of the mill was obviously lower if it was in bad repair. An extent of 1351 for Kilmactalway values the mill at 4 marks, "and not more because it is old and tumble down and there are not many of the king's tenants to use it."[80]

The variety of ways in which the value of a mill might be calculated as well as the conditional factors such as state of repair and arrangements for maintenance means that caution must be exercised in comparing the value of one mill with another. Nevertheless, some general observations can be made. In the period 1250-1350 the average annual value of a watermill was somewhere between one and two pounds. There were some mills with values significantly greater than this, for example the mills at Dublin Castle and at St. Sepulchre's. More surprising are the valuable mills at Newcastle McKenegan and Dunlavin, Co. Wicklow, in the southeast, said to be worth £5 and £4 respectively, and at Ballymore Eustace, Co. Kildare, where two mills had a combined value of £10 in 1326. In 1540, of the eighteen mills valued not one could match the £5 valuations cited above. However, the average mill value had risen to between three and four pounds per annum. Two mills were valued at £4, one of which, that belonging to the Hospital at Kilmainham, was a double mill with two pairs of millstones under one roof.

In considering the overall pattern of values depicted in Figure 7, the central importance of the city area is once again clear, but higher values are also apparent at a remove from it. On the edges of the study area, whether to the north, in the southwest in the vicinity of Naas, or in the southeast at Newcastle McKenegan, mill values are noticeably higher than they are in the intervening areas. At Newcastle McKenegan, it is no doubt because the royal mill was the only milling facility in the larger neighbourhood, and it is centrally placed along this narrow coastal belt to service most requirements. Values are available for mills owned by lay lords as well, and these tend to be relatively low, suggesting once again that these mills served local interests only. The evidence for lay mills is nevertheless sufficient to argue that the documentary material within the larger Dublin area is not socially selective. This is an important observation because the received view is that the sources reveal little about people who lived outside the two institutions of Church and Crown. The Dublin study tries to make the common voice heard.

Concluding Remarks

This paper has taken a different approach to the study of medieval mills in Ireland. Instead of focussing on the details of design, as in internalist approaches to the history of technology, the emphasis has been to look beyond the essential construction of mills in an attempt to gauge the degree to which mill sites can inform broader issues that, in this instance, look at the economic bases of the country. The result has perhaps achieved little beyond suggesting future possibilities. Yet I would contend that the early mill sites, and in particular tidal mills, prompt us to reassess the essential economic paradigm that has been formulated to characterise development in Ireland during the early middle ages. In turn, and by isolating references to milling alone, there is sufficient material in Ireland to articulate a discussion on the organization of the later medieval countryside; a discussion that can be carried out within a context that economic historians have developed to understand the growth of the medieval economy in England. Internalist historians of technology can all too easily remain fixated on the detail of the apparatus that is their primary point of reference. Yet it is incumbent on us, as demonstrated by many of the papers in this volume, to reach beyond the particular to try to place the findings within the broader context, and indeed to see whether the technology can in its own way help to illuminate and modify mainstream paradigms of cultural development.

Acknowledgements

I am grateful to Donald Murphy and Matthew Seaver for allowing me to report on their current excavations in advance of their completion; to Mike Baillie and David Brown at the Palaeoecology Centre, Queen's University Belfast, for sending me a current list of dendrochonologically-dated sites; and to Colin Rynne for ensuring that my reading of his work was up to date. The paper has been read by Charles Doherty, Adam Lucas, Finbar McCormick, and the volume's editor. I greatly appreciate their insight and comments which have helped to tighten up the presentation. Errors and inadequacies remain my responsibility. My colleagues within the Discovery Programme's Medieval Rural Settlement project have also contributed assistance in various ways, especially Michael Potterton who prepared Figures 4-7, Anne Connon who carried out some searches of the earlier sources, and Margaret Murphy who prepared the later sources and commented on a draft of the paper. To each I owe my thanks and appreciation.

Notes

[1] A short list of recent work will suffice: P.A. Rahtz, "Medieval Milling," *Council for British Archaeology Reports* 40 (1981); Örjan Wikander, "Archaeological Evidence for Early Water-mills—an interim report," *History of Technology* 10 (1985): 151-79; Richard Holt, *The Mills of Medieval England* (Oxford: Blackwell, 1988); Miquel Barceló, "The Missing Watermill: a question of technological diffusion in the High Middle Ages," in Miquel Barceló and François Sigaut (eds.), *The Making of Feudal Agricultures?* (Leiden: Brill, 2004), pp. 255-314; John Langdon, *Mills in the Medieval Economy. England 1300-1540* (Oxford: Oxford University Press, 2004).

[2] A.T. Lucas, "The Horizontal Mill in Ireland," *Journal of the Royal Society of Antiquaries of Ireland* 83 (1953): 1-37; E.M. Fahy, "A Horizontal Mill at Mashanaglass, Co. Cork," *Journal of the Cork Historical and Archaeological Society* 61 (1956): 13-57; Colin Rynne, "The Introduction of the Vertical Watermill into Ireland: some recent archaeological evidence," *Medieval Archaeology* 33 (1989): 21-31; Colin Rynne, *Technological Change in Anglo-Norman Munster,* Barryscourt Lectures 3 (Cork, 1998; rpt. in *Medieval Ireland. The Barryscourt Lectures I-X* [Kinsale: Barryscourt Trust, 2004]), pp. 65-95; Colin Rynne, "Waterpower in Medieval Ireland," in P. Squatriti (ed.), *Working with Water in Medieval Europe. Technology and Resource-Use* (Leiden: Brill, 2000), pp. 1-50; T. McErlean and N. Crothers, "The Early Medieval Tide Mills at Nendrum: an interim statement," in Thomas McErlean, Rosemary McConkey, and Wes Forsythe (eds.), *Strangford Lough: an archaeological survey of the maritime cultural landscape* (Belfast: Blackstaff Press, 2002), pp. 200-211.

[3] Research in England indicates the potential of addressing milling in broader contexts; see especially Holt, *The Mills of Medieval England* and Langdon, *Mills in the Medieval Economy*.

[4] "Ancient Irish water-mills," *Transactions of the Kilkenny Archaeological Society* 1 (1849-51): 154-64.

[5] R. MacAdam, "Ancient Water-mills," *Ulster Journal of Archaeology* 4 (1856): 6-15; H.T. Knox, "Notes on Gig-mills and Drying Kilns near Ballyhaunis, Co. Mayo," *Proceedings of the Royal Irish Academy* 26C (1906-07): 265-73; Lucas, "The Horizontal Mill in Ireland."

[6] E.C. Curwen, "The Problem of Early Water-mills," *Antiquity* 18 (1944): 130-46; Miquel Barceló, "The Missing Water-mill," pp. 260-61.

[7] M.G.L. Baillie, "A Horizontal Mill of the Eighth Century A.D. at Drumard, Co. Derry," *Ulster Journal of Archaeology* 38 (1975): 25-32; M.G.L. Baillie, *Tree-Ring Dating and Archaeology* (London: Croom Helm, 1982), p. 182.

[8] Rynne, "The Introduction of the Vertical Watermill" (note 2), pp. 24-26; see also Fahy, "A Horizontal Mill" (note 2).

[9] However, not everyone agrees that Rynne has offered a convincing argument: see Dáibhí Ó Cróinín, *Early Medieval Ireland 400-1200* (London: Longman, 1995), p. 96, n. 77.

[10] Baillie, *Tree-Ring Dating and Archaeology*, p. 182.

[11] Rynne, "The Introduction of the Vertical Watermill" (note 2), p. 26; Denis Power (ed.), *Archaeological Inventory of County Cork. Volume 2: East and South Cork* (Dublin: Stationary Office, 1994), p. 165.

[12] Rynne, "Waterpower in Medieval Ireland" (note 2), pp. 9, 19-40.

[13] Gearóid Mac Eoin (ed. and trans.), "The early Irish vocabulary of mills and milling," in B.G. Scott (ed.), *Studies of Early Ireland: Essays in honour of M. V. Duignan* (Belfast: Association of Young Irish Archaeologists, 1982), pp. 13-19, at pp. 14-15. For a similar survey of slightly later Anglo-Saxon references to water mills, see Philip Rahtz and Donald Bullough, "The Parts of an Anglo-Saxon Mill," *Anglo-Saxon England* 6 (1977): 15-37. It is of interest that the Laws do not consider the presence of vertical wheeled mills, and this gap is perhaps worth exploring further on another occasion. I am grateful to Adam Lucas for pointing out this matter.

[14] McErlean and Crothers, "The Early Medieval Tide Mills at Nendrum" (note 2), pp. 201-11.

[15] I am grateful to Matthew Seaver, site director, for this information ahead of publication, and to Cultural Resources Development Services Ltd. for permission to bring attention to the site at this early stage of its post-excavation work on behalf of Meath County Council and the National Roads Authority. See Matthew Seaver, "Run of the mill? Excavation of an early medieval site at Raystown, Co. Meath," *Archaeology Ireland* 19.4 (2006): 9-12.

[16] I am grateful to Donald Murphy for this information ahead of publication, and to his company Archaeological Consultancy Services Ltd. for permission to bring attention to the site at this early stage of its excavation on behalf of Waterford County Council and the National Roads Authority. He has also supplied the following detail: two samples from planks on the site have returned calibrated dates of 1530±60 BP - 2 Sigma Calibration Cal (AD 410 to 650), and 1510±60 BP - 2 Sigma Calibration Cal (AD 340 to 600) respectively.

[17] It should be noted that the dates returned have a wide standard deviation, and further analysis of the site data may refine this view.

[18] Michael Duignan, "Irish Agriculture in Early Historic Times," *Journal of the Royal Society of Antiquaries of Ireland* 74 (1944): 124-45, at p. 144.

[19] The earliest reference appears to be at Kilscanlan, near Old Ross, Co. Wexford, dated 1281, and cited in Rynne, *Technological Change* (note 2), p. 79.

[20] Rynne, *Technological Change*, p. 86.

[21] Maurice Hurley, *Excavations at the North Gate, Cork, 1994* (Cork: Cork Corporation, 1997), pp. 45-49; and cited in Rynne, "Waterpower in Medieval Ireland" (note 2), p. 45.

[22] Colin Rynne, "The Patrick Street Watermills," in Claire Walsh (ed.), *Archaeological Excavations at Patrick, Nicholas and Winetavern Streets, Dublin* (Dingle: Brandon, 1997), pp. 81-89.

[23] Howard Clarke, *Dublin Part I, to 1610*, Irish Historic Towns Atlas no. 11 (Dublin: Royal Irish Academy, 2002), p. 26.

[24] Charles McNeill (ed.), *Calendar of Archbishop Alen's Register, c.1172-1534* (Dublin: Royal Society of Antiquaries of Ireland, 1950), pp. 171, 220.

[25] See Clarke, *Dublin to 1610*, p. 9; and Roberta Magnusson, "Public and Private Urban Hydrology: Water Management in Medieval London," ch. 8 in this volume.

[26] Certain later sites, highlighted on the map as outline symbols, are included because dates exist for them, although strictly speaking they fall outside the time-frame under review.

[27] To take the millstones home would guard against illegal use of the mill, an abuse that is noted in the laws: D.A. Binchy (ed.), *Corpus iuris hibernici* (Dublin: Institute for Advanced Studies, 1978): 383.32-33; W.N. Hancock, *et al.* (eds.), *Ancient Laws of Ireland* (Dublin: HMSO, 1865-1901), I:162.23-24.

[28] Matthew Stout, *The Irish Ringfort* (Dublin: Four Courts Press, 1997), p. 54.

[29] Comparison has been made with the *General Soil Map of Ireland*, 1:575,000, 2[d] ed. (Dublin: National Soil Survey, 1980).

[30] The distribution of hand querns has not been plotted in recent years but they remain a common occurrence, and a survey of finds from ringforts published in 1961 serves as a background study: V. Proudfoot, "The Economy of the Irish Rath," *Medieval Archaeology* 5 (1961): 94-122.

[31] Niall Brady, "Reconstructing a Medieval Irish Plough," in *Primeras Jornadas sobre Tecnologia Agraria Tradicional*, (Madrid: Direccion Gral. De Bellas Artes y Archivos, 1993), pp. 31-44.

[32] See Raghnall Ó Flóinn, "The Archaeology of the Early Viking Age in Ireland," in Howard Clarke, Máire N'Mhaonaigh, and Raghnall Ó Flóinn (eds.), *Ireland and Scandinavia in the Early Viking Age* (Dublin: Four Courts Press, 1998), pp. 131-65, at p. 151. The distribution of plough irons is presented in Niall Brady, *The Plough in Early Historic and Medieval Ireland*, M.A. thesis, University College Dublin, 1986.

[33] On the original pattern of construction, see Baillie, *Tree-Ring Dating and Archaeology* (note 7). I am particularly grateful to Mike Baillie and David Brown at the Palaeoecology Centre of the Queen's University Belfast for supplying a revised list of tree-ring-dated sites.

[34] Eoin MacNeill, "Ancient Irish Law: the law of status or franchise," *Proceedings of the Royal Irish Academy* 36C (1921-24): 265-316, at p. 286, n. 2.

[35] Michael Ryan, "Furrows and Browse: some archaeological thoughts on agriculture and population in early medieval Ireland," in Alfred P. Smyth (ed.), *Seanchas. Studies in Early and Medieval Irish Archaeology, History and Literature in Honour of Francis J. Byrne* (Dublin: Four Courts Press, 1999), pp. 30-36.

[36] P.A. Rahtz, "Medieval Milling," in D. W. Crossley (ed.), *Medieval Industry*, CBA Research Report 40 (London: Council of British Archaeology, 1981), pp. 13-14.

[37] Donnchadh Ó Corráin, "Viking Ireland—afterthoughts," in Clarke *et al.*, *Ireland and Scandinavia* (note 32), pp. 421-52, at pp. 428-31.

[38] Michael Ryan, "The Significance of the Hoard," in Michael Ryan (ed.), *The Derrynaflan Hoard, volume 1, a preliminary account* (Dublin: National Museum of Ireland, 1983), pp. 36-41, at pp. 40-41.

[39] D. Binchy, "Secular Institutions," in Myles Dillon (ed.), *Early Irish Society* (Dublin: Colm O Lochlainn for the Cultural Relations Committee of Ireland, 1954), pp. 52-65, at p. 54.

[40] See for instance, Nerys Patterson, *Cattle-Lords and Clansmen: Kinship and rank in early Ireland* (New York: Garland, 1991), pp. 67-68.

[41] See for example, Charles Doherty, "Exchange and Trade in Early Medieval Ireland," *Journal of the Royal Society of Antiquaries* 110 (1980): 67-89; John Bradley, "Urbanization in Early Medieval Ireland," in Catherine E. Karkov, Kelly M. Wickham-Crowley, and Bailey K. Young (eds.), *Spaces of the Living and the Dead: An Archaeological Dialogue*, American Early Medieval Studies 3 (1999): 133-47.

[42] Kevin Down, "Colonial Society and Economy," in Art Cosgrove (ed.), *A New History of Ireland. II. Medieval Ireland 1169-1534* (1987; rpt. Oxford: Oxford University Press, 2001), pp. 439-91, at p. 481.

[43] Lucas, "The Horizontal Mill in Ireland" (note 2), p. 3.

[44] Baillie, "A Horizontal Mill" (note 7), p. 25.

[45] Fergus Kelly, *Early Irish Farming* (Dublin: Dublin Institute for Advanced Studies, 1997), p. 482.

[46] *Ibid.*, p. 484.

[47] Rynne, "Waterpower in Medieval Ireland" (note 2), pp. 6, 18-19.

[48] Colin Rynne, "Some Observations on the Production of Flour and Meal in the Early Historic Period," *Journal of the Cork Historical and Archaeological Society* 95 (1990): 20-29, at p. 21.

[49] H.C. Lawlor, *The Monastery of Saint Mochaoi of Nendrum* (Belfast: Belfast Natural History and Philosophical Club, 1925).

[50] McErlean and Crothers, "The Early Medieval Tide Mills at Nendrum" (note 2), p. 211.

[51] McErlean *et al.*, *Strangford Lough* (note 2), p. 76.

[52] *General Soil Map of Ireland* (note 29).

[53] T. McErlean and A. O'Sullivan, "Foreshore Tidal Fishtraps," in McErlean *et al.*, *Strangford Lough* (note 2), pp. 144-85, at pp. 182-83.

[54] I am especially grateful to Charles Doherty for this comment, in advance of his note on the historical evidence for Nendrum's connections with Armagh: Charles Doherty, "Nendrum: a note," forthcoming.

[55] Doherty, "Exchange and Trade"; see also Charles Doherty, "Some Aspects of Hagiography as a Source for Irish Economic History," *Peritia* 1 (1982): 300-23; Charles Doherty, "Settlement in Early Ireland: a review," in Terry Barry (ed.), *A History of Settlement in Ireland* (London: Routledge, 2000), pp. 50-80.

[56] Doherty, "Some aspects of hagiography," p. 320.

[57] *Ibid.*, p. 302.

[58] Bradley, "Urbanization in early medieval Ireland" (note 41), pp. 142-43.

[59] John Bradley (pers. comm., December 2004).

[60] Unfortunately historical references to Little Island in the early period are few and unclear; it is currently not possible to indicate who owned the mill site. I am grateful to Anne Connon for looking into the possibilities for me.

[61] Holt, *The Mills of Medieval England* (note 1), pp. 88-89.

[62] D. A. Binchy, "Irish Law Tracts Re-edited i. *coibnes uisci thairidne*," *Ériu* 17 (1955): 52-85, at pp. 68-71.

[63] I am not aware of a law tract that requires payment of compensation in the construction of an intertidal millpond, while the laws take the view that the issues of the sea belong to either the owner of the adjacent land or to the finder: Fergus Kelly, *A Guide to Early Irish Law* (Dublin: Dublin Institute for Advanced Studies, 1988), pp. 107-8.

[64] In the absence of rivers and streams in the immediate vicinity, the tidal mill at Nendrum capitalized on the presence of a tidal regime. On other aspects of tidal mills, see Langdon, *Mills in the Medieval Economy* (note 1), pp. 78-79.

[65] The sites are Knocknacarragh, Co. Galway; Tahilla, Co. Kerry; Donaghmore, Co. Cork; Little Island, Wallingstown, Co. Cork; Killoteran, Co. Waterford; Great Island, Co. Wexford; Ballymascanlan, Co. Louth.

[66] Indeed, John Langdon argues that later medieval tidal mills in England needed to be located close to areas of high population density to ensure that sufficient profits would be forthcoming from milling to support the long-term maintenance costs: Langdon, *Mills in the Medieval Economy*, p. 79. This line of enquiry is worth following up with further research in Ireland.

[67] The possibility of broadening the spectrum of research into agrarian practices in Ireland is suggested by a short note on corn-drying kilns: Muiris O'Sullivan and Liam Downey, "Corn-drying Kilns," *Archaeology Ireland* 19.3 (2005): 32-35.

[68] The following data is drawn from the Discovery Programme's Medieval Rural Settlement project, which is examining archaeological and historical sources to describe patterns of land use, land ownership, and land value within the hinterland of Dublin: Niall Brady, *Exploring Irish Medieval Landscapes* (Dublin: Discovery Programme, 2003).

[69] *Ibid.*, p. 29; A.J. Otway-Ruthven, "The Medieval Church Lands of Co. Dublin," in J.A. Watt, J.B. Morrall, and F.X. Martin (eds.), *Medieval Studies Presented to Aubrey Gwynn* (Dublin: O'Lochlainn, 1961), pp. 54-73.

[70] The references up to 1550 have been collated by Margaret Murphy, while those for the seventeenth century have been collated by Michael Potterton.

[71] The recent excavation of a mill in the Liffey valley at Chapelizod by Claire Walsh has yet to be published, as has the site of Carrickmines to the southeast of the city excavated by Mark Clinton for Valerie J Keeley Ltd., archaeological consultancy.

[72] *Calendar of Documents Relating to Ireland, 1171-1251* [etc.] (hereafter *CDI*) (London: Public Record Office, 1875-86), I:438; *CDI*, V:4.

[73] *CDI*, V:81-83.

[74] James Mills (ed.), *Calendar of the Justiciary Rolls, or proceedings in the court of the justiciar of Ireland preserved in the Public Record Office of Ireland 1295-1303* [etc.], (Dublin: HMSO, 1905, 1914), III:156.

[75] It would however be wrong to assume that no mills were built in the mountains. The *Annals of Tigernach* for 1177 record a great bursting forth of water through the centre of Glendalough, which is located within the Wicklow mountains, and this flood swept away bridges and mills of the town and left some fish in the town. Whitley Stokes, *The Annals of Tigernach* [rpt. from *Revue Celtique* 1896/97] (Llanerch: Felinfach, 1993), p. 298. I am grateful to Charles Doherty for this reference.

[76] *CDI*, IV: 225.

[77] M.J. McEnery and Raymond Refaussé (eds.), *Christ Church Deeds* (Dublin: Four Courts Press, 2001), no. 578.

[78] I am grateful to Margaret Murphy for the following.

[79] *Calendar of Archbishop Alen"s Register* (note 24), p. 222.

[80] London, The National Archives [Public Records Office], C47/10/22/7.

Waterwheels and Garden Gizmos: Technology and Illusion in Islamic Gardens

D. Fairchild Ruggles
(University of Illinois, Urbana-Champaign)

With so little garden archaeology undertaken for the medieval Islamic world, we must often rely on descriptions for information on the appearance and plan of gardens. Some, with descriptions of golden trees and mechanical singing birds, have been dismissed as the narrators' fabrications, but the technology did exist to create such spectacles. Ordinary irrigation techniques such as waterwheels, water-raising levers, and siphons that were used in the landscape to improve agriculture could also be used to animate palace fountains and make water seem to appear miraculously from hidden sources. The fact that such devices were employed for theatricality and pleasure is seen in a group of Arabic treatises on *automata*, small-scale contraptions that used water and weights to make mechanical figures pour jugs of water, birds whistle, and ducks peck at seeds. Clearly engineering ingenuity was used for more than agricultural irrigation: it also served the whims of an elite class of garden patrons who wished for extravagant spectacles that far exceeded the possibilities of nature.

Waterwheels and Technology

Historically, Islamic agriculture from Iran to North Africa was challenged by the lack of rainfall. Crops survived and flourished by means of artificial irrigation. This is true today and certainly was true a thousand years ago during the "medieval" period—although the connotation of "medieval" works well for Western history, it does not accurately describe the Islamic world in the year 1000. The ninth through twelfth centuries was a period of brisk trade, freedom of movement by means of excellent transportation, and communication facilitated by the spread of one language—Arabic—that served as the *lingua franca* for

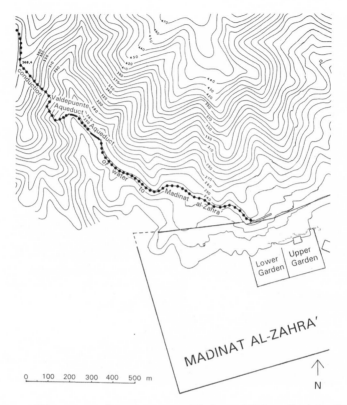

Figure 1: The water conduction system at Madinat al-Zahra, Cordoba, Spain;
by the author

not only religion but also for law and commerce.[1] It was a glorious age for art, architecture, and science: the illustrated book emerged in the eleventh century as a result of the new medium, paper; the irrigated garden emerged as a significant art form; and agriculture flourished as a result of botanical diversification and a more intensified application of technology.

Traces of a number of great gardens survive from the Islamic Mediterranean in this period. In Cordoba, the seat of government of the Hispano-Umayyad dynasty (756-1031), a new garden-city was founded in the agricultural green belt outside the walls of the medieval city in 936: Madinat al-Zahra' had two large gardens with raised walkways dividing the space into four sunken quadrants (Fig. 1). In these and smaller gardens at the site, pavilions overlooked a lush environment where pools, water channels, and fountains transformed the quotidian act of irrigation into an exciting spectacle. Water was carried down from

Figure 2: The bath patio at Madinat al-Zahra, Cordoba, Spain; photo by the author.

the mountains via a repaired Roman aqueduct, flowing into the north side of the palace city and from there through the halls and gardens. It filled an enormous fish tank as well as smaller garden pools and an ornamental basin in the baths adjoining the principal reception hall and garden[2] (Fig. 2). Seville's Alcazar in the late eleventh and twelfth centuries likewise had numerous gardens within its luxurious walled precinct. This palace and the garden estates outside of the city of Seville were irrigated first by water lifted from the Guadalquivir river and later, as more settlement and cultivation increased the need for water, a Roman aqueduct was revived to supply the demand.[3] The fortified twelfth-century Castillejo of Monteagudo (Murcia) was organized around a central quadripartite courtyard with sunken garden beds. Intersecting water channels erupted in a fountain at their point of juncture and flowed into rectangular pools at either end

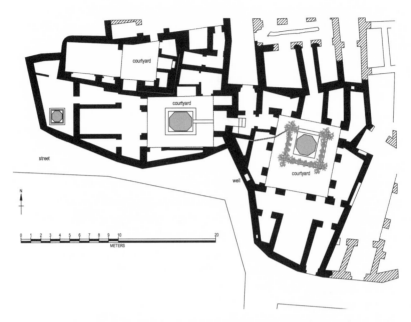

Figure 3: **Plan of a house excavated in Fustat, near Cairo**; after
Aly Bahgat and Albert Gabriel, *Fouilles d'al-Foustat* (Paris, 1921).

of the courtyard. The Castellejo stood on a tall hill, and the water for its inhabitants and vegetation was lifted up from below by means of a waterwheel.[4]

These are examples of grand palaces and fortresses, but humble households
also had gardens. Excavations at Fustat (outside of Cairo) revealed one- and
two-story courtyard houses dating from the mid-ninth through the twelfth century. The houses had at least one, and sometimes several courtyards, with basins,
beds for vegetation, and some large shrubs or small trees[5] (Fig. 3). These required water from an artificial source since Egypt receives virtually no rainfall.

In all of these, irrigation was a challenge. Water is always available from
some source, whether a river, mountain stream, or deep aquifer, but the essential
problem is how to lift it from its source, often a low point in the landscape, to the
field or household where it is needed. The techniques for doing this in the pre-
modern Islamic world included the waterwheel, sweep lever (*shaduf*), and underground conduits (*qanats*), in conjunction with canals, aqueducts, and siphons.

Waterwheels in Islam consisted of a wooden spoked wheel to which ceramic
vessels were attached either directly or suspended on a long looped chain. In the
saqiya version, the containers hang along the length of a chain or rope loop which

is attached to a horizontal bar, like an ordinary yard well (fig. 4A). A draft animal such as an ox or donkey walks in an endless circle, propelling a horizontal bar that rotates a shaft attached to one or more larger cogged wheels. A chain of buckets is attached to the wheel: as the chain rotates upward, the buckets tilt at the highest point and the water splashes into a raised trough through which it flows to the agricultural field, garden bed, or basin where it is to be stored or used. This system is ideal for lifting water from a deep but confined source, like a well or cistern. Although the *saqiya* transports water in relatively small quantities, it can be lifted from a very low point of storage to a very high point of delivery, depending on the length of the chain.

A slightly different version of the waterwheel consisted of a wheel with cups attached directly to it so that, as the wheel circulates, the cups dip into the source below and then dump their contents as they reach the summit of the wheel's rotation (Fig. 4B). Because this kind of wheel typically used the natural water current for propulsion, it is the most economical and rapid means of lifting water into an irrigation system.[6] The same technology is used to power mills, sometimes taking advantage of places of especially rapid current such as the spaces between the piers of bridges.[7]

Another water-lifting device is the *shaduf*, a long lever with a bucket at one end and a counterweight at the other (Fig. 4C). A person dips, raises, and guides the bucket from the source up to the water canal that carries the water into the field. Sometimes *shadufs* are stacked in a series, so that water is raised in stages from one terrace to another. *Shadufs* are ideal for areas such as the Nile River valley where the source of water is only a bit below the level of the agricultural field.[8] It is not a particularly efficient system, since it can move water only at a rate of one bucket at a time, requires a human operator, and supplies only a small plot of land, but *shadufs* were used as early as 2000 BCE and are still used today by poor farmers because they are inexpensive and easy to build.[9]

Finally, the Archimedean screw was also used throughout the Islamic world. (Fig. 4D) This was essentially a thick pipe with two to four internal partitions around a central shaft. The partitions spiraled around the central shaft like a modern helical drill bit and, being tightly fitted, formed a series of troughs up the length of the pipe. The whole pipe was set at a shallow angle with tis base in the water source (river or irrigation canal) and as the central shaft to which the chambers are attached was turned, the water trapped inin each chamber climbed up the pipe and spilled out the top. Although very efficient, the Archimedean screw was limited in both its length because of construction considerations, and in the height it could lift water by operational considerations. This screw pump

A) Saqiya

B) Waterwheel with attached cups

Figure 4: Irrigation technologies in the premodern Islamic world;
drawings by author after Thorkild Schiøler, *Roman and Islamic Water-
Lifting Wheels* (Odense, Denmark: Odense University Press, 1971)

is inexpensive and moves water fairly rapidly, but it too requires a human operator and cannot lift water very high.

In each of these cases, machinery is propelled by animal or human labor to
raise a container of water to a certain height in order to deliver it into the irrigation system. Hence, the benefit of cultivating crops with these types of irrigation
techniques must be offset against the cost of labor and the capital investment of
construction. Furthermore, these systems are limited in that the supply of water cannot be far away from the field that it irrigates. An altogether different
means of transporting water was the *qanat* (Fig. 5), a subterranean tunnel that
carries water from an elevated source where there is a steady water supply, such

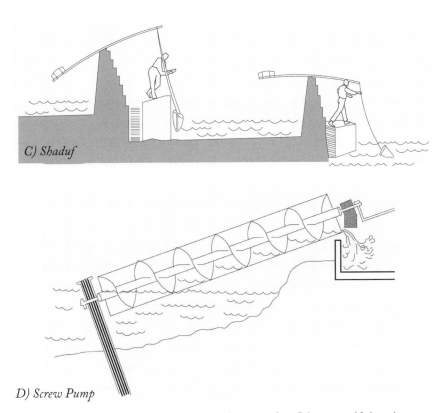

C) Shaduf

D) Screw Pump

Figure 4: **Irrigation technologies in the premodern Islamic world** *(cont.)*; drawings by B. Variava and D. F. Ruggles

as a mountain with melting winter snows, to a lower point that may be a considerable distance away. *Qanat*s were used in Iran during the Achaemenid Empire (6th-4th centuries BCE) and possibly earlier, although it is unclear whether earlier *qanat*s were drainage channels for mining runoff or true irrigation conduits.[10] In any case, *qanat* technology spread to Iraq, Syria, the Arabian Peninsula, and India; the Romans carried it across northern Africa; and Muslims brought the technique to the Iberian Peninsula and Sicily. Water is tapped at the base of a mountain where the water table is high. It is then carried at a slope that declines slightly less than that of the natural water table. Many miles distant, where the water table has dropped considerably below the ground surface, the *qanat* spews

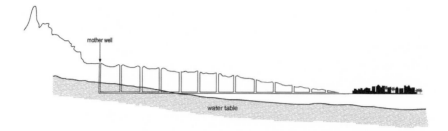

Figure 5: **Diagram of a Qanat water supply system;**
drawing by B. Variava and D. F. Ruggles

forth water.[11] The system is efficient because, once constructed, no human or animal labor is required to move the water, which flows like a natural stream. The *qanat* transports large quantities of water, twenty-four hours a day, often providing irrigation to an entire settlement, and in arid areas the *qanat* has the advantage over above-ground aqueducts or seasonal streams because the water does not evaporate. Thus, in the dry landscape of Syria, Iraq, and Iran, *qanat*s were used through history to transform the desert by providing farms and orchards with abundant quantities of necessary water.

These devices for obtaining water were used in conjunction with devices for transporting water, such as aqueducts, surface canals, and siphons. Roman engineers were famed for their skill in the construction of aqueducts, spanning deep valleys on slender tiered arches that withstood earthquakes and the passing of millennia. Like many other aspects of Roman engineering, the aqueduct was a form taken up by Arabs who in some cases repaired and rebuilt Roman aqueducts that had fallen into ruin in the early medieval period. In other cases they actually built new structures, albeit on a smaller scale. The principle is quite simple: to permit water to flow at a constant rate on an incline that is neither too level (and therefore slow) nor too steep (and therefore fast). The aqueduct is a response to natural topography because it creates an evenly sloping conduit where a natural stream would cascade recklessly over rocks and collect lethargically in stagnant pools. The graceful bridges of the aqueducts—such as those at Segovia, Spain, or the Pont du Gard near Nîmes, France—are usually the most visible portion of longer canals that run at ground level and tunnel through mountains. A different solution to the same topographic challenge is the inverted siphon. Instead of water traversing a nearly horizontal surface, it drops in a closed pipe from a high point, across a valley, and rises again on the other side, although necessarily to a point *lower* than the original point of departure.

These techniques, passed down apparently unbroken from Antiquity and used in various combinations, enabled farmers to transform the earth, making arid landscapes green with staple food crops as well as more unusual foods for export such as figs, saffron, and nuts. They also allowed more exotic botanical experiments and finally gardens that were enjoyed for beauty, fragrance, and cool shade. Some—aqueducts and *qanats*—required complex social organization to build and manage the system and to allocate its benefits.[12] Others—wheels and *shadufs*—could be constructed by individuals wishing to improve the productivity of a specific farm or garden.

Garden Gizmos and Illusion

There are two kinds of gardens studied by Islamic historians. One type is the real garden, such as Madinat al-Zahra', the Castillejo of Monteagudo, and the houses of Fustat, for which we have material evidence consisting of standing remains as well as archaeological traces discernible by excavation or techniques such as aerial survey. The other is the textual garden that survives only in the form of words: either narrative descriptions made by travelers, chroniclers, and geographers, or odd historical fragments in the form of correspondence, contracts of sale, dowry lists, and court proceedings that record land and water disputes. Some of these written accounts describe fantastic gardens that existed only in the literary imagination.

The classic Arabic folktales of *The 1001 Nights* (sometimes known as *The Arabian Nights*) contain several such imaginative accounts. One story tells of the city of Iram, built by Shaddad who had read a description of the pavilions and gardens of paradise in ancient books and vowed to build such a place. He commanded his men: "Go ye forth therefore to the goodliest tract on earth and the most spacious and build me there a city of gold and silver, whose gravel shall be chrysolite and rubies and pearls.... Fill it with palaces, whereon ye shall set galleries and balconies and plant its lanes and thoroughfares with all manner of trees bearing yellow-ripe fruits and make rivers to run through it in channels of gold and silver."[13]

Shaddad assembled the greatest architects, engineers, and craftsmen and for 300 years they worked, building him the foundations, pavilions, and fountains with water channels, all lavishly adorned. But Shaddad, who had dared to try to rival paradise with his city, was struck down by God before he could enter the gates. All roads to the city were hidden, so that, although the city of dreams continued to exist in mineralized perfection, it could not be seen by human eyes.

The story of the Copper City is a similar tale. The narrator Sheherazade related that the governor of the Maghreb, Musa ibn Nusayr, went there and found a magnificent place of domes and pavilions, but it was entirely walled with locked gates and could not be entered. Eventually Musa looked over the walls from a nearby hilltop and saw a great, handsome city, "with dwelling places and mansions of towering height, and palaces and pavilions and domes gleaming gloriously bright and sconces and bulwarks of strength infinite; and its streams were a-flowing and flowers a-blowing and fruits a-glowing." All those who tried to scale the walls died in the attempt. When a group finally did succeed in gaining entry, they found unimaginable wealth, heaps of jewels, caskets of pearls, richly colored silken textiles and brocades, alabaster fountains, marble water basins, and streams flowing in channels incised in the floor as well as a floor of shining marble inlaid with gems that looked like a shimmering surface of water. But as they explored further, the group was shocked to discover that all the inhabitants of the palace were completely desiccated, dead.[14]

The story is a *vanitas*—a gruesome reminder of the ephemerality of life on earth. There is a clear fascination with a world of mineralized splendor that permeates the description despite the message that such a place may be dangerous, the work of Satan. Although the sight of death in every hall was disturbing and repugnant, the description of the treasure encountered there is tremendously appealing. Moreover, the reference to a floor that shimmered like water recalls the famous meeting of the wise king Solomon (Sulayman) and the Queen of Sheba. Sulayman's palace floor was of polished glass which caused the Queen to lift her skirts, believing it to be of water (Quran, 27: 44).

Finally, in the Christian Broker's Tale there is a description of an elevated hall overlooking a garden "that delighted the eye with running streams and all kinds of fruits and birds. In the middle of the hall there was a square fountain at whose corners stood four snakes made of red gold, spouting water, as if it were jewels and pearls."[15]

The Quran also describes wondrous places of luxury and ease, and nature made perfect. According to the Quran, paradise is a tranquil garden with four rivers and shady blooming trees with low-hanging fruit that is forever ripe. The inhabitants of Paradise will recline on couches studded with gold and gems, attended by maidens (*houris*) with big eyes like lustrous pearls, drinking wine, eating fruit and fowl (Quran, 2: 25; 29: 58; 47: 15; 56: 12-38). The *hadith* (sayings of Muhammad) also elaborate upon the architecture of paradise in detail, describing pavilions made of a single enormous pearl and gem-studded palaces' with glowing floors of mother-of-pearl, sometimes laid with rugs woven from pearls, rubies, and lapis lazuli with stripes of silver and gold.

Arabic fiction and even Islamic religious texts often describe gardens in fantastic terms that test the listeners' credulity. These were mythic places that were never supposed to be seen: the *1001 Nights* is a collection of stories—fictions— and the Quran describes a place—paradise—which no one will see in earthly life. But at the same time there were real gardens where nature was similarly exaggerated to inspire awe in the viewer and to evoke the imaginary scenes and mythic places described in literature. For example, the palaces of the Abbasid caliphs of Samarra, a sprawling expanse of palaces built 60 miles north of Baghdad in the mid-ninth century, had extraordinary gardens. When the Byzantine ambassador arrived in Samarra in 917, the palace of the caliph al-Muqtadir was the scene of great ceremony. The ambassador was led through a succession of great halls, corridors, and courtyards, eventually arriving at the New Palace where there were gardens with a metal-rimmed pool surrounded by four hundred tall date palm trees. These were draped with painted textiles hanging from golden rings. From there the visitors went to the Tree Court where, in the middle of a great pool, stood a tree with eighteen gold and silver branches with multi-colored leaves that fluttered as if in the breeze. In the tree, gold and silver birds twittered and sang. Finally they arrived in the domed hall where the caliph awaited them. On his command, a tree slowly emerged from the ground, rising until it filled the air. Mechanical birds sang overhead while perfumed fountains spouted in the air.[16]

The over-the-top splendor of this palace at Samarra parallels the mythic palaces of the *1001 Nights*, and it is no coincidence that the setting of the narrative tale recalls the architecture of Samarra.[17] A significant difference, however, is that while the Copper City was a legend, the Samarra palace was quite real. Little remains of that palace except the words with which the medieval chroniclers described it, and these were probably as exaggerated as any description intended to inspire awe, but the palace itself was certainly not a storyteller's fabrication. There are too many historical mentions of extraordinary halls and gardens in disparate areas of the early Islamic world to discount them as pure fable.

For comparison, in late-ninth-century Cairo, the ruler Ibn Tulun built a country palace with gardened courtyards stocked with palms, fruit trees, water-lilies, manicured myrtle, roses, saffron, and exotic plants brought from far away. Magnificently plumed peacocks roamed freely. But controlling nature by cultivating a splendid garden was not enough for this patron. He had the trunks of the palm trees sheathed with copper and gilded so that they would not tarnish, and his engineers hid lead tubing under the sheathing in order to pipe water upwards so that the palms sprouted not only fronds but a spray of water as well. The water fell into basins and from there irrigated the rest of the garden. Elsewhere in the palace there was a golden chamber with a large tank filled with mercury on which Ibn Tulun, an insomniac, slept on an inflated leather mattress.[18]

In Islamic Spain, in the tenth-century Cordoban palace, Madinat al-Zah'ra, the regent al-Mansur had a large basin with croaking tortoises and water pouring from the jaws of a lion fountain made of black amber and wearing a necklace of pearls. Elsewhere in the palace, waterlilies grew in one of the large pools. When al-Mansur was visited by the ambassadors of a potentially hostile neighbor, assessing the strength of his kingdom, he ordered that silver and gold chunks be inserted into the lilies while they were still closed in the cool early morning. Later that day as the lilies opened to the sun, the lilies were plucked, gathered on a tray, and presented to the guests who could not have failed to comprehend the metaphor. Seeing that the flowers of al-Andalus miraculously yielded silver and gold, they realized the extent of al-Mansur's agricultural resources and were suitably impressed.[19]

The illusion of gold-blooming flowers at Madinat al-Zahra', an effective device for representing economic wealth and power, was not hard to produce. But in other gardens, more sophisticated mechanical skill was required to make inanimate objects move and speak. For example, from twelfth-century Iran a bronze incense burner in the form of a large feline, nearly a meter in length, breathed smoke through its fangs for a dramatic effect.[20] From tenth-century Spain comes a bronze stag with internal plumbing that suggest that it spewed water into a pool; the Monzón Lion was part of a fountain structure in an eleventh-century Islamic palace in Palencia; and a fierce-looking eleventh-century bronze lion, also nearly a meter long, had a mouth aperture clearly fitted for a pipe.[21] A bronze spigot from twelfth- or thirteenth-century Syria had the form of a lion's head while the handle took the form of a peacock.[22] In the hills above Cordoba stood a stone fountain in the shape of an elephant or boar; water poured from its mouth into a rectangular reservoir and flowed from here through along an open-faced aqueduct. There is also the well-known fountain of twelve stone lions bearing a basin on their haunches that occupies the center of the Court of the Lions at the Alhambra palace (Fig. 6). Indeed, these are just a few cases of intact examples: there are a great many fountain fragments from Spain and the Maghreb that suggest that zoomorphic fountains were a very popular garden feature.[23]

Figure 6: **Court of the Lions, Alhambra Palace, Granada, Spain;**
photo by Steven A. Walton.

To pipe water through an inert stone sculpture requires hydraulic skill of a very basic sort, and so the illusion of animation was easy to achieve. But many fountains were engineered to do more than simply pour. Mechanical birds actually sang and tortoises croaked, presumably because they were crafted with moving parts and acoustic mechanisms. While too few of these ingenious garden gizmos survive, we can find the plans for their design in a genre of treatises written about amusing contraptions called *automata*. The best known of these treatises is that by al-Jaziri, completed in either 1204 or 1206 in east central Turkey. Al-Jaziri's *Book of Ingenious Devices* deals with topics such as clocks, drinking vessels, and mechanical pitchers. Inspired by classical works on *automata* by Heron, Philon, and Ctesibius, al-Jaziri's treatise provides clear, working drawings and descriptions of both ancient and contemporary hydraulic, pneumatic, and mechanical wonders.

One sign of the immense popularity of al-Jaziri's treatise on *automata* is the existence today of at least eleven partial or wholly surviving copies, including one made for one of the Mughals of India and one made as late as the eighteenth century. The treatise is divided into six categories on subjects such as clocks, drinking vessels, and pitchers and basins for phlebotomy and washing. Category IV is "On the construction in pools of fountains which change their shape, and of machines for the perpetual flute," and Category V is "On the construction of machines for raising water from standing water which is not deep, and from a running river."[24] These were not entirely driven by water; one illustration is of a wind-driven wheel.[25] The explanations, quite specific and clear in their own right, were greatly enhanced by the 173 accurately drawn illustrations that accompanied them. One illustration explains the mechanics for raising water with waterwheels. Although the instructions refer to a small toy with a figure of a cow, the illustration shows a *saqiya* and a cupped wheel moved by vertical and horizontal shafts with cogs, the same mechanics that were used to supply water to gardens and farms. In all cases, the descriptions indicate that mechanical toys of diminutive size were intended, but there is no reason why such engineering skill could not be realized on an expanded scale for gardens.

Al-Jaziri's treatise was not the first of its kind. There is a ninth-century Arabic manual on mechanical devices called the *Kitab al-Hiyal* by three brothers called the Banu Musa bin Shakir.[26] The illustrations made for the early copies of the *Kitab al-Hiyal* are particularly interesting for a garden historian because they show hydraulic devices with figural spouts. Among them, there is a machine with spouts in the shape of two rams' heads and another in the form of a lion head (Fig. 7). This entertaining mixture of technology and figural animation that pleased courtly audiences on a small scale was also realized in architectural environments, as a painting from the *Bayad wa Riyad* manuscript (13th-14th century Islamic Spain), shows (Fig. 8). Although the figures of the human beings, the swimming ducks, and the rabbit were meant to suggest living creatures, the horse heads spewing water into the pool were sculptural figures like those seen in the *Kitab al-Hiyal*.[27] The important thing to remember here is scale. The *automata* use the same engineering skill employed in irrigation systems for raising water by means of waterwheels, siphons, levers, and pumps.

In addition to the treatises on *automata*, there were related works such as Ridwan al-Sa'ati's treatise on clocks, written 1203.[28] This writer was the son of a clock-maker who between 1154 and 1167 had designed for the Great Mosque of Damascus a wonderful clock with a waterwheel, pulleys and weights, a revolving zodiac disk, and the sounding of the hours by dropping balls from birds' beaks

Figure 7: **Fountain with lion spout from the** *Kitab al-Hiyal*; redrawn by B. Variava.

into resonant metal basins. The Damascus clock is illustrated in al-Sa'ati's manuscript,[29] making visible the direct relationship between scientific treatise and actual application. A treatise of the Pseudo-Archimedes (in Arabic but ascribed to the Greek scientist) described a tree with silver birds that whistled in alarm in response to two silver snakes that emerged from the mountains at its feet each hour; it was animated by compressed air (Fig. 9). A similar figure, animated not by air but by the pouring of wine, was described in the work of Philo of Byzantium (*c.*200 BCE).[30] The treatises of al-Jaziri, the Banu Musa ibn Shakir, and Ridwan al-Sa'ati owed a considerable debt to Hellenistic and Byzantine precursors, and text-based historians have argued that Byzantine authors transmitted the Hellenistic science to Islamic society. However, because the Byzantine palace gardens date to the same period as the Abbasid gardens, it cannot be stated for certain which one begat the other.[31]

Historians of the Arabic book have studied these manuscripts as early examples of Islamic book illustration, often classifying them together with astronomical treatises and other forms of early scientific, as opposed to narrative, il-

Figure 8: **Garden scene from** *Bayad wa Riyad*; ©Biblioteca
Apostolica Vaticana (Vatican), MS Ar. 368.

Figure 9: **Clock illustration from the Treatise of Pseudo-Archimedes**; redrawn by B. Variava.

lustration. Historians of technology have been interested in the texts as evidence of mechanical knowledge and have redrawn many of the contraptions in order to clarify their mechanics. In so doing, the mechanically extraneous animal figures and waterspouts are invariably omitted. However, these details provide important evidence that the devices were used in actual garden settings, and they call attention to the role that technology played in the art of the built environment and, by extension, imaginative literature. The *automata* and horological treatises allow us to understand that extraordinary gardens with gilded palms, bejewelled vegetation, mechanical birds, and exuberant waterworks were not pure fantasy: they were actual elements in real gardens. Of course only the richest patron could afford these elaborate entertainments and could secure the services of the expert artisans who designed and built them, which was partly the point of making them in the first place. But the transmutation from the ephemeral beauty of nature to the permanent magnificence of gold and gems had a meaning that went beyond mere conspicuous display, for on a more profound level they suggested an enduring form of power: the ability to defeat the natural cycle of life and its invariable successor, death.

Notes

[1] S.D. Goitein, "The Unity of the Islamic World," in Goitein, *Studies in Islamic History and Institutions* (Leiden: E.J. Brill, 1966), pp. 296-307.

[2] D. Fairchild Ruggles, *Gardens, Landscape, and Vision in the Palaces of Islamic Spain* (University Park: Pennsylvania State University Press, 2000), pp. 53-109.

[3] J. Bosch Vilá, *Historia de Sevilla: La Sevilla Islámica, 712-1248* (Seville: Universidad de Sevilla, 1984), pp. 227-30; R. Manzano Martos, "Casas y palacios en la Sevilla Almohade. Sus antecedentes hispánicos," in J. Navarro Palazón (ed.), *Casas y Palacios de al-Andalus, Siglos XII y XIII* (Barcelona and Madrid: D.L. Lunwerg, 1995), pp. 315-52; and Ruggles, *Gardens, Landscape, and Vision*, pp. 141-47.

[4] L. Torres Balbás, "Monteagudo y 'El Castillejo,' en la Vega de Murcia," *Al-Andalus* 2 (1934): 366-72; Julio Navarro Palazón and Pedro Jiménez Castillo, "El castillejo de Monteagudo: Qasr Ibn Sa`d," in Palazón (ed.), *Casas y Palacios*, pp. 63-103.

[5] Aly Bahgat and Albert Gabriel, *Fouilles d'al-Foustat* (Paris, 1921); Antoni Ostrasz, "The Archaeological Material for the Study of the Domestic Architecture at Fustat," *Africana Bulletin* 26 (1977): 57-87; and George Scanlon, "Housing and Sanitation: Some Aspects of Medieval Egyptian Life," in A.H. Hourani and S.M. Stern (eds.), *The Islamic City: A Colloquium* (Oxford: Bruno Cassirer, 1970), pp. 185-94.

[6] The literature on waterwheels is vast because there are many variants: the best technical source on all forms of waterwheels is Thorkild Schiøler, *Roman and Islamic Water-Lifting Wheels* (Denmark: Odense University Press, 1971).

[7] Donald Hill, *Islamic Science and Engineering* (Edinburgh: Edinburgh University Press, 1993), pp. 110-11; Thomas Glick, *Islamic and Christian Spain in the Early Middle Ages* (Princeton: Princeton University Press, 1979), p. 23.

[8] On *shaduf*s, see Donald Hill, *Islamic Science and Engineering* (Edinburgh: Edinburgh University Press, 1993), p. 92; Karl Butzer, *Early Hydraulic Civilization in Egypt* (Chicago: University of Chicago Press, 1976), p. 47; and Glick, *Islamic and Christian Spain*, p. 227.

[9] On antiquity, see M. Rostovtzeff, *Social and Economic History of the Hellenistic World* (Oxford: Clarendon Press, 1941), p. 363; and Lynn White, *Medieval Technology and Social Change* (Oxford: Clarendon Press, 1962), pp. 80-82.

[10] Norman Smith, *Man and Water: A History of Hydrotechnology* (New York: Scribner, 1975), ch. 6.

[11] There is an ample bibliography on the *qanat* as a technique as well as regional applications. Two classic works are Henri Goblot, *Les Qanats: une technique d'acquisition de l'eau* (Paris: Mouton, 1979), pp. 59-73; and Paul English, "The Origin and Spread of Qanats in the Old World," *Proceedings of the American Philosophical Society* 112 (1968): 170-81; and a more popular one is H.E. Wulf, "The Qanats of Iran," *Scientific American* 218 (1968): 94-105.

¹² The literature on "hydraulic societies" is huge; Glick gives a concise summary of the arguments as applied to the Andalusian context in *Islamic and Christian Spain*, pp. 68-78.

¹³ *The Book of the Thousand Nights and a Night*, trans. and ed. Richard Burton ([s.l]: The Burton Club, 1885), IV: 116.

¹⁴ *Ibid.*, VI: 102-12. The story can also be found in Abu Hamid al-Garnati (flourished in al-Andalus in the early 12th century), *Tuhfat al-Albad*, ed. Gabriel Ferrand in *Journal Asiatique* 207 (1925): 1-148, 193-304 esp. 55-60.

¹⁵ *The Arabian Nights*, ed. Muhsin Mahdi, trans. Husain Haddawy (New York: W.W. Norton, 1990), p. 222. The Burton translation of this same story has birds instead of snakes. My thanks to Janina Safran for bringing this to my attention.

¹⁶ Al-Khatib, *Tar'ikh Baghdad*, I: 100-4 cited in Guy Le Strange, "A Greek Embassy to Baghdad in 917 A.D.," *Journal of the Royal Asiatic Society*, [no series] 7 (1897): 42, and María Jesús Rubiera Mata, *La arquitectura en la literatura árabe* (Madrid: Editora Nacional, 1981), pp. 69-74.

¹⁷ The precise origins of the *1001 Nights* are unknown. They were a collection of stories of Indian, Persian, and Arab origin circulated orally for centuries—at least as early as the tenth century—until it was written down in the second half of the thirteenth century. There are two manuscript genealogies: a Syrian branch, which had fewer stories in it, and an Egyptian branch which was more heterogeneous and incorporated later stories, some of which were new inventions and some of which were older folktales that were simply folded into the vehicle of the *1001 Nights*. Husain Haddawy, "Introduction," in Mahdi (ed.), *The Arabian Nights*, esp. pp. xi-xiii.

¹⁸ Al-Maqrizi, *al-Khitat*, II: 108-9, trans. in Rubiera Mata, *La arquitectura en la literatura árabe* (Madrid: Ediciones Hiperión, 1988), pp. 82-86.

¹⁹ Ruggles, *Gardens, Landscape, and Vision* (note 2), p. 124.

²⁰ *The Islamic World* (New York: Metropolitan Museum of Art, 1987), cat. no. 27.

²¹ The Cordoba stag and the Monzón Lion are reproduced in *Al-Andalus: The Art of Islamic Spain*, ed. Jerrilynn D. Dodds (New York: Metropolitan Museum of Art, 1992), pp. 210 and 270; the bronze incense-burning lion appeared in the Christie's catalogue, "Islamic Art, Indian Miniatures, Rugs, and Carpets," October 19, 1993.

²² Reproduced in Christine V. Bornstein and Priscilla Soucek, *The Meeting of Two Worlds: The Crusades and the Mediterranean Context* (Ann Arbor: University of Michigan Museum of Art, 1981), catalogue entry no. 30.

²³ For examples, see Marilyn Jenkins, "Al-Andalus: Crucible of the Mediterranean," in *The Art of Medieval Spain, A.D. 500-1200* (New York: The Metropolitan Museum of Art, 1993), pp. 73-84.

²⁴ Isma'il Ibn al-Razzaz al-Jaziri, *The Book of Knowledge of Ingenious Mechanical Devices*, trans. and ed. Donald Hill (Dordrecht: D. Reidel, 1974); Eilhard Wiedemann and Fritz Hauser, *Über die Uhren im Bereich der islamische Kultur*, Nova Acta Abhandlungen der Kaiserlich Leopoldinisch-Carolinisch Deutschen Akademie der Naturforscher 100/5 (Halle, 1915), pp. 58-166.

[25] Safwan Kh. Tell, "Two Illustrated Pages on Automata in the Metropolitan Museum of Art," *Annual of the Department of Antiquities, Jordan* 25 (1981): 95-104; see fig. 2 (p.99).

[26] Banu (sons of) Musa bin Shakir, *The Book of Ingenious Devices* (*Kitab al-Hiyal*), trans. Donald Hill (Dordrecht: D. Reidel, 1979); Ahmad Y. al-Hassan (ed.), *Kitab al-Hiyal: The Book of Ingenious Devices* (Aleppo: University of Aleppo, 1981).

[27] The only manuscript of the *Bayad wa Riyad* is in the Vatican collection.

[28] There are two surviving manuscripts of Ridwan al-Sa'ati's treatise, one of which (Istanbul, 1260) was copied directly from the original. On this horological treatise and its relationship to *automata*, see Finbarr Flood, *The Great Mosque of Damascus* (Leiden: E.J. Brill, 2001), pp. 114-38, and Donald Hill, *Arabic Water-Clocks*, Sources and Studies in the History of Arabic-Islamic Science, History of Technology Series 4 (Aleppo: University of Aleppo, 1981).

[29] Flood, *The Great Mosque of Damascus*, plate 59.

[30] The treatise was compiled in an additive manner beginning in the late 10th century or earlier, but Donald Hill believes the portion describing the tree with singing birds was written no earlier than the 12th century; Hill: *On the Construction of Water-Clocks* (*Kitab arshimidas fi'amal al-binkamat*), Occasional Papers 4 (London: Turner and Devereaux, 1976), pp. 6-9, 30-33. See also Flood, *The Great Mosque of Damascus*, pp. 127-29.

[31] Charles Barber, "Reading the Garden in Byzantium: Nature and Sexuality," *Byzantine and Modern Greek Studies* 16 (1992): 1-19.

The Role of the Monasteries
in the Development of Medieval Milling

Adam Lucas
(University of New South Wales, Australia)

Introduction

For more than seventy years, historians from several different sub-disciplines have argued that the monasteries of Western Europe played an important role in promoting technological progress and the transition to modernity. While perhaps not the earliest, two of the most influential publications to make the case appeared within a year of one another in 1934 and 1935. Lewis Mumford's *Technics and Civilization* (1934) and Marc Bloch's "Avènement et conquêtes du moulin à eau" (1935) approached the subject from different intellectual backgrounds, and differed substantially in the depth of their analyses, but the basic elements of the narrative which they outlined were the same.[1]

Both contended that although the watermill was invented in classical times, the Romans and their contemporaries made little use of it. Christian monks were largely responsible for its dissemination in medieval times, introducing it to areas where knowledge of it had died out or never existed. Monastic mills and their associated waterworks thus provided technological exemplars for other social groups to emulate. The monks' activities were, indeed, paradigmatic of a revolution in humanity's approach to nature and technology that occurred during the second half of the Middle Ages.[2]

Mumford's and Bloch's accounts diverge significantly, however, in their interpretation of the monks' interests in promoting the widespread adoption of water-powered milling. Whereas Mumford regarded the monks' role as an essentially benign one of encouraging mechanical relief from boring, repetitive work, Bloch believed that the "advanced technology" of the watermill was imposed by an ecclesiastical élite intent on surplus extraction from peasants and townsfolk who preferred the simpler and cheaper technology of milling by hand at home using rotary querns.

Bloch's 1935 paper was in some respects a summary and development of a thesis first articulated by Richard Bennett and John Elton in their four-volume *History of Corn Milling* (1898-1904).[3] For Bloch, like Bennett and Elton, monastic ownership of mills and the monks' promotion of watermilling technology have to be seen within the framework of feudal lordship; in particular, the emergence of seigneurial monopolies as a privilege either granted by monarchs to powerful magnates as a reward for their vassalage, or claimed as a customary right by such magnates and enforced through tyranny. With the emergence of various feudal systems toward the end of the first millennium of our era, the ownership of mills became exclusively a privilege of lordship: a seigneurial monopoly. Known as a *banalité* in France and "suit of mill" or "mill soken" (*mulctura*) in England, this particular seigneurial monopoly was one of the most important of the rights of private justice that were granted to lords by their monarchs, first in France during the tenth century, and slightly later in England in the late eleventh and early twelfth centuries.[4]

The tenants of a lord who held suit of mill were legally obliged to grind their grain at the lord's mill and pay the lord a proportion of the milled grain as tollcorn. Bloch observed that by the thirteenth century, French legal theory regarded suit of mill as "one of the highest judicial rights." He recorded numerous instances of peasants and townsfolk who resisted the imposition of suit of mill by continuing the centuries-old practice of grinding the household grain at home on a rotary handmill, and how such flagrant flouting of the law incurred the wrath of lay and (more often) ecclesiastical lords in such famous cases as St. Albans, Peterborough, and Cirencester, where handmills were confiscated and destroyed, the transgressors fined and beaten, and, in the worst cases of rebellion, jailed and even executed.[5]

Bloch's views emerged from a Marxist tradition which held that it was material conditions, and especially class relations, that shaped the structure and development of the medieval economy. Lords were the dominant players in medieval economic relations, and exercised their authority by monopolising production and trade and relegating the lower orders of society to the margins of economic activity. The abbots and priors of the large monasteries were amongst the earliest members of the new feudal élite, and tended to be as oppressive as their lay counterparts, zealously maintaining their feudal privileges. Bloch suggested that the interest of lords in replacing the handmill with the watermill was not based on the desire to increase productivity, but rather, to strengthen their economic domination of the lower orders. It was not a case of the mode of production (in this case, the technology of the watermill) determining social relations, as Marx's famous aphorism proclaimed, but of social relations (*i.e.*, the feudal relationship between lord and vassal) determining the mode of production.[6]

On the other hand, Mumford's views on the development of medieval milling as expressed in *Technics and Civilization* emerged from an already well-established movement among liberal intellectuals to recuperate the Middle Ages as a legitimate object of study.[7] His account of how monkish inventiveness was responsible for the dissemination of powered milling throughout medieval Europe was subsequently elaborated upon by Lynn White, Jr., Bertrand Gille and Mumford himself over the next four decades. What eventually became a full-blown theory of monastic innovation shaped the views of at least two generations of historians of technology.[8]

According to this theory, positive Christian attitudes to technological innovation encouraged the use of watermills and other machines that harnessed new sources of power, such as the tide mill and the windmill. Like Bloch, these historians argued that Christian monasteries reintroduced watermilling technology to Western Europe after the collapse of the Roman Empire. Unlike Bloch, proponents of what might be called the "monastic innovation thesis" argued that the monks were leaders in the promotion of new and positive attitudes toward the mechanical arts. The role which they attributed to the monasteries in the process of medieval technological development was thus far more benign—and indeed beneficent—than that envisaged by Bloch and other neo-Marxists.[9]

One of the most common claims made by proponents of the monastic innovation thesis is that the Benedictines adopted a standard plan for their monasteries which included one or more watermills. Their primary purpose in adopting such technology was to spare their brethren from the mind-numbing but necessary tasks of milling, fulling, and sawing by hand, in order to liberate more time for them to engage in prayer and other spiritually rewarding tasks.[10] Picking up on these themes and articulating them at length in a number of his own publications, White argued that the Cistercians took the Benedictines' ideas to new heights, applying the technology of the watermill to a range of new industrial applications, including forging iron, sawing timber, and crushing and smelting ore, all the while embracing a reformed commitment to the original ideals of the Benedictines. White credited the Cistercians with having "often ... led the way in the use of [water]power," telling us that "[s]ome of their abbeys had four or five water wheels, each powering a different workshop."[11]

According to Mumford and White, therefore, it was a philanthropic, for-ward-looking, and proto-humanist monastic order—the Benedictines—and their reformed offshoot—the Cistercians (the "White Benedictines")—who em-braced the advanced technology of the watermill in the design and construction of their monasteries and who led their lay counterparts by example through their rapid adoption of, and innovations in, water- and wind-powered milling technol-ogy between the tenth and fourteenth centuries. While the essential elements of this narrative appear to have been derived from Bloch, it is a sanitized version of Bloch's story that neglects the central issue of milling monopolies and lordly power.

Both accounts of the role of the monasteries in medieval technological development have proven to be extraordinarily resilient and influential, with Mumford and his followers largely holding sway in the history of science and technology, and Bloch in medieval studies. And yet, while there has been a veritable explosion in milling studies in several disciplines and sub-disciplines over the last two decades, relatively few scholars have subjected either account to sustained critical scrutiny.[12] This paper is therefore an attempt to utilize the burgeoning research in medieval milling to determine to what extent Mumford's and Bloch's canonical claims are consistent with the current state of empirical knowledge.

Because most of the detailed research on medieval milling has been con-ducted on England, most of the evidence cited here will be drawn from there, although some comparative evidence will also be taken from medieval Ireland, Wales, France, and northern Italy. The process sheds light on the question of whether the widespread medieval use of the watermill was primarily an expres-sion of lordly coercive power, as Bloch argued, or was instead the result of a lib-eratory interest in relieving monks and tenants from the drudgery of milling by hand, as Mumford and proponents of the monastic innovation thesis have ar-gued.

The Role of Monasticism in the "Reintroduction" of the Vertical-Wheeled Watermill to Western Europe

Bloch, Mumford, and Lynn White, Jr. are probably the best-known exponents of the view that the Western monastic orders, and particularly the Benedictines, were responsible for having "reintroduced" vertical-wheeled watermills to West-ern Europe after the collapse of the Roman Empire.[13] According to this particular "myth of origins", the Middle Ages in general and the monasteries in particular played a crucial role in the development of modern technology, whereas the classical period in general and lay institutions and commoners in the medieval period were far less important. There is, however, a growing body of evidence to suggest that this view requires substantial revision and qualification. With respect to the use of watermills during the late classical period, it is now clear that the Romans and their contemporaries were not only far more involved in watermilling than earlier scholars have believed, but that the most developed regions of early medieval Europe (modern France and Italy) continued many of the milling practices that had first emerged under the Romans.[14] On the margins of the Empire, the evidence from the British Isles presents a different picture of the development of milling, but one that is also not particularly supportive of the central role attributed to the monasteries by Mumford and Bloch.[15]

Early medieval France inherited water transmission systems and watermills from the Romans, including watermills in various locations and urban aqueducts in Paris, Le Mans, Béziers, and Pézenas, most of which saw service or were rebuilt during the early Middle Ages.[16] Around 500, Gregory of Tours wrote a detailed description of the construction of a watermill complex at Loches, as well as the watermills installed in the defensive walls of Dijon. Visigothic, Alamannic, and Frankish legal codes all indicate that watermills and their associated water networks were important to the economies of the post-Roman kingdoms and a source of some litigation.[17] While a number of early monasteries (such as the Abbey of Saint-Bertin *c.*650) built their own watermills, they were also granted parcels of land that included watermills built by lay people of varying status. In Carolingian times, watermills were amongst the most prized possessions of the new feudal élite, drawing substantial revenues for the aristocracy and religious houses, but also for free peasants in some rural areas. The archaeological evidence from the ninth century onward suggests that most of these mills were vertical-wheeled watermills located on small waterways, although horizontal-wheeled watermills appear to have predominated in southern France, just as they did in the neighbouring Spanish caliphates and kingdoms.[18]

Early medieval Ireland had a continuous tradition of water-powered milling from at least the late sixth century onwards. According to Irish legend, watermills were an import from pagan Britain.[19] Legal texts of the period lend some support to this oral tradition, indicating that the arrival of watermills in the Irish kingdoms predates the arrival of Christianity.[20] Although the earliest firmly dated millsites to date are all monastic, and include the earliest recorded horizontal- and vertical-wheeled tide mills from the first half of the seventh century, the pre-Christian provenance of water-powered milling in Ireland is supported by the fact that of the almost 100 watermill sites that have been dated to the period before 1150, less than 10% were the vertical-wheeled types that we usually associate with the monasteries.[21]

In Britain, eight well-confirmed ancient watermill sites have been excavated throughout the country, suggesting that the technology was used extensively in the former Roman province. Following the withdrawal of Roman governance in the early fifth century, there is neither archaeological nor manuscript evidence for the existence of watermills up until the late seventh century. The six or seven archaeological sites dated to the later Anglo-Saxon period are all royal, and not monastic, however, as are most of the fifty or so charter references to Anglo-Saxon mills. The archaeological remains are also predominantly from horizontal-wheeled mills.[22]

A better idea of the proportion of Anglo-Saxon watermills that were held in ecclesiastical hands can be gained from examining the property held by different social groups in late eleventh-century England as recorded in Domesday Book. The English Church held about a quarter of the country's wealth in 1086, with the Crown, tenants-in-chief, and lesser gentry holding the remainder in roughly equal proportions. If we assume that mill ownership was directly correlated to property ownership, the Church held a quarter of the more than 6,000 watermills that were recorded in the survey. A breakdown of Domesday mill ownership by social sector remains to be done, however.

Richard Holt and John Langdon have both found evidence that ecclesiastical lords were quicker at exploiting their waterways for the construction of watermills than were lay lords.[23] A more recent study of the mill holdings of thirty English religious houses suggests that while the Benedictines may well have held as many as 2,000 watermills throughout the country at Domesday, it is very unlikely that the Black Monks were responsible for building all of these mills, as a reasonably high proportion of ecclesiastical properties both before and after Domesday was acquired from lay lords, many of which included already constructed watermills, just as they did in France.[24]

The Italian case provides some interesting parallels with contemporaneous developments in France and Spain. Paolo Squatriti has found that both vertical- and horizontal-wheeled watermills were being built and used in different parts of early medieval Italy, depending on the hydrological and demographic conditions. Vertical-wheeled watermills tended to be built on major waterways within or near urban centres (following the example set by the Romans), while horizontal-wheeled watermills tended to be built on precipitous or drought-prone streams in rural or mountainous areas that had not previously been served by watermills.[25] He argues that most of the early medieval charter references are to horizontal-wheeled watermills, based partially on the number of references to "mobile" watermills and the many references to watermills that were located in or on top of streams.[26] Whereas Bloch asserted that horizontal-wheeled watermills were an atavistic return to a more primitive type of technology used by "peoples accustomed to a very crude level of material existence,"[27] Squatriti suggests that they played an important role in the post-Imperial economy.[28]

Squatriti's findings suggest that there were two major reorientations in the technological base of the powered milling sector between late Imperial times and the High Middle Ages. The first was from a sector dominated by government-operated vertical watermills and animal-powered mills in late Imperial times, to privately (and communally) operated vertical and horizontal watermills in the Italian micro-states of the early Middle Ages. The second change took place between the eighth and tenth centuries, as feudal rulers appropriated large tracts of land for redistribution to their vassals. The nobles and ecclesiastical authorities who were the beneficiaries of the appropriation of communally-owned mills and lands went on to operate those mills as their own. It is not clear, however, whether this shift in watermill ownership was accompanied by a reduction in the number of horizontal watermills in favour of the more expensive and efficient vertical types, although that is clearly an implication.[29] The evidence from Italy nonetheless indicates that a general shift in patterns of ownership and control of mills occurred in favour of the monasteries and the aristocracy at the expense of the peasantry and townsfolk towards the end of the first millennium. The same appears to be true of France and England. As different feudal systems began to take shape between the eighth and tenth centuries, many watermills that had previously been built and held communally or privately by people of lesser social rank were appropriated by rulers and magnates.[30]

To the extent that the élites can be said to have "reintroduced" the vertical-wheeled watermill to the Italian countryside therefore, they certainly did not do so out of any sense of philanthropy; they did so because such watermills were useful, profitable, and conferred status and authority on those who owned them.[31] Because ecclesiastical officials and institutions were the first and largest beneficiaries of the process of feudal appropriation, it is hardly surprising that earlier scholars have tended to mistake the rapid acquisition by the Church of so much property, including mills, for a remarkable enthusiasm to build new watermills when they were, in fact, only one of the social groups involved in their construction. There is, however, clear evidence that the process of élite appropriation of communal lands and property did not progress so far in Italy as it did in France and England.[32]

While it is therefore evident that in France, Italy, England, and Ireland the arrival of the watermill predates Christian monastic activity, the extent to which the monasteries contributed to the introduction or reintroduction of vertical watermills to each region remains under-determined. The indications are nevertheless strong that the monks were neither the only social group nor the main social group responsible for building watermills during the first half of the Middle Ages.

Milling Monopolies and Lordly Control

Bloch argued that seigneurial milling monopolies were virtually ubiquitous throughout medieval France but less pervasive in England. They persisted until the late eighteenth century in France, the early nineteenth century in Prussia, and well into the nineteenth century in some parts of Canada.[33] They were regarded as one of the many forms of feudal tyranny by those on whom they were imposed,[34] and sometimes extended beyond the bounds of the manor to "neighbouring lordships whose lords were too feeble or too unskilful to succeed in winning this privilege on their own account."[35]

According to Bloch, lordly monopolies extended over most forms of milling, although they were more difficult to enforce in rural areas.[36] Only high-ranking townsfolk escaped their jurisdiction.[37] Commoners were not allowed to own or build water- or windmills, and were expected to procure a license and pay a fee if they used their own handmills or owned a horse mill.[38] Suit of mill was a privilege that ensured tidy profits for the lords concerned.[39]

Bloch describes a number of disputes between French and English tenants and their lords over handmilling in the thirteenth and fourteenth centuries to illustrate his argument that peasants and burgesses resented the imposition of suit of mill and the obligation which that entailed to use powered mills rather than the household handmill, the use of which was of course much more difficult to monitor and tax. His most striking example involves a vivid account of the long history of conflict between the monastery of St. Albans and the artisans who were its main tenants. Unlike the lords of some other urban centres such as Newcastle, Cardiff, and Tewkesbury, the monks of St. Albans refused to grant their tenants any concessions in relation to suit on the town's corn, malt, and fulling mills. Over the course of more than a century between 1274 and the

1381 Peasants' Revolt, a series of violent skirmishes between the tenants and abbatial officials culminated in the granting of a number of liberties to the tenants, all of which were annulled by royal decree following the supression of the Peasants' Revolt.[40] For Bloch, such disputes were indicative of the more widespread phenomenon of peasant and bourgeois resistance to new technologies generally, rather than, for example, resistance to social and economic exploitation.[41]

The picture that he paints is nevertheless compelling. It is also fundamentally at odds with the benign and philanthropic portrayal of monastic innovation that Mumford and White and their followers promoted. However, Bloch's view that ecclesiastical lords were just as oppressive and exploitative as their lay counterparts, if not more so, requires further qualification, and in certain crucial respects, substantial correction.

First of all, Bloch's assertion that the Normans and French effectively introduced seigneurial privileges to England after the Conquest is incorrect.[42] Already in the ninth century some of the larger English ecclesiastical lords were acquiring such rights.[43] By the eleventh century, seigneurial monopolies had become widespread in England. Holt has argued that we have no reason to believe that the vast majority of the more than 6,000 watermills recorded in Domesday Book did not have suit attached to them.[44] But far from being a period during which seigneurial privilege became entrenched in England, the twelfth century was witness to many lords abandoning their claims to such privileges.

To give him his due, Bloch did say that seigneurial monopolies were less pervasive in England than they were in France, and that a number of towns managed to secure charters of liberty with respect to suit of mill in the twelfth century.[45] But he nevertheless gave the strong impression that suit of mill was virtually ubiquitous in England from the twelfth century onwards. Because he drew the evidence for his position from northern England and the larger manorial estates in the south, he did not realize that while French lords may well have kept a stranglehold on their feudal monopolies over many centuries, English lords lost or abandoned effective control of a large number of mills from the very time they were supposed by Bloch to have been imposing such monopolies for the first time. This difference in estate management techniques had profound implications for the structure of lordship in the French and English milling industries, and leads to the second issue in Bloch's thesis that requires substantial correction.

Although the Anglo-Saxon period is not well documented with regard to the structure of mill ownership in England, we do know that whereas manorial employees and household slaves were the main caretakers of mills on behalf of lords during the pre-Conquest period, the evidence from Domesday Book indicates that within twenty years of the Conquest, a large number of mills were held at will from lay and ecclesiastical lords by tenants paying cash rents.[46] The subsequent economic downturn of the early twelfth century made many English lords reconsider their role in mill management.

Despite fluctuations in mill profitability, French lords continued to jealously guard their ownership of mills and the seigneurial monopolies that accompanied them throughout the twelfth century and beyond.[47] English lords were not so phlegmatic, however. The downturn in the English economy in the early twelfth century was followed by political turmoil and economic instability under the reign of Stephen.[48] These events led to a major restructuring of property relations between English tenants and lords that was definitely to the advantage of the lower orders.

Essentially, seigneurial monopolies in many parts of England were allowed to fall into abeyance. Traditionally, feudal lords had retained direct control of their possessions, collecting revenues for their own benefit without leasing them out. During the first half of the twelfth century, however, lordly revenues from such demesne possessions declined, while their maintenance costs remained the same. As a consequence, many lay and ecclesiastical lords allowed their demesne possessions to fall into hereditary tenure. Such possessions were let to free tenants as well as customary villein tenants for a life, or even for two or three lives, in order for the lord to diminish his or her ongoing costs for expensive enterprises like milling by shifting those costs onto tenants.[49] But because lords charged fixed rents on these mills which could only be varied once the tenant died or the mill in question was passed on to a third party via grant, sale, or lease, it also meant that lords forfeited to their tenants any increase in profitability once economic conditions improved.

If a mill was held by a lord within the demesne and was directly managed, the lord collected all of the revenue from the mill, but was also responsible for all the costs of maintenance and repairs (typically around 15-20% of the mill's income over its lifetime).[50] But if a mill needed to be partially or totally rebuilt, such costs could significantly reduce lordly profits during a time of low revenues. Allowing mills to fall into hereditary tenure was a common lordly strategy for minimising costs during such periods. However, an unforeseen consequence, first during the twelfth century, and later in the wake of the Black Death, was that a significant number of these mills could no longer be effectively controlled by their lords. As a result, many lords sued their tenants (or those who had illegally appropriated their mills) for recovery when their profitability improved.[51]

The degree to which such mills had autonomy from lordly control has prompted some debate about their exact status in the context of the English manorial system, and by extension, the most appropriate term to use when describing them. Holt has described such mills as "independent mills", while Langdon has called them "tenant mills." Holt's reasoning for choosing the former term is that these mills were granted out in free or hereditary villein tenure and paid fixed rents from that time onwards. They were, therefore, relatively independent of lordly control.[52] Langdon's reasoning for choosing "tenant mills" is that although these mills fell into hereditary tenure, the lord still had some control over the mill. The person (or persons) who held the mill under hereditary or free tenure was, therefore, still a tenant. Theoretically at least, the lord of the mill could still reclaim the mill from his or her tenant if its cash or labour rent was not paid, or if the tenant died without an heir and had not sold or bequeathed it to someone else. In other words, these mills were not "independent" in the sense that they were not completely beyond lordly control.[53]

The advantage of Holt's "independent mills" is that it gives a clear indication of the relative autonomy of these mills from lordly jurisdiction; the disadvantage of Langdon's "tenant mill" is that it makes it difficult to differentiate between mills that were held at farm on short- or fixed-term leases, and those held in hereditary tenure. There clearly was a difference in the two types of tenure, and the use of the term "tenant mills" arguably obscures that difference.

While fixed-term leases on mills (mills "at farm") varied somewhat in their conditions, most transferred rights of multure (*i.e.*, the miller's right to take a percentage of the corn milled as a fee) to the lessee.[54] In exchange, the lessee was expected to pay for the maintenance of the mill, the cost of which was usually offset by the lord through the ongoing provision of timber for maintenance, and/or the provision of extra land from which to draw this and other resources, such as fruit from orchards, or fish and eels from the mill's pond and leet.[55] Generally speaking, such leases stipulated whether the tenant concerned also acquired suit of mill from the lord, and whether the lord's household was exempt from having to pay multure or retained other milling privileges, such as the right to mill his or her own grain before other customers.[56]

Mills let out in hereditary tenure had much the same conditions attached to them as fixed-term leases. However, as noted previously, one of the defining characteristics of such tenancies was that while the mill may have initially been let for a market rent, because of the nature of the tenure, the lord was unable to increase the rent until either the tenant died or the lord was able to bring the mill back into demesne tenure.[57] In practice this meant that the rents on such mills remained fixed despite any fluctuations in grain prices or other costs. As profits increased, therefore, a greater share of the profits went to the tenant, rather than the lord. The main beneficiaries of such practices were free peasants, artisans, merchants, and the minor gentry, although bonded peasants were also given customary rights over a significant number of mills that subsequently acquired hereditary status.[58] While lords in some parts of twelfth- and thirteenth-century England did not pursue these policies, such as in the north and in certain areas where ancient religious houses held most of the property (such as Huntingdonshire), many lords in England south of the Humber did do so.[59] As with fixed-term leases, however, it is not always clear how many of these mills were permitted to continue to draw suit, although it seems reasonable in most cases to assume that if the mill concerned was not granted or leased as part of a whole manor, drew low revenues compared to others on the manor or nearby, and the relevant documents do not stipulate that suit was included as part of the agreement, the mill did not hold suit.[60] Holt found that by the mid- to late thirteenth century, between a third and a half of the mills in many parts of southern England were held in hereditary tenure.[61] These findings are supported by Langdon's studies of mill ownership in the West Midlands from 1086 to 1500 and the *Inquisitiones Post Mortem* for the reign of Edward II,[62] and by my own study of the mill holdings of more than thirty English religious houses.[63]

When economic conditions improved in the late twelfth and thirteenth centuries, many of the lords who had earlier let their mills fall into hereditary tenure tried to draw these mills back into the demesne, from where they could enjoy their by now considerable profits. At the same time, many of them sought to re-impose or even to increase the labour and other services required of both free and bonded tenants. Such strategies often included the rigorous enforcement of suit of mill. In response, many villeins who had held property under customary or hereditary tenure on cash rents during the previous period sought to argue a legal case for their free status, although in most cases appear to have been unsuccessful.[64] By the early fourteenth century, English lords had managed to recover most of the mills that had fallen out of their direct control.[65] Despite their success, however, a relatively large number of mills remained effectively beyond seigneurial control throughout southern England, particularly in East Anglia. In the wake of the Black Death, a significant number of demesne mills once again reverted or were converted to customary tenure due to the difficulties of securing a stable income from hugely depleted manorial populations.[66]

Ecclesiastical lords were just as, if not more, enthusiastic as lay lords at pursuing alienated mills, although they often had to take their tenants to court in order to regain them. This sometimes involved the payment of considerable sums of money to compensate the disenfranchised tenant for lost future revenue, as at the mills of Neford and *Apechildewude* held by the Abbey of Holy Trinity, Caen, and of the mills of Wye held by Battle Abbey.[67] However, some of the smaller religious houses and those administering property from afar had neither the financial resources nor the will to pursue such cases through the courts. This meant that they might never recover direct control of what had once been profitable manorial mills, and had to remain content with drawing a fixed and relatively low income from those mills, or indeed, no income at all. Holy Trinity and the Priory of St. Denys in Southampton provide instances of both kinds of houses that allowed alienated mills to remain outside the demesne, or were unable to collect the mill rents due them from recalcitrant tenants.[68] On the other hand, if a free or customary tenant refused to relinquish control of a mill with suit, the lord could starve the mill of custom by failing to enforce suit on its tenants, and/ or by building a new manorial mill. Battle, Bec, and Glastonbury Abbeys are just some of the houses that pursued such policies.[69]

Clearly, there were marked differences between the abilities and willingness of lords to take their tenants to court to regain direct control of mills and other properties that had been part of their demesnes, just as there was to sue neighbouring lords and the descendants of donors who had illegally disseised them. Some cases could drag on for decades and cost the lords concerned more money than the properties were worth. Examples include Lancaster Priory's seventy-year-plus dispute over seisin of the mills of Caton with a local knightly family; St. Denys' Priory's century-long dispute over rents due to it from the mill of King's Sombourne; Furness Abbey's dispute with the Neville family over land and mills in Ulverstone; Holy Trinity's disputes over seisin of its mills in Minchinhampton, Felsted, and Avening; and Battle's disputes over seisin of its mills in Wye.[70]

The claim that mills in hereditary tenure were still effectively under lordly control is therefore undermined by three demonstrable facts:

1) the profits from mills in hereditary tenure generally accrued to their tenants, rather than their lords;
2) lords frequently had to sue their tenants to regain seisin of mills in hereditary tenure; and
3) even when lords were successful in regaining seisin, they were often forced to pay tenants considerable compensation for lost future revenue.

Holt's initial assessment that many mills in customary and hereditary tenure were relatively autonomous is therefore more consistent with the evidence, although Langdon is correct to note that such mills nevertheless remained under lordly jurisdiction by law, if not in practice. I will, however, adopt Holt's term "independent mill" to register the relative autonomy of these mills from lordly jurisdiction.[71]

Independence from feudal obligations, and especially suit of mill, was seen as a desirable and legitimate goal by many peasants and townsfolk throughout England, especially from the twelfth and thirteenth centuries onwards. The fact that some had been able to collectively free themselves from such feudal burdens after the Conquest is illustrated by a case in the borough of Tamworth, Staffordshire, where a lay lord was accused by the townspeople in 1275 of depriving them of their customary rights, which had previously included "the choice of their own bailiffs; a fixed farm; and freedom from suit of mill."[72] But while lay lords appear to have been relatively indulgent in allowing such rights to persist, it was far more common for ecclesiastical lords to deny them.[73] The resistance of free and bonded tenants to suit of mill was part of a broader rebellion in the towns and on the larger manorial estates by mercantile and craftwork associations and whole communities against what were regarded as part of a more general system of oppressive rule.[74]

Just how oppressive the imposition of suit had become by the fourteenth century is well illustrated by the fact that lords were frequently prepared to commute suit of mill for individuals and even whole communities to an annual licence fee. Holt records a number of instances where the lord concerned no longer owned a functioning mill on a manor but nevertheless insisted that a licence fee be paid, showing that such behaviour clearly illustrates that seigneurial mills were regarded by both users and owners "as little more than a means of transferring wealth from the former to the latter."[75]

Despite the coercion involved in milling at the manorial mill, however, peasants and townsfolk do not necessarily appear to have preferred to mill their corn with handmills, as Bloch and Pierre Dockès argued. The long-term survival of a large number of powered mills outside the demesne clearly demonstrates that they drew custom from a variety of social strata. Although most independent mills may not have been as profitable as manorial mills, a reasonable number of them were sufficiently profitable to survive the Black Death and other problems.[76] Their existence demonstrates that Bloch was wrong to argue that milling monopolies were the norm throughout the later Middle Ages in England, while the fact that independent mills did not require coercion to maintain their custom demonstrates that peasants and burgesses were not necessarily averse to the "advanced technology" of the watermill.[77] Bloch was correct, however, to note that suit of mill conferred tidy profits on the lords concerned.

On the other hand, it is clearly not the case that the majority of watermills and windmills were built and acquired by lay and ecclesiastical lords in order to relieve their tenants from drudgery, as proponents of the monastic innovation thesis have argued.[78] To the contrary, they built and acquired new mills to try to make a profit and to impress their power and authority upon the lower orders.[79] Indeed, the evidence from the thirteenth century indicates that, despite the widespread growth in the number of watermills and windmills, ecclesiastical lords were actively engaged throughout this period in imposing additional feudal burdens and unfree status upon their villeins, and significantly increasing the rents extracted from their free tenants.[80] Further, because suit of mill was imposed by law in many parts of England and France, White's characterization of the spread of powered milling as "a chapter in the conquest of freedom" requires serious qualification. It was only in those places where there was a competitive market or where a relatively independent sector of the milling industry existed that there was a genuine lack of compulsion in this particular economic exchange.

Monastic Mill Construction and Innovation

What is the evidence for the monasteries' involvement in mill-building in the second half of the Middle Ages, and for them being great innovators in industrial milling practices? The best evidence to date comes from medieval England and Wales. Three major orders—the Benedictines, Augustinians, and Cistercians — and a dozen or more minor orders owned and operated mills throughout England between the eighth and sixteenth centuries. The Benedictines were by far the most powerful and widespread of the monastic orders in the country before the Conquest. It was they who were the primary benefactors of Anglo-Saxon aristocratic largesse between the early seventh and eleventh centuries and who owned the largest amount of property (including mills) of any of the orders both before and after the Conquest.

The Benedictines' prosperity, therefore, had little to do with the "orderly routine" followed by the monks, or their "mastery of technical activities," as Mumford claimed. Their prosperity (in England as elsewhere) was, in fact, primarily due to the generosity of their benefactors and the extensive nature of their estates. As the oldest and wealthiest of the major orders, the Benedictines were able to establish themselves in many parts of England without any competition from other religious orders or lay lords; they had built or acquired hundreds of manorial mills before the other orders had even arrived in the country.[81] A reasonable idea of their dominance of the ecclesiastical milling sector can be gained by examining the relative numbers of mills held by the various religious orders in the early fourteenth century, the peak of medieval milling activity.

Eight of the ten Benedictine houses sampled held just under 275 mills between them, while the ten Augustinian houses sampled held only 73 mills between them, and the five Cistercian houses, 51 mills. This gives us an average of more than 34 mills per house in the case of the Benedictines, just over 7 mills per house for the Augustinians, and just over 10 mills per house for the Cistercians. The Benedictines thus held more than three times as many mills per capita as the Cistercians and five times as many as the Augustinians. While there is somewhat of a bias in the figures for the Benedictines due to the number of wealthy houses in the sample,[82] and a heavy reliance on charter evidence for the Augustinian houses, it is nevertheless clear that the Benedictines had a strong edge over their ecclesiastical competitors in the milling industry. Furthermore, virtually every religious house examined, whether large or small, held more mills than it needed to feed its own people.

Perhaps unsurprisingly, the only monastic order that was ever involved in extensive mill-building at any stage during the Middle Ages was the Benedictines. The second and third largest orders, the Augustinians and Cistercians, acquired at least 70% of their mills through grants, appropriations, and purchases of their mills from lay lords, most of whom were members of the knightly class.[83] The first major phase of monastic mill construction probably took place in the century or so leading up to the Domesday survey (1086), after the monasteries had first been granted seigneurial privileges. It was almost undoubtedly the larger Benedictine houses that were building most of these mills, although how the Benedictines acquired the majority of their mills before the Conquest has yet to be determined. Given their substantial property base, however, it seems reasonable to assume that this enabled them to make significant investments in mill construction, much as they did in the thirteenth century.

The thirteenth century marked the second phase of monastic mill construction, when mill profitability was at an all-time high and the English population was growing rapidly. Most of the second phase of mill-building involved the construction of windmills, and most of these were built in areas where there were insufficient supplies of running water to meet local demand for milled grain with watermills. The main area for windmill construction was East Anglia—some houses tripled their mill holdings over the period of six or seven decades[84]—although Lancashire and Sussex also experienced somewhat of a windmill building boom during the thirteenth century.[85] Across the whole of England, a significant number of the wealthier Benedictine houses doubled their mill holdings between Domesday and the early fourteenth century: a doubling which reflects population growth over the same period and clearly indicates the desire and ability of the large houses to take advantage of the growing market for finely milled grain.[86]

Although the Black Monks may have been building more mills than most other lords between the ninth and eleventh centuries, by Domesday they were starting to lose their preeminence—probably shared with the king—with respect to the ownership of mills. But it was not the other religious orders who were challenging their better-established brethren. Particularly from the thirteenth century onwards, it was lay lords, and to a lesser extent free men, who were building the majority of new mills, many of which appear to have been operating independently. As many as a fifth of the new mills being built in the early fourteenth century were constructed by "small men", and probably twice that number in the wake of the Black Death.[87] The plague had a remarkable effect on breaking down feudal monopolies and freeing up property and investment for the lower orders in England. It therefore played a significant role in providing the social and economic foundations for the early modern period.

What then of the role of the monasteries in mill innovation, and especially the application of waterpower to industrial processes such as those associated with fulling, brewing, tanning, timber-cutting, tool-sharpening, and metallurgy? Industrial mills in England and Wales were uncommon generally, although they were slightly less so for ecclesiastical estates. Around 10% of the mills held by Benedictine houses and around 14% of those held by Cistercian houses in the late thirteenth and early fourteenth centuries were industrial mills,[88] a significantly higher proportion than that of 3.5% found for lay lords across England in the early fourteenth century,[89] but roughly in accord with the figure of 10% across the board that Langdon found in the West Midlands between the thirteenth and fifteenth centuries.[90] These figures are also consistent with the recent findings of researchers for the Discovery Programme in Ireland, who found fifteen fulling mills out of 178 mills (*i.e.*, 8.4%) identified in the medieval sources for the region around Dublin between *c.*1180 and 1550.[91]

Although the religious houses did not necessarily document all of the industrial mills that existed on their estates—as archaeological digs on houses such as Kirkstall, Bordesley, and others have subsequently revealed—a trawl of archaeological reports from the early 1950s onwards suggests that the numbers of English industrial mills pre-1500 can hardly have been more than double those revealed by the manuscript sources.[92] By far the largest involvement by English ecclesiastical lords in any kind of industrial milling (nearly 85%) was in the fulling industry. Other forms of industrial milling, such as grinding bark to extract tannin to cure leather, tool-sharpening, and manufacturing iron were comparatively rare. Furthermore, the extensive evidence for the use of waterpower in a range of industrial applications as seen in France and northern Italy was not in evidence in England until the sixteenth century.[93]

The broader context within which monastic mechanized fulling took place is partially revealed through a sectoral analysis of almost three centuries of the Welsh mechanized fulling industry: from 1270 to 1550, just under a fifth of all the Welsh fulling mills identified were held by religious houses. Although the vast majority were controlled by a handful of wealthy noble families, half the ecclesiastical sector of Welsh fulling was dominated by just a quarter of the Welsh houses that held such mills. The situation was probably much the same in England, although the research remains to be done.[94] It would seem reasonable to assume that as much as a third of the Welsh fulling industry in the late thirteenth century was controlled by religious houses, but that this figure had been reduced to as little as a fifth by the fourteenth and fifteenth centuries, similar to the situation in northern Italy in the fourteenth century.[95] The fact that 45% of the fulling mills identified in documents dating from 1270 to 1299 were owned by ecclesiastical estates also suggests that although the monasteries became involved relatively early in mechanized fulling, they were soon eclipsed by lay lords.

Of those religious orders that were involved in mechanized fulling in England, the Cistercians appear to have been the most active in the fulling industry per capita, largely due to their major involvement in the wool trade, with the Benedictines running a close second. The Cistercians also appear to have been pioneers in the use of watermills for manufacturing iron, as most of the earliest recorded sites in England are Cistercian. Two of the five Cistercian houses sampled had workshops and iron foundries that used waterpower (*i.e.*, Kirkstall and Beaulieu, with Beaulieu also holding a tanning mill and a horse-driven tool-sharpening mill in its shoe workshop in the late thirteenth century). While three of the five Cistercian houses studied do not appear to have held any industrial mills, the fact that by the early fourteenth century the other two held seven out of the nineteen mills which they held between them does give some credence to the monastic innovation thesis, and therefore warrants further study.

The Monasteries' Role in the Independent Milling Sector

The involvement of the monasteries in the independent milling sector was largely shaped by the kinds of property which they held, and the places where they held it. There was, therefore, a significant difference between the kinds of independent mills held by the Benedictines, and those held by two other major orders, the Augustinians and Cistercians. Because of their relatively late arrival in England, the Augustinians and Cistercians did not benefit nearly so much as the Benedictines from large grants of ancient demesne by members of the royal family and other tenants-in-chief. Most of the Benedictines' grants consisted of whole manors, many with existing mills. Most of the Augustinian and Cistercian houses, if they held whole manors at all, tended to acquire them from their founding benefactors. The Cistercians, Premonstratensians, and some other minor orders were able to compensate for this disadvantage to some extent by founding their houses in relatively isolated areas and subsequently consolidating their holdings nearby. The Augustinians, however, tended to build up their estates in a far more piecemeal way. The smaller and medium-sized houses in particular were the beneficiaries of disparate and often small holdings that were parts of widely scattered manors previously held at fee by knights. Understandably, most found such holdings difficult to manage effectively.

These differences in the composition of their estates meant that while the larger Cistercian houses and most of the minor orders were able to consolidate their holdings sufficiently well to establish suit of mill* over a fairly significant proportion of their tenants (even in cases where they had not been granted whole manors or mills with suit), the Augustinians were far less successful at doing so. By the early fourteenth century, the Augustinians held suit only on about 25% of their mills, the Cistercians slightly more at around 37% of their mills, while the

---

*Some questions remain as to how we determine whether certain mills held suit while others did not, and to what degree holding suit was the norm. If a grant or lease of a mill stipulated that the mill held suit, then it clearly did. In those cases where a house held a whole manor and the mill(s) on the manor were either directly managed or leased on fixed-term leases, we assume that the mill(s) *did* hold suit (confirmation could sometimes be gained by comparing mill revenues across manors). If a grant or lease of a mill did not include the whole manor and suit of mill is not mentioned in the relevant documents, we assume that the mill *did not* hold suit. If a manorial account registered a mill as being in free, customary, or hereditary tenure, and the mill was drawing a very low or nominal rent in comparison to other mills held by the same house that were known to hold suit, we assumed that mill also *did not* hold suit. The same assumption was made for multiple mills on a single manor, if only one was directly managed and was drawing a significant income compared to the others.

minor orders held suit on between 71% and 80% of their mills. The figures for the Benedictines, however, ranged far more widely, with anywhere between 55% and 95% of their mills holding suit, depending on the region[96] [see Tables 1-3].

The extant evidence suggests that there was a significant difference between the origins and status of independent mills held by the Benedictines and those held by the Augustinians and Cistercians. Whereas the Benedictines' manorial mills held suit from the time they were first acquired and subsequently lost it, the Augustinians and Cistercians were granted a large number of mills that did not hold that privilege, and in relatively few cases later acquired it. Most of their mills were donated to them by members of the knightly class, and appear to have been held in hereditary tenure prior to being donated. How such mills had fallen out of the demesne in the first place is not always clear. Some had probably been initially built by knightly families on fees for the use of their households only. Others may have been held by peasants, townsfolk, or members of the lesser gentry prior to the Conquest and were never effectively brought into the demesne, while still others may once have been demesne mills, but for one reason or other were abandoned, sold off, or rented for a nominal rent, and replaced by newer, more powerful, or more reliable mills that were subsequently given suit at the expense of the other mill(s) on the manor in order to maximise lordly returns. These mills, which did not have seigneurial status at the time of their acquisition from lay lords, constitute a newly-identified category of independent mills.

A cogent illustration of the co-existence on the same manor of manorial and independent mills is illustrated by a dispute between Glastonbury Abbey and Bradenstoke Priory in Wiltshire in the late thirteenth century. In April 1287, Abbot John of Glastonbury appointed Abbot William of Malmesbury as his attorney to "put the prior of Bradenstoke into full seisin of the suit of mill of the abbot's men of Glastonbury to the prior's mill in Christian Malford, as before."[97] Glastonbury held two mills on the same manor, but neither of them held suit, and one of them was already at farm for two lives by this time. A declaration by the abbot of around the same time lists fifty-one of his tenants who owed suit to the Christian Malford mill, eight of whom were women.[98] The dispute over suit of the mill appears to have arisen because the prior of Bradenstoke had until then refused to swear fealty to the abbot of Glastonbury. This was presumably because he knew that Bradenstoke held suit on the manor after it was granted to the canons by a local knightly family, and the abbot was refusing to instruct his own tenants to do suit to the prior's mill, thus providing his own mills with a larger clientele.[99]

Table 1

SUIT OF MILL AND AVERAGE MILL REVENUES FOR SIX RELIGIOUS HOUSES IN LATE THIRTEENTH- AND EARLY FOURTEENTH-CENTURY ENGLAND

Name and order of religious house	Number of mills held	% of mills with suit	Average annual mill revenue
Abbey of Bec* (French foundation)	23	87%	£3 13s.
Hereford Cathedral Priory (Benedictine)	21	95%	£3 14s.
Beaulieu Abbey (Cistercian)	12	75%	£5
Grove Priory (French dependency)	5	100%	£4
Treasury of St Peter's Church, York (Augustinian)	5	100%	£6 3s.
Durham Cathedral Priory (Benedictine)	35	95%	£15

*English manors only

Even though between 63% and 75% of the mills held by the Cistercians and Augustinians had independent status, in terms of overall numbers there must have been far more of the former Benedictine mills that were independent, simply because the Benedictines always held more mills than the other orders. The significant difference between the two types of independent mill was that the Benedictines no longer directly managed those mills (having leased them to customary and free tenants instead), whereas the Augustinians and Cistercians often directly managed their mills or let them on fixed-term leases. Both orders therefore played a significant role in providing independent milling alternatives to manorial tenants and others.

According to Langdon, 40% of the overall milling market in England in the early fourteenth century was handled by the demesne sector, less than 20% by "tenant" mills, 20% by "borough" mills (or mills in English towns and villages that had secured charters of liberty and were therefore outside lordly control), while another 20% or more of the market was handled by domestic handmills and a much smaller number of horse mills. Based on the assumption that ecclesiastical lords held around a quarter of the country's wealth at the time, they probably therefore controlled only about 20% of the watermills and windmills throughout the country in the early fourteenth century, although they may have held as many as 40% of the mills in the north.[100] This means that their share of the powered milling sector overall had diminished significantly between the late eleventh century and the early fourteenth century, the remainder having been picked up by lay lords and, presumably, a growing number of "small men" (*i.e.*, artisans, craftsmen, merchants, and some of the wealthier peasants).

On the basis of these data, it is now possible to make a meaningful assessment of a claim made by Langdon using the *Inquisitiones Post Mortem* (*IPM*s) for the reign of Edward II (1307-27) regarding the extent to which the tenants of lay lords tended to utilize ecclesiastical mills as an alternative to the manorial mills of their own lords. In his study of the *IPM* material, Langdon suggests that lay demesne mills south of the Humber were processing only about half of the millable grain on their manors, suggesting that some custom was lost to ecclesiastical mills. He suggests that this is unlikely, however, because of the rapacious reputation of ecclesiastical lords, whose own tenants often sought to take their grain outside the manor to be milled, including to neighbouring lay mills.[101]

While it is true that many of the larger religious houses were rapacious and sought to extract the maximum revenues from their mills with suit, many houses—and even some of the older and wealthier houses—held significant numbers of independent mills from which they were drawing low revenues. The two categories of independent ecclesiastical mills just described were clearly being used by some manorial tenants. Even those that were directly managed by religious houses (*i.e.*, demesne mills without suit) were drawing custom away from lay lords and other ecclesiastical lords.

Most of the religious houses studied collected revenues from mills that did not have seigneurial status. Even without the compulsion of suit, some of these mills collected quite reasonable revenues for their ecclesiastical lords, indicating that they were not considered an irksome imposition by the people who frequented them. Although such mills did not generally draw very high incomes, or on the whole very high levels of custom, they most certainly did provide an important alternative to the manorial mills with suit held most frequently by the Benedictines and lay tenants-in-chief. The ecclesiastical lords who held these mills were, therefore, not necessarily rapacious. Furthermore, because a significant number of the smaller Augustinian and Cistercian houses directly managed mills without seigneurial status in competition with seigneurial mills, such competition presumably fuelled a certain amount of conflict.

That disputes between lords with competing milling interests did indeed occur is borne out by the previous example of Glastonbury Abbey's conflict with Bradenstoke Priory over suit in the manor of Christian Malford. That such disputes were fairly common is illustrated by the fact that all five of the Cistercian houses in the sample were involved in at least two or three mill-related water and land disputes with local lay lords, while Sibton was involved in several. Four of the ten Augustinian houses were involved in mill-related water disputes, and three of the five houses of the minor orders were involved in disputes over access to watercourses or lands pertaining to mills. A number of these disputes were clearly related to competition for mill custom, and sometimes went on for decades.[102]

This research provides a substantial body of additional evidence to confirm Holt's and Langdon's previous findings that the existence of mills without suit was far more common in England than Bloch acknowledged. It also demonstrates that there was more than one category of ecclesiastical mill that can be construed as independent, and that such mills constituted a viable alternative for tenants who were dissatisfied with the milling options offered by their own lords.

Milling Profitability and its Shaping Factors

Monastic mills provided an important source of revenue for religious houses and a relatively secure income stream. In the thirteenth and fourteenth centuries, it was not at all unusual for 6-10% of a monastery's total income to be derived from its mills, compared to an average of 5-8% of all manorial income for both lay and ecclesiastical lords over the same period.[103] In some parts of northern England at the same time, milling contributed as much as a third of rental income, with the average in the north being around 14%.[104] Milling generally remained a profitable enterprise between the late eleventh century until the second half of the fourteenth century, when profits experienced a marked decline in the wake of the Black Death.[105]

That English lords fully appreciated the profitability of powered milling is well illustrated by the rationalisation of milling resources that took place after the Conquest. Whereas Anglo-Saxon lords had tolerated a large number of relatively unprofitable mills on marginal streams and rivers, or those far from population centres, within two hundred years of their arrival French and Norman aristocratic families had concentrated their milling assets on major waterways and in or near population centres. Furthermore, milling efficiency was increased by as much as 30% with the construction of bigger and more powerful water-mills, particularly in the late thirteenth century.[106]

Profitability of various kinds of milling enterprises—or lack thereof—depends most importantly on the cost of building, repairing, and maintaining mills. The only other significant cost was the employment of the miller, who could be a demesne employee paid directly by the lord, or a bonded or free tenant who paid rent to the house which held the mill. Often, the miller used a boy or apprentice to help run the mill. If the miller was a demesne employee, he was often paid in tollcorn, supplemented by a cash stipend. Despite the considerable expertise required, the total sums (in cash and tollcorn) paid to millers with vil-lein status appear to have generally corresponded to that of a low-skilled worker in the early fourteenth century: around £1 5s. per annum.[107] Millers who were free men could command higher wages, partially because they were responsible for meeting the mills' essential running costs.[108]

With respect to the costs of construction, repairs, and maintenance, the av-erage cost of building windmills and watermills in late thirteenth- and early fourteenth-century England was around £10 in the case of an average post wind-mill, and from £9 to £15 for rebuilding a watermill on an already existing site. In the case of watermills, however, if watercourses, milldams, ponds, sluices, and weirs had to be built from scratch, the cost was considerably higher: it was not unusual for £20 or more to be spent on building mill ponds and sluices for a new watermill in the late thirteenth century.[109] In terms of repairs and maintenance, the cost of repairing watermills averaged around 20% of the overall income from the mill over a few decades, while the cost of repairing windmills was around 30-35%.[110] These costs could be reduced slightly by recycling parts such as mill-stones, or using timber harvested from the mill-owner's property.

Windmills were, therefore, significantly cheaper to build than watermills, but were more expensive to maintain. Furthermore, they produced on average only about half the revenues of watermills.[111] If a lord had the choice between re-building an existing watermill on a reliable watercourse or building a new wind-mill, he or she would understandably opt for the former due to the lower ongoing maintenance costs and higher revenues. The utility of windmills was therefore largely restricted to areas with restricted supplies of running water and steady prevailing winds, such as parts of East Anglia, the West Midlands, Lancashire, and Sussex.[112] Despite these differences in construction and maintenance costs as well as utility and profitability, the profits that were to be had from operat-ing a conventional grain mill were considerable. Given that a watermill paid on average around 20% of its income on expenses, and a windmill about 30%, the average profit for mills engaged in grain-milling was high, at around 70-80% of total revenue. Although these kinds of profits were generally restricted to mills with suit, independent mills located in population centres with relatively little competition could expect a similar level of profitability.

Industrial mills, on the other hand, were far less profitable. While data on the revenues for English fulling mills is relatively abundant, that for other types of industrial mill is virtually non-existent. Fulling mills earned on average only around a quarter to a third as much as conventional watermills. While some of the data from Wales suggests that they were cheaper to build than water-powered grain mills (possibly because they did not require expensive millstones), the costs of maintaining and repairing them can hardly have been much lower.[113] They were, therefore, practical propositions only where there was an abundance of running water and an existing expertise in industrial commodity production.[114]

It is becoming increasingly clear that, despite the early enthusiasm of some of the larger religious houses for industrial applications of waterpower, ecclesiastical and lay lords alike were primarily involved in the milling industry for profit, and generally only supported those mechanised milling practices which brought in a decent income. The larger religious houses in particular were often entrepreneurial in seeing opportunities for profit-making, particularly during the thirteenth century, but with respect to the adoption of new mill designs or new applications for powered mills, the Cistercians appear to be the only order that was consistently more innovative than their lay counterparts.

The extent to which a house held suit on its mills largely determined its level of income from those mills, which of course explains why so many ecclesiastical lords in the thirteenth and fourteenth centuries sought to remind their tenants of the privilege by occasionally fining those who ignored it and confiscating their handmills. Generally speaking, the more mills with suit, the higher the revenues. This latter observation is clearly reflected in the average annual mill revenues of six religious houses in the late thirteenth and early fourteenth centuries. One of these houses was Cistercian, one was Augustinian, two were Benedictine and the other two were French abbatial lands or dependencies [Table 1].

The average annual mill revenue differences between houses are largely related to differences in the strength of lordship in the regions where the respective houses were located, which in turn largely determined the levels of mill revenue in those regions. The estates of Beaulieu, Bec, and Hereford were all located in the south of England where there was significant competition for milling cus-

Table 2

SUIT OF MILL AND AVERAGE MILL REVENUES FOR FOUR CATEGORY I RELIGIOUS
HOUSES IN LATE THIRTEENTH- AND EARLY FOURTEENTH-CENTURY ENGLAND

Name and order of religious house	Number of mills held	% of mills with suit	Average annual mill revenue
Holy Trinity Abbey, Caen* (French foundation)	10	10%	9s. 9d.
Canterbury Cathedral Priory** (Benedictine)	14	15%	11s. 3d.
Battle Abbey (Benedictine)	20+	50% (?)	£1 5s. 3d.
Glastonbury Abbey (Benedictine)	40	40%	£2

Manor of Minchinhampton only   **Sussex manors only*

tom, with manorial mills competing against mills in customary and hereditary tenure and others without seigneurial status. Such mills did not generally hold suit and charged lower rates of multure than those that did. Competition from independent mills in the south tended to keep overall mill revenues and rates of multure lower than in the north, where much stronger lordship ensured that such mills were generally not tolerated, and higher rates of multure could be maintained. Multure rates in the north could be as high as 1/13 for villein tenants, whereas those in the south were generally around 1/20 to 1/24, but could be as low as 1/32.[115]

The relative earning capacities of mills with suit and those without is clearly revealed by comparing the high average mill revenues of those religious houses that mostly held suit with the low average mill revenues of those houses that mostly held mills without suit. As explained earlier, there were two categories of mills without suit. The first category consisted of mills that had been alienated from the demesne and were held in customary or hereditary tenure, while the second category consisted of mills which did not have seigneurial status before they were acquired by the religious houses concerned. Generally speaking, most of those houses which held mills in the first category were Benedictine and had been part of ancient demesne lands that were alienated or appropriated during the eleventh and twelfth centuries, while most of those in the second category were Cistercian or Augustinian mills that had been granted to the houses con-

Table 3

SUIT OF MILL AND AVERAGE MILL REVENUES FOR FOUR CATEGORY 2 RELIGIOUS HOUSES IN LATE THIRTEENTH- AND EARLY FOURTEENTH-CENTURY ENGLAND

Name and order of religious house	Number of mills held	% of mills with suit	Average annual mill revenue
Lacock Priory (Augustinian)	5	0%	12s.
St. Denys Priory (Augustinian)	8	20%	£1 7s.
Sibton Abbey (Cistercian)	9	33%	£1 7s.
Cirencester Abbey (Augustinian)	19	40%	£1 13s.

cerned by knightly benefactors during the twelfth and thirteenth centuries. The two types of mill have been called Category 1 and Category 2, respectively, in Tables 2 and 3.

The contrast between the average annual mill incomes of the houses that mostly held suit on manorial mills and those whose manorial mills had been alienated, or which had been donated independent mills, is thus very clear. Generally speaking, the higher the proportion of mills in independent tenure, the lower the average mill revenues. The highest average mill earnings in Categories 1 and 2 are still only around half of the lowest average mill earnings of the houses with high proportions of mills with suit. The lowest average mill earnings in Categories 1 and 2 are about one-seventh of the lowest average mill earnings of the houses with high proportions of mills with suit. They are about one-thirtieth of those of the most extractive ecclesiastical lord in the country, that is, the bishop of Durham. There were, therefore, huge variations in the amounts of revenue which could be extracted from mills in different parts of England. Bloch's assumption that seigneurial monopolies were virtually ubiquitous throughout England cannot account for these variations and why they should have been the case.

Conclusion

What then can be said about the various claims made by proponents of the monastic innovation thesis and the seigneurial monopoly model? With respect to those made by advocates of both theories that the monasteries reintroduced the vertical-wheeled watermill to medieval Europe after the collapse of the Roman Empire, we have seen that although the Romans introduced the vertical-wheeled watermill to the regions that we now call Italy, France, and Britain, the early medieval development of powered milling in Italy and Britain involved the widespread construction and use of horizontal-wheeled watermills. From the ninth and tenth centuries onwards, feudal rulers appropriated communal lands for distribution to their vassals, one of the consequences being that horizontal-wheeled watermills were replaced by vertical-wheeled watermills. At least three powerful social groups were responsible for this technological transition, the monks being only one of them. There is also reason to believe that while the (mainly Benedictine) monks may have held most of the watermills in Western Europe by the end of the first millennium, it is unlikely that they built most of those mills themselves.

With respect to the claims made by advocates of the monastic innovation thesis that the Benedictines embraced and encouraged technological development, while valuing frugal living and manual labour, we have seen that the reality was somewhat different. By the tenth and eleventh centuries, the Benedictines were already drawing fire from other religious orders for their extraordinary wealth and luxurious living conditions. Nor did they work the land themselves, as Mumford and White seem to have believed, but used bonded tenants to do it for them, people whose dependent relationship to them they sought to intensify rather than relax as the centuries wore on. If we want to praise any of the monasteries for their efforts at making milling more affordable, and for encouraging more equitable relations with their tenants, we should probably single out the smaller Augustinian and Cistercian houses, and not the Benedictines.

When we turn to the topic of monastic innovation, the picture is more complicated. The larger Benedictine houses seem to have indeed built a large number of mills, but they did not do so to free up their tenants' time: they did it to better manage their milling resources and make a handsome profit from tenants compelled to mill their grain at the manorial mill. On the other hand, the larger Cistercian houses may well have been innovators in some aspects of industrial milling technology, but the notion that it was some philanthropic bent that motivated them is unlikely given their record of exploiting their feudal position in a similar fashion to their Benedictine brethren. A more plausible explanation is given by Holt, who argues that "[the Cistercians'] overriding intention—driven by the strict interpretation of the monastic ideal—was to provide for their own needs, to contain production within their own precincts, and to achieve all this without hired labour."[116]

With respect to the central claims of the seigneurial monopoly model, we have seen that a large number of watermills and windmills in England south of the Humber were effectively outside seigneurial control from the very time that Bloch claimed that the French and Normans had introduced the seigneurial system to England. In the mid-thirteenth and early fourteenth centuries, as many as half of the mills in southern England did not have seigneurial status. Half of these mills were located in towns and villages that had secured exemptions from suit of mill as part of a charter of liberties, while the other half were held by a mixture of knights, tenants-in-chief, religious houses, and customary and free tenants on rural and urban properties. A significant but as yet undetermined proportion of the independent sector consisted of mills that had formerly been directly controlled by the larger Benedictine houses. A lesser proportion of mills without seigneurial status were held by Augustinian and Cistercian houses and directly managed or let to tenants on fixed-term leases. This second category of ecclesiastical mill without seigneurial status provided direct competition to the seigneurial mills of lay lords and the larger religious houses.

One of the main attractions of mills to lords was their profitability, which was largely a function of whether or not they held suit. The efforts of lay and ecclesiastical lords to rationalise their mill holdings in the thirteenth century and to secure suit of mill for as many of their mills as possible clearly indicate that their main concern was with making a decent profit. The ownership of windmills and watermills generated high profits for lords whose mills held suit, but mills without suit could attract sufficient custom to be economically viable. As Bloch maintained, therefore, economic exploitation was a primary motivating factor for English lords. Nevertheless, the fact that many people throughout England from the twelfth century onwards chose to take their grain to be ground at independent mills demonstrates that Bloch was wrong to conclude that most peasants and townsfolk preferred to mill their grain at home, as does the growing number of mills built by commoners from the late thirteenth century onwards. Clearly, many households preferred the convenience of using powered mills over handmills, especially if they were not compelled to do so and were not unduly taxed for the privilege.

Although the evidence presented here tends to favour a modified version of the seigneurial monopoly model over most of the elements of the monastic innovation thesis, the seigneurial monopoly model fails to give sufficient credit to the lower social orders and the smaller religious houses in establishing and promoting a large independent milling sector in which a fair economic exchange was the norm rather than the exception. It is upon this sector that we should be focusing our attention if we want to better understand the emergence of bourgeois enterprise in the early modern period, and not the élites, whether they be monastic or aristocratic.

Notes

[1] See Lewis Mumford, *Technics and Civilization* (1934; rpt. Orlando: Harcourt & Brace, 1963), and Marc Bloch, "Avènement et conquêtes du moulin à eau," *Annales d'histoire économique et sociale* 7 (1935): 538-63, first published in English as "The Advent and Triumph of the Watermill," in *Land and Work in Mediaeval Europe: Selected Papers by Marc Bloch*, trans. J.E. Anderson (London: Routledge, 1967), pp. 136-68.

[2] See Adam Robert Lucas, "Industrial Milling in the Ancient and Medieval Worlds: A Survey of the Evidence for an Industrial Revolution in Medieval Europe," *Technology and Culture* 46.1 (2005): 1-30, for a critical discussion of the influential thesis that there was an industrial revolution in medieval Europe. Cf. Richard Holt, "Mechanization and the Medieval English Economy," in Elizabeth Smith and Michael Wolfe (eds.), *Technology and Resource Use in Medieval Europe: Cathedrals, Mills, and Mines* (Aldershot: Ashgate, 1997), pp. 149-56.

[3] Richard Bennett and John Elton, *History of Corn Milling* (1898-1904; rpt. New York: Burt Franklin, 1964). In an earlier critique of Bloch's thesis, John Langdon used the term "seigneurial-exploitation model": "Lordship and Peasant Consumerism in the Milling Industry of Early Fourteenth-Century England," *Past and Present* 145 (1994): 22.

[4] Bloch, "Advent and Triumph," pp. 151-53, 156: In France, there were also "monopolies concerning the use of the baking-oven, the wine-press, the breeding-boar or bull, the sale of wine or beer ... [and] the supply of horses for treading out corn." Of these, the seigneurial monopoly on milling was "probably the most ancient and certainly the most widespread."

[5] *Ibid.*, pp. 153, 157-58. Bloch's views about lordly exactions are endorsed by Pierre Dockès, *Medieval Slavery and Liberation*, trans. Arthur Goldhammer (London: Methuen, 1982), pp. 22-25, 174-96, and by Zvi Razi, "The Struggles between the Abbots of Halesowen and their Tenants in the Thirteenth and Fourteenth Centuries," in T.H. Aston, *et al.* (eds.), *Social Relations and Ideas: Essays in Honour of R.H. Hilton* (Cambridge: Cambridge University Press, 1983), pp. 166-67. *Cf.* Richard Holt, *The Mills of Medieval England* (Oxford: Oxford University Press, 1988), pp. 47-53, for a critical examination of Bloch's thesis.

[6] Marx's much-debated aphorism that "[t]he handmill gives you society with the feudal lord; the steam-mill, society with the industrial capitalist," appears in Karl Marx, *The Poverty of Philosophy* (New York: International Publishers, 1963), p. 109. It occurs at the end of a passage about Proudhon, who, Marx says, "has not understood... that these definite social relations are just as much produced by men as linen, flax, etc. Social relations are closely

bound up with productive forces. In acquiring new productive forces men change their mode of production; and in changing their mode of production, in changing the way of earning their living, they change all their social relations." One of Dockès' central arguments in *Medieval Slavery and Liberation* is that Bloch provides an account of the development of the watermill in the Middle Ages that is more consistent with the evidence than Marx's bald statement.

[7] See Mumford, *Technics and Civilization* (note 1), pp. 112, 113-18. Mumford's precursors included Charles Homer Haskins, Lynn Thorndike, George Sarton, and Abbott Payson Usher.

[8] See, for example, Lewis Mumford, *The Myth of the Machine: Technics and Human Development* (London: Secker & Warburg, 1967), pp. 263-271; R.J. Forbes, "Metallurgy and Technology in the Middle Ages," in S. Lilley (ed.), "Essays on the Social History of Science", *Centaurus* 3 (Copenhagen: 1953): pp. 50-51; Lynn White, Jr., *Dynamo and Virgin Reconsidered: Essays in the Dynamism of Western Culture* (Cambridge, Mass.: MIT Press, 1968), pp. 63-6; Bertrand Gille, "The Problems of Power and Mechanization," in Maurice Daumas (ed.) and Eileen B. Hennessy (trans.), *A History of Technology and Invention: Progress Through the Ages* (New York: Crown, 1969), I:559-62; Terry S. Reynolds, *Stronger than a Hundred Men: A History of the Vertical Water Wheel* (1983; rpt. Baltimore: Johns Hopkins University Press, 2004), pp. 109-14; George Basalla, *The Evolution of Technology* (Cambridge: Cambridge University Press, 1988), p. 148; J. Kenneth Major, "Water, Wind and Animal Power," in Ian McNeil (ed.), *An Encyclopaedia of the History of Technology* (London: Routledge, 1990), p. 232.

[9] White was particularly exuberant in his praise for the Benedictines, to whom he attributed a form of humanism that encouraged industrialisation. See White, *Dynamo and Virgin Reconsidered*, pp. 63-67 (the relevant essay was first published in 1958). He emphasised the Benedictines' supposed valuation of frugal living and manual labour and the general effect this had on medieval and later Protestant attitudes to work. Monastic discipline encouraged the monks to combine both practical and theoretical concerns in their everyday lives, thereby helping to "create a social atmosphere favorable to scientific and technological development." Mumford had already articulated similar views in *Technics and Civilization*, but his most extended reflections on the subject are contained in *The Myth of the Machine*, where he concluded that "[t]hrough its regularity and efficiency the monastery laid a groundwork for both capitalist organization and further mechanization: even more significantly, it affixed a moral value to the whole process of work, quite apart from its eventual rewards." See Mumford, *Myth of the Machine*, p. 266.

[10] *Ibid.*, p. 270. Mumford argued that these labour-saving devices contributed to the "changeover to free industry" thought to have begun around the tenth century. He repeated the claim that the widespread institution of slavery had prevented the Romans and their contemporaries from making any extensive use of watermilling technology [*Ibid.*, p. 268]. This claim looks increasingly implausible, however, as more archaeological evidence is uncovered of the widespread use of watermills during Roman times, on which see Örjan Wikander, "The Watermill," in *idem* (ed.), *Handbook of Ancient Water Technology* (Leiden: Brill, 2000), pp. 371-400; also George Brooks, "The 'Vitruvian Mill' in Roman and Medieval Europe," ch. 1 of this volume. Mumford concluded that the Benedictines' extensive use of watermills instituted "technological advances... which released labor for other purposes and immensely added to the total productivity of the handicrafts themselves" (Mumford, *Myth of the Machine*, p. 270).

[11] White, *Dynamo and Virgin Reconsidered*, pp. 66-67.

[12] The few scholars who have done so are Richard Holt, John Langdon, and Paolo Squatriti. See Richard Holt, "Whose were the Profits of Corn-Milling? An aspect of the changing relationship between the Abbots of Glastonbury and their tenants, 1086-1350," *Past and Present* 116 (1987): 4-6, 22-23; Holt, *Mills of Medieval England* (note 5), pp. 36-37, 40, 47-48, 52-53, 145-46; "Mechanization," pp. 142-43, 156-57 (note 2); Langdon, "Lordship and Peasant Consumerism," pp. 3-46 (note 3); Paolo Squatriti, "'Advent and Conquests' of the Water Mill in Italy," in *Technology and Resource Use*, pp. 125-38.

[13] Mumford, *Technics and Civilization* (note 1), p. 114; Bloch, "Advent and Triumph," p. 152 (note 1); White, *Dynamo and Virgin Reconsidered*, pp. 63-67. *Cf.* Holt, "Whose were the Profits of Corn-Milling?", pp. 4-5, and *Mills of Medieval England*, p. 36, who notes Bloch's assignation "to the major monastic communities the major role in the harnessing and utilisation of waterpower." Squatriti's "'Advent and Conquests'," p. 131 n.16-17, cites a number of French and Italian scholars who similarly ascribe the most significant dissemination of watermilling technology to the period between the ninth and eleventh centuries and "the growth of large, self-sufficient, lord-owned estates."

[14] The best summaries of this evidence can be found in Örjan Wikander, *Exploitation of Water-Power or Technological Stagnation? A Reappraisal of the Productive Forces in the Roman Empire*, Scripta Minora Regiae Societatis Humaniorum Litterarum Lundensis (Lund: 1984); Wikander, "Archaeological Evidence for Early Water Mills—An Interim Report," *History of Technology* 10 (1985): 151-79; "The Watermill" (note 11); Paolo Squatriti, *Water and Society in Early Medieval Italy, AD 400-1000* (Cambridge: Cambridge University Press, 1998), ch. 5.

[15] The best summaries of this evidence can be found in Holt, *Mills of Medieval England* (note 5), ch. 1, and Colin Bernard Rynne, "Waterpower in Medieval Ireland," in Paolo Squatriti (ed.), *Working with Water in Medieval Europe: Technology and Resource-Use* (Leiden: Brill, 2000), pp. 1-50.

[16] Paul Benoit and Joséphine Rouillard, "Medieval Hydraulics in France," in *Working with Water in Medieval Europe*, pp. 166-67, 169.

[17] *Ibid.*, pp. 169-70. Also Wikander, *Exploitation of Water-Power*, p. 31.

[18] *Ibid.*, pp. 170-71, 180, 203-4.

[19] The legend is first recorded in a poem by Cuan O'Lochain, which is dated to the late tenth or early eleventh century. See Robert Mac Adam, "Ancient Water-Mills," *Ulster Journal of Archaeology* 4 (1856): 10; E. Cecil Curwen, "The Problem of Early Water-mills," *Antiquity* 18 (1944): 138-39; Colin Rynne, "Waterpower in Medieval Ireland," in Squatriti (ed.), *Working with Water in Medieval Europe*, pp. 1-50 at 18-19.

[20] See *Ibid.*, pp. 4, 14, for the Irish sources.

[21] See Niall Brady, "Mills in Medieval Ireland: Looking Beyond Design," ch. 2 of this volume. Also Rynne, "Waterpower in Medieval Ireland," pp. 4-6, 9, 14; Wikander, *Exploitation of Water-Power*, pp. 31-2. The relevant evidence is summarised in Adam Lucas, *Wind, Water, Work: Ancient and Medieval Milling Technology* (Leiden: Brill, 2006), ch. 2.

[22] See Holt, *Mills of Medieval England* (note 5), ch. 1, and Lucas, *Wind, Water, Work*, ch. 2, for summaries of this evidence.

[23] See Holt, *Mills of Medieval England*, ch. 7, and John Langdon, "Water-mills and Windmills in the West Midlands, 1086-1500," *Economic History Review* 44 (1991): 431-32.

[24] Adam Robert Lucas, *Machinariarum Nihil Ex Deo: the role of the Church in the development of powered milling in high medieval England*, University of New South Wales D. Phil. thesis, 2003.

[25] Squatriti, *Water and Society*, pp. 127, 133-36 (note 14). Benoit and Rouillard make a similar argument with respect to the different types of watermill used in France. See Benoit & Rouillard, "Medieval Hydraulics in France" (note 16), pp. 203-4.

[26] Squatriti, *Water and Society*, pp. 130, 134, 136, 138. According to Wikander, however, there is no archaeological evidence for the use of horizontal-wheeled watermills in Italy before the ninth century (pers. comm., November 2002).

[27] See Bloch, "Advent and Triumph" (note 1), p. 142. Cf. Miquel Barceló "The Missing Water-mill: a question of technological diffusion in the high Middle Ages," in Miquel Barceló and François Sigaut (eds.), *The Making of Feudal Agricultures?* (Leiden: Brill, 2004), pp. 255-314. Barceló's paper examines the legacy of Bloch's negative assessment of the contribution of the horizontal-wheeled watermill to medieval technological development. My thanks to Thomas Glick for drawing my attention to Barceló's work.

[28] Squatriti, *Water and Society*, ch. 5.

[29] *Ibid.*, pp. 133-38, 144-45.

[30] A similar process has been revealed with somewhat greater clarity in medieval Spain after the Christian conquest of the thirteenth and fourteenth centuries. See Lucas, *Wind, Water, Work* (note 21) , ch. 2.

[31] Squatriti, *Water and Society*, pp. 135-36.

[32] See Bloch, "Advent and Triumph," with regard to France, and Holt, *Mills of Medieval England* (note 5), with regard to England. It should be noted, however, that an overall increase in mill numbers did not necessarily occur as a result of the élite appropriation of milling resources. In fact, if vertical-wheeled watermills were replacing horizontal-wheeled watermills, the increased milling capacity of the former may have even contributed to a *decrease* in the numbers of mills *per capita*, essentially what happened in England after the Conquest as Anglo-Norman lords rationalised the location and increased the size and power of their vertical-wheeled watermills. See Holt, *Mills of Medieval England*, pp. 112-13. Cf. John Langdon, *Mills in the Medieval Economy: England 1300-1540* (Oxford: Oxford University Press, 2004), ch. 1.

[33] Bloch, "Advent and Triumph" (note 1), pp. 153, 156, 165 n. 46. Similarly, a milling monopoly in the Wakefield district in West Yorkshire was not abolished until 1853. See W.L. Norman, "The Wakefield Soke Mills to 1853," *Industrial Archaeology* 7 (1970): 176. In England, milling monopolies on some estates, such as the manor of Otterton in Devon, continued until the early twentieth century: Desna Greenhow, "More Water by the Mill; the restoration, machinery and history of Otterton Mill, Devon," *Industrial Archaeology* 14 (1979): 315-17.

[34] Bloch, "Advent and Triumph," p. 156.

[35] *Ibid.*, p. 153.

[36] *Ibid.*, p. 155.

[37] *Ibid.*

[38] *Ibid.*, p. 156. Although Bloch does not specifically mention this fact, it was also the case that if tenants built mills without permission, they could be lawfully destroyed by, or taken into the possession of, the lord.

[39] *Ibid.*, p. 152.

[40] *Ibid.*, pp. 157-58.

[41] *Ibid.*, pp. 154-60. The latter position is argued by Holt *contra* Bloch in *Mills of Medieval England* (note 5), pp. 40-41.

[42] *Ibid.*, p. 156.

[43] See Bennett and Elton, *History of Corn Milling*, II:122-23; III:206-7. Cf. Holt's comments on their confusion on this issue in Holt, *Mills of Medieval England*, pp. 37-38.

[44] *Ibid.*

[45] Bloch, "Advent and Triumph" (note 1), pp. 156-57.

[46] Holt, *Mills of Medieval England*, pp. 68, 70.

[47] See Bloch, "Advent and Triumph," pp. 153-6; Holt, "Whose were the Profits of Corn-Milling?" (note 14), pp. 5-6; *Mills of Medieval England*, p. 70.

[48] See Holt, "Whose were the Profits of Corn-Milling?," pp. 6-7, and n. 15, for a bibliography of the debate between M.M. Postan and R.V. Lennard and their followers on the English economy during the twelfth century, as well as Edward Miller's comments on the subject in "England in the Twelfth and Thirteenth Centuries: An Economic Contrast?," *Economic History Review* 24 (1971): 1-14. Holt argues that the evidence of mill revenues and tenures on Glastonbury Abbey's estates clearly support Postan's contention that there was a twelfth- century economic recession. Subsequent research conducted by Holt, Langdon, and myself, provides further support for Postan's position.

[49] Property held in customary tenure was held outside the demesne in exchange for feudal services, sometimes commuted to a nominal cash rent in the twelfth and thirteenth centuries and subsequently.

[50] Lucas, *Machinariarum* (note 26), pp. 572-73. Cf. Holt, *Mills of Medieval England* , pp. 86-7.

[51] See Holt, "Whose were the Profits of Corn-Milling?," pp. 7-8, 13-14; *Mills of Medieval England*, ch. 4; Langdon, "Lordship and Peasant Consumerism" (note 3), pp. 5-6.

[52] See Holt, *Mills of Medieval England* (note 5), pp. 54-55.

[53] John Langdon (pers. comm., September 2004). Also Langdon, *Mills in the Medieval Economy* (note 34), p. 17.

[54] Grants and leases of mills by both lay and ecclesiastical lords included the mill "with its appurtenances." In the case of a watermill, this included the wheel, millhouse, and other associated buildings, as well as its "waters and lands", which might include roads and footpaths to and from the mill, as well as leets, ponds, dams, trenches, and other waterworks such as sluices and gates, along with the meadows in which the whole complex was located. In the case of windmills, the lease was usually restricted to the post-mill itself and the mound and meadow in which it was located. In a reasonably large number of instances, however, the lease on either a wind- or watermill might also include a messuage or croft, as well as a significant parcel of land. Occasionally, long-term leases might include suit of mill, although this has normally been thought of as an exclusively lordly privilege. See John Langdon, "The Birth and Demise of a Medieval Windmill," *History of Technology* 14 (1992): 56-57, and "Lordship and Peasant Consumerism", p. 6, n. 12, in which he describes how the "tenant" watermill of Turweston was granted suit of mill by its lord in the thirteenth century, a privilege that was not able to be overturned when a demesne windmill was subsequently built on the manor.

[55] Holt, *Mills of Medieval England*, pp. 57, 59, 63.

[56] Although the example to follow is a grant rather than a lease, it does illustrate the principle involved. Some time before 1217, Osbert de Henham granted the watermill of Henham

to Blythburgh Priory. Osbert's grant included the suit of the men of Henham, but exempted his own household from having to pay multure when grinding at the mill. See C. Harper-Bill (ed.), *Blythburgh Priory Cartulary, Part 1* (Trowbridge: Suffolk Records Society, 1980), ms. 304. The right to mill "hopper-free" (*i.e.*, to jump to the head of the queue) is recorded by Holt, *Mills of Medieval England*, p. 49, and Langdon, *Mills in the Medieval Economy*, pp. 274, 277.

[57] For example, the canons of Cirencester leased their mill of Boycott to Richard of Radcliff, miller, for life some time between 1236 and 1240. When Richard died, the land and mill were to be given over to the life-long lessee of their other lands in Boycott, and the total rent increased by half a mark. See C.D. Ross (ed.), *The Cartulary of Cirencester Abbey, Gloucestershire* (London: Oxford University Press, 1964), ms. 649.

[58] Holt, *Mills of Medieval England* (note 5), pp. 54-55.

[59] Langdon's study of the *inquisitiones post mortem* material for the reign of Edward II illustrates this most clearly. See Langdon, "Lordship and Peasant Consumerism" (note 3).

[60] For example, many of the mills granted to the Augustinians appear to have been mills held in hereditary free tenure by knights of varying status, but only a small percentage of the relevant grants specify that the mills held suit. The Bishop of Hereford, on the other hand, appears to have collected rents on a number of mills let in free and hereditary tenure that did continue to hold suit for reasons which remain unclear. See Lucas, *Machinariarum* (note 26), chs. 3 & 4.

[61] *Ibid.*, ch. 4.

[62] Langdon, "Water-mills and Windmills in the West Midlands"; *idem*, "Lordship and Peasant Consumerism."

[63] Lucas, *Machinariarum* (note 24), ch. 3, 4, 5, 6 & Conclusion.

[64] See Rodney Hilton, "Freedom and Villeinage in England," *Past and Present* 31 (1965): 3-19. See also Bloch, "Advent and Triumph" (note 1), pp. 156-57, and Holt, *Mills of Medieval England* (note 5), p. 38. One exception was the successful effort by the people of the township of Ormskirk under the jurisdiction of the Augustinian priory of Burscough; see Lucas, *Machinariarum*, App.K, §2.0.

[65] For example, Holt has demonstrated that on 23 manors held by Glastonbury Abbey between 1086 and 1189 mill incomes in many cases doubled over that hundred-year period. By 1189, 30 out of 31 of these mills had been let out under customary or hereditary tenure. A little over one hundred years later, however, 2/3 of these independent mills were back under seigneurial control, with their total revenues more than quadrupling over this period. See Holt, "Whose were the Profits of Corn-Milling?" (note 14), pp. 11-13, 18; *Mills of Medieval England*, p. 14.

[66] Holt, "Whose were the Profits of Corn-Milling?," p. 14.

[67] See Lucas, *Machinariarum*, ch. 3, §7.0; ch. 6, §6.0, App.J & M.

[68] See *Ibid.*, ch. 4, §9.0; ch. 6, §6.0; App.K & M.

[69] *Ibid.*, ch. 3, §2.0, 5.0 & 7.0; also Holt, *Mills of Medieval England* (note 5), pp. 64-65.

[70] See *Ibid.*, ch. 3, §3.0 & 7.0; ch. 4, §9.0; ch. 6, §6.0; App.J, K, L, & M.

[71] Ian Jack has used the terms "private" and "free" mills to designate such mills, but they similarly do not fully capture the kinds of tenure in which these mills were held: Ian Jack, "Fulling-Mills in Wales and the March before 1547," *Archaeologia Cambrensis* 130 (1983): 70-130. The term "commercial mills" used by Glick and Squatriti to distinguish Spanish and

Italian mills run for profit rather than as lordly monopolies also does not fully capture the mixed status of these English mills.

[72] Hilton, "Freedom and Villeinage in England," p. 14, citing *Calendar of Patent Rolls, 1272-81*, p. 123. According to Bloch, "Advent and Triumph," p. 156 (note 1), such exemptions from suit of mill for English townsfolk were "totally unknown in French and German urban charters"

[73] The famous cases of Cirencester, Peterborough, Halesowen, and St. Albans clearly bear this out; See Bloch, "Advent and Triumph," pp. 157-59; Razi, "Struggles between the Abbots" (note 5); Holt, *Mills of Medieval England*, pp. 40-45: Lucas, *Machinariarum* (note 24), ch. 4, §4.0.

[74] See Holt, *Mills of Medieval England*, ch. 3; Lucas, *Machinariarum*, App.A, §A.4.5.

[75] Holt, *Mills of Medieval England*, pp. 44-47.

[76] *Ibid.*, ch. 4.

[77] Langdon, "Lordship and Peasant Consumerism" (note 3), pp. 40-41.

[78] It was, in fact, primarily the labour of women in the household that was being freed up by the use of watermills and windmills. As the work of Ruth Schwartz Cowan has shown with respect to improvements in domestic technology in the twentieth century, and numerous other sociologists with respect to the computerization of the workplace, the mechanization and automation of tasks within a variety of different contexts does not necessarily lead to less work for those concerned. See Ruth Schwartz Cowan,"The 'Industrial Revolution' in the Home: Household Technology and Social Change in the Twentieth Century," *Technology and Culture* 17 (1976): 1-23; *More Work for Mother: The Ironies of Household Technology from the Open Hearth to the Microwave* (New York: Basic Books, 1983); Donald MacKenzie and Judy Wacjman (eds.), *The Social Shaping of Technology: How the Refrigerator got its Hum* (Milton Keynes: Open University Press, 1985).

Whatever time women may have saved by having the household's flour milled mechanically, this task was invariably replaced by others which could not be, or had not yet been, mechanized. In other words, although many women may have been relieved of the task of hand grinding by the growth of the powered milling sector, their overall workload probably remained fairly constant. In *The Evolution of Technology* (note 8), p. 148, Basalla puts forward a similar argument to Reynolds about the growth of powered milling being stimulated by labour shortages, first within the monasteries (and presumably upon monastic estates), and later, upon lay estates, where lay landowners were also "in need of new revenues." No evidence is presented to support the thesis that such labour shortages existed, however, and it is simply assumed that "a diminishing and more costly labour force" automatically favoured the construction of more watermills by lords, although Basalla does also note that suit of mill was a guaranteed source of additional lordly profits. *Cf.* Reynolds, *Stronger than a Hundred Men* (note 8), pp. 32, 34-35, 36, 112-13.

[79] George Ovitt, Jr. has argued that the positive attitudes towards technological innovation expressed by some medieval Churchmen was more a reaction to events that were already taking place, rather than a forward-looking orientation that served as an example to laypeople. See George Ovitt, Jr., "The Cultural Context of Western Technology: Early Christian Attitudes toward Manual Labor," *Technology and Culture* 27 (1986): 486, 497-98, 500. These ideas are further developed in his *The Restoration of Perfection: Labour and Technology in Medieval Culture* (New Brunswick, NJ: Rutgers University Press, 1987).

[80] See the detailed discussion of this issue in Lucas, *Machinariarum* (note 24), App. A, §A.4.3.

[81] See John Compton Dickinson, *Monastic Life in Medieval England* (London: Adam & Charles Black, 1961), p. 4.

[82] Three of the eight houses (Glastonbury, Bury, and Ramsey) were amongst the ten highest-earning houses at the Dissolution.

[83] This percentage only includes those mills whose origins could be definitely determined.

[84] See Holt, *Mills of Medieval England*, pp. 23-27, 116, summarised in Lucas, *Machinariarum*, pp. 120-21. The mills concerned were built by Ramsey, Bury St Edmunds, Norwich Cathedral Priory, and the Bishop of Ely. Holt's findings were supported by evidence uncovered in relation to the East Anglian houses of Blythburgh, Butley, Sibton, and Leiston. See *idem*, chs. 4, 5, & 6.

[85] On East Anglia, see Holt, *Mills of Medieval England* (note 5), ch. 2, 7 & App.1. On Lancashire and Sussex, see Lucas, *Machinariarum*, ch. 4, §2.0 & 10.0, ch. 6, §2.0.

[86] See the conclusion to Lucas, *Machinariarum*, ch. 3.

[87] See Lucas, *Wind, Water, Work* (note 21), ch. 9.

[88] Lucas, *Machinariarum*, conclusions to chs. 3 & 5. None of the ten Augustinian houses studied appear to have held any industrial mills before the mid-fourteenth century. See *ibid.*, conclusion to ch. 4.

[89] Langdon, "Lordship and Peasant Consumerism" (note 3), pp. 12-14.

[90] Langdon, "Water-mills and Windmills in the West Midlands," p. 434, table 2. It would seem significant that almost three-quarters of the 104 manors sampled by Langdon belonged to religious houses. See *ibid.*, p. 429.

[91] Niall Brady, "Water and its uses in Late Medieval Ireland, with particular reference to Mills and Milling in the Hinterland of Dublin City," paper presented at *Wind and Water: the Medieval Mill*, a conference at Pennsylvania State University, 16-17 April 2004, p. 11 and his "Mills in Medieval Ireland: Looking Beyond Design," ch. 2 of this volume.

[92] Lucas, *Wind, Water, Work*, ch. 8.

[93] See Lucas, "Industrial milling". Cf. Holt, "Mechanization" (note 2), pp. 149-56.

[94] See Lucas, *Wind, Water, Work*, ch. 9.

[95] See John Muendel, "The Distribution of Mills in the Florentine Countryside during the Late Middle Ages," in J.A. Raftis (ed)., *Pathways to Medieval Peasants* (Toronto: Pontifical Institute of Medieval Studies, 1981), p. 99.

[96] Generally speaking, the older Benedictine houses in southern England which never recovered possession of mills that had been alienated from their possession between the eleventh and twelfth centuries held an average of around half their mills with suit. The average determined for the five Benedictine houses studied in detail was 70%, whereas a rough calculation of the (mostly East Anglian) houses studied by Holt came to around 57%. For the estates studied in detail, the percentages ranged wildly from 14% for Canterbury's Sussex mills, to 95% for Durham's and Hereford's mills.

[97] Vera C.M London (ed.), *Cartulary of Bradenstoke Priory*, Wiltshire Record Society 35 (1979), ms. 154.

[98] *Ibid.*

[99] *Ibid.*, p. 65 n. 1. See Langdon, *Mills in the Medieval Economy* (note 32), p. 278, for a comparable case at Wyberton in Lincolnshire, where a windmill was recorded as being worth only 10s. in 1325 "and no more because of the smallness of the soke [*i.e.*, the number of tenants observing suit of mill to the windmill] and because there are mills on either side of it."

[100] Langdon, "Lordship and Peasant Consumerism" (note 3), pp. 28-31. The figure of 20% of all the powered mills in the early fourteenth century is based on the assumption that ecclesiastical lords controlled about a third of the demesne sector (13.3% of the total market) and possibly an equal proportion of the independent sector (around 6% of the total). This last figure does not include former seigneurial mills held mostly by the Benedictines that had fallen into customary or hereditary tenure but were never recovered.

[101] Langdon, "Lordship and Peasant Consumerism," pp. 27-28.

[102] Lucas, *Machinariarum* (note 24), Appendices J, K, L, & M.

[103] Holt, *Mills of Medieval England* (note 5), pp. 82-86; Langdon, "Lordship and Peasant Consumerism," p. 5.

[104] Holt, *Mills of Medieval England*, pp. 79-82; Langdon, "Lordship and Peasant Consumerism", p. 13. The Bishop of Durham, for example, was drawing around a quarter of his rental income from mills in the early fourteenth century, on which see Lucas, *Machinariarum*, ch. 3, §2.0. Lords in some other parts of England were also able to extract high rental incomes from their mills, such as in East Anglia, where the Earl of Norfolk earned more than 15% of his total revenues in the late thirteenth century from mills, although the average proportion for the whole region in the early fourteenth century was only 6.1%.

[105] See Holt, *Mills of Medieval England*, chs. 5 & 10; "Milling Technology in the Middle Ages: The Direction of Recent Research," *Industrial Archaeology Review* 13 (1990): 57, and the discussion at the end of Lucas, *Machinariarum*, ch. 2. The Welsh mechanized fulling industry also seems to have experienced a marked decline in the 1310-30s that was presumably related to inflation and the cattle murrains of that period. See Ian Kershaw, "The Great Famine and Agrarian Crisis in England 1315-1322," *Past and Present* 59 (1973): 3-50. There is also evidence of declines in cornmilling income for some houses such as Bolton Priory for this period, as discussed in detail in Lucas, *Machinariarum*, App.A, §A.4.4.

[106] Holt, *Mills of Medieval England*, pp. 111-13.

[107] Holt notes that "a peak of seigneurial authority [in the thirteenth century] coincided with increasing population pressure, and so enabled lords to exact an inflated price for grinding from the peasant customers, while paying extremely low wages to the employees who worked and maintained the mills" (*Mills of Medieval England*, p. 170).

It should be noted that some women were employed as millers and/or ran mills with their husbands or on their own using male employees. For example, four of ten English mills held by the Abbey of the Holy Trinity, Caen, in its manor of Minchinhampton in the early fourteenth century were held by women tenants, three of whom let the mill in their own right. See Lucas, *Machinariarum*, pp. 204, 219, 227, 235, 238, 249, 282, 305, 354, 388, 393.

[108] See Holt, *Mills of Medieval England*, ch. 6. Also Lucas, *Wind, Water, Work* (note 21), p. 138, in which the wages for eight millers employed by Beaulieu Abbey in 1269/70 are recorded. Six of these men were demesne employees, and were paid cash stipends of between 4s. 2d. and 10s. each. These sums and the associated conditions are consistent with those found by Holt. In contrast, two free men were paid £2 4d. and £5 1s. 9d. respectively. Both of the mills that they operated cleared around £1 in "profit" for that financial year, although Beaulieu

appears to have been minimising its profits from its mills by using its tollcorn to pay *famuli* and listing such payments as expenses.

[109] See Lucas, *Wind, Water, Work*, ch. 4, for a summary of the relevant data. Langdon records that as much as £80 was spent on building and rebuilding watermills in the higher wage conditions of the fifteenth century. See Langdon, "Water-mills and Windmills in the West Midlands," p. 436.

[110] Lucas, *Machinariarum*, p. 327; Holt, *Mills of Medieval England* (note 5), pp. 86-87. While the data on windmills is drawn from only two estates, those for watermills are drawn from almost a dozen.

[111] Holt, *Mills of Medieval England*, pp. 77-78; Langdon, "Water-mills and Windmills in the West Midlands," p. 434.

[112] See Lucas, *Machinariarum*, ch. 1, §2.2.4, for discussions of Holt's and Langdon's work; ch. 4, §2.0 for a discussion of the Lancashire windmills of Burscough; and ch. 4, §10.0 for a discussion of the Sussex windmills of Chichester.

[113] See Lucas, *Wind, Water, Work*, ch. 4. On the lack of profitability of fulling mills as opposed to grain mills, see Holt, *Mills of Medieval England*, pp. 155-60; Langdon, "Water-mills and Windmills in the West Midlands," p. 435; "Lordship and Peasant Consumerism" (note 3), pp. 14-15; Lucas, *Machinariarum*, chs. 3, 5 & 6.

[114] See Lucas, *Machinariarum*, ch. 1, §2.2.2, ch. 5, §7.0, and App.B, C, & D.

[115] Beaulieu's ability to earn higher average mill revenues than most of its southern counterparts (despite having fewer mills with suit) was somewhat of an aberration: it faced less competition in those areas of Hampshire and neighbouring counties in which it held mills. Holt, *Mills of Medieval England*, pp. 49-50.

[116] Holt, "Mechanization" (note 2), p. 153.

Lords' Rights and Neighbors' Nuisances: Mills and Medieval English Law

Janet S. Loengard (Moravian College)

The amount of litigation involving mills in medieval England would send shivers down the spine of a modern cereal company. Suits about milling contributed to the plea rolls and Year Books[1] and manor court records in numbers far beyond the expectation of a modern lawyer. Once the lawyer looked at those plea rolls and records, though, the reasons for all the litigation would become clear. For one thing, there were a lot of mills: one modern author has counted 6082 water mills in Domesday Book alone.[2] But more importantly, mills were economically significant; they had the capacity to do injury to other people's lands; and quite simply, they represented power, sometimes an abuse of power. Arguments based on economics—often involving mill repairs or use—frequently reflected vertical relationships, but suits based on injury to property frequently involved relationships among peers as well. So there are suits by lords against tenants, by tenants against lords, between lords, between tenants, by the king against towns and by towns against outsiders, by millers, against millers, and between millers. In other words, litigation about mills involved almost every segment of society, lay and religious. A variety of situations frequently provoked that litigation. There were disputes about upkeep, disputes about physical injury done by or to a mill, and claims by a lord to have the right to compel others to grind at his mill, not to mention issues involving millers themselves, who were both the plaintiffs and defendants in so many suits.[3]

I

Medieval England knew mills designed for various purposes—for grinding grain, for fulling cloth, for powering forges. Forges are rarely mentioned in the legal records. Nor, apparently, did the fulling mills *per se* attract a high volume of litigation. I have found only two instances where a mill caused dispute specifically because it was a fulling mill: one in connection with the tenants' contention with the abbot at St. Albans in 1275, discussed below, and one in 1302, when the demand that a grantor's heir warrant a charter for a fulling mill was challenged because the purchaser of the mill had turned it into a corn mill in violation of the agreement.[4] It was corn mills that fattened the plea rolls, and the watermill and millpond on a stream or river was a leading source of litigation.[5]

Water was not the only source of power for the medieval mill, of course; it was followed closely by the wind. The windmill—*molendinum ad ventum*, or *molendinum ventriticum*—was obviously more useful where there were no fast-flowing streams, but it presented its own set of issues resulting in litigation.[6] Beyond wind and water there were the horse mills, used far back in antiquity but surviving through the Middle Ages and thereafter, but these rarely motivated lawsuits. The handmill, or quern, on the other hand, undoubtedly the oldest of all, was frequently the subject of contention.

Water mills and windmills excited litigation because they were both expensive to build and maintain and at the same time highly profitable. *The Estate Book of Henry de Bray* records that in 1299 Henry spent £9 6s 4d to make a mill and its pond. The next year, he spent an additional £4 13s 4d for amending it because it had been badly made, and he spent more money on a bridge. But he also records that the mill rendered him two marks—£1 6s 8d—a year and free multure.[7] That is a return of about eight percent a year not counting the free multure and assuming that he had leased out the mill so that he was not responsible for all the repairs, which otherwise would have significantly reduced his income.[8] Watermills, especially, produced income from a number of sources. A mill owner could farm it out to a miller for a tidy rent, or could keep it in his own hands, appoint a miller, and of course charge for grinding—often assuring a steady source of customers by obliging his tenants to patronize it. One could fish for the fish in the millpond,[9] cut the grass growing on the banks of that pond (presumably for hay),[10] or harvest the eels which seem to have lived in abundance in every medieval millrace. One might also sell the willows or flax growing on the shore of the millpond,[11] or charge for passage if there were a bridge crossing the stream at the milldam. On the other hand, one could be guilty of letting the mill become ruinous or of not keeping the bridge in repair,[12] or for allowing the willows, cut, to fall into the millstream thereby blocking it,[13] or for taking too much multure, or for raising the level of one's millpond and consequently flooding someone else's land, or for diverting the course of a stream by means of cutting a channel to keep one's wheel turning but thereby impairing the grinding ability of a neighboring mill downstream. Windmills did not cause the flooding and water-diversion problems, but they were subject to other complaints: the sails were in poor repair

or the mill was too high or so close to a neighbor's windmill that it hindered the
neighbor's grinding. Sometimes the very existence of a looming, noisy mill was
enough to provoke lawsuits. Interference with common of pasture—probably by
the sails' noise or motion frightening animals—must have been a common complaint, since a provision in the Statute of Westminster II specifically provides
that no one (presumably no mill owner) shall be harassed by an assize of novel
disseisin for common of pasture because of his windmill.[14]

Any discussion of profits from a mill, then, must balance income and potential expenditure, whether extraordinary or simply the recurring costs of upkeep. Since perhaps the most unavoidable element of expense was repairs, it is
easy to understand the constant quarrels about them. Most of a watermill, except for the stones themselves and a few metal parts, was made of wood. Gears
and shafts were usually wood. The wheel, often oak and always wood, was constantly in water.[15] Repairs were an annual chore and a chore that mill owners
were eager to pass on to the miller himself, villein tenants, or even freeholders.
In dealing with millers who had leased the mill or with men who did not hold
land on a plaintiff's manor, suits about repairs or non-repairs to both water and
windmills could be brought by the action of covenant in cases where defendant
had bound himself to make them; in other situations, if the non-repair resulted
in the breach of a pond bank or similar injury, an action lay to compel the defendant (often the miller) to correct the situation.[16] As for tenants of a plaintiff's
manor, over and over again custumals specify that men are to aid at the mill, or
find a man for mending the mill. At the manor of Cashio in 1238, there was a
dispute about whether the vill had to carry millstones and timber to the mill; the
vill denied it, was shown wrong by the record, and was fined as an entirety.[17] At
Elton, the dispute was over whether free tenants as well as villeins had to help
repair the millpond; they did.[18] A recalcitrant tenant who owed such service as a
condition of tenure might find himself distrained—that is, his beasts taken from
him—until he complied.[19]

Where a miller farmed the mill, he could be bound to any repairs specified
in the lease. At the manor of "Busshopeston" (Bishopston), the lord was to find
the miller timber and the miller was to do the work at his own cost.[20] In 1395,
when John the Miller took the windmill at Walsham le Willows in Suffolk, he
agreed to pay a rent in grain, to provide at his own cost cloth for the sails of the
mill, and to put in place the cogs and staves on the back of the mill and on its
trundle-wheels.[21] A century earlier, in 1287, Walter of Horseth took the mill on
the Ramsey Abbey manor of Chatteris for 40 shillings a year, agreeing that he
would keep the mill in the condition in which he found it; the abbot would pro-

vide the iron spindle and other named parts at his expense; and Walter was responsible for providing other necessaries. The wheels were measured, and when
Walter gave up the mill before the end of the term, they were again measured
and he was charged for the wear.[22] There are suits involving millers who did not
meet their obligations either of rent or of repair; one in particular illustrates the
risks a mill-farmer might take. In Michaelmas term 31 Edward I (1303) a lessor
demanded payment of rent in arrears for a mill. The defendant lessee explained
that the mill had been burnt by the Scots, presumably on a raiding foray. But the
lessor had brought a writ of covenant based on the lease, and the lease provided
that the defendant would leave the mill at the end of the term in as good condition as he had found it. Therefore the defense was invalid. The Year Book entry
reads simply "whereby he was bound without exception."[23]

II

The bulk of the litigation concerning mills, however, arose because of physical
damage done to or by them in specific situations. Physical injury to or by a mill
involved harm of several sorts. Injury could be done by the raising or lowering
of a mill dam, the diversion of water to feed a mill stream, the cutting off of road
access by a mill bridge, the building of a windmill too close to someone else's, or
similar acts; all those situations were classed as *nocumentum* (nuisance). The kind
of injury complained of determined how and where a complaint would be heard,
since they were not all handled by the same procedure or in the same courts.[24]
When a free tenement was at issue, matters classed as *nocumentum* were handled
either by the sheriff at the county level or before the judges called justices in assize, the travelling justices who were sent out from Westminster regularly after
1166. The two jurisdictions had complementary, not identical, competence. The
Register of Writs dictated that actions concerning millponds or dams, diversions
of watercourses, and road impairments (*de stagno levato vel prostrato, cursu aquae
diverso*, and *via arctata vel obstructa*) were to be heard in an action called the assize of nuisance before the travelling justices. But it went on to add that complaints about other named structures, including mills, belonged to the sheriff in
county court; the mills there referred to are windmills. In other words, disputes
involving injury to or by water mills were handled by assize, since most water
mill nuisances arose from a millpond or watercourse, but windmills were, at least
theoretically, handled in the county court.[25]

   As a result, one who raised his millpond and flooded out his neighbours or
diverted the course of a stream into a new channel to feed his millwheel thereby

starving out the wheel of the miller downstream would, after 1166, find himself the defendant in an assize of nuisance:[26] twelve free men of the neighbourhood would be called to meet the king's travelling justices when they came into the county, to say whether defendant's act amounted to a violation of the Assize of Novel Disseisin. On the other hand, a defendant whose windmill damaged another mill—perhaps by taking the wind out of its sails—would appear in county court before the sheriff under what was called a viscontiel writ.[27]

To fall into the category of actionable nuisance, an act did not have to be in itself necessarily wrongful. The theory underlying the action came to be enunciated in the rule that one must not use one's own property to injure that of another, an idea repeated over and over again in treatises and opinions into the early modern period. The treatise called *Fleta* refers to a statutory basis for the assize of nuisance, and perhaps even for the viscontiel writ as well. It remarks "There is also a constitution of law that no one shall act wrongfully on his own land, namely that he shall not make a pond or raise or lower its level whereby he may injure his neighbour, and similarly he shall not make any house, bridge, pond, weir, sluice or mill whereby his neighbour is unlawfully harmed."[28] The "constitution of law" that *Fleta* describes almost certainly refers to the Assize of Novel Disseisin.

It was nuisance to raise a millpond (*stagnum*) so that one's neighbor's meadow was flooded if there was a spate of water or when the mill was shut.[29] It was nuisance to divert a watercourse by making a trench across a stream[30] or to move land in the channel of a river to reverse the flow of water into a different channel, so one's own mill could grind but another person's mill could not.[31] It was nuisance to raise a bank or a house over a plantiff's right of way through a meadow to a mill.[32] Conversely, the right of way itself could be a nuisance. Two formularies, the mid-thirteenth-century *Brevia Placitata*[33] and the fifteenth-century *Articuli ad Novas Narrationes*,[34] have sample nuisance writs. Both allege that the defendant raised a windmill *ad nocumentum* because people crossed plaintiff's land to get to and from the mill.[35] All those nuisances were actionable—unless, of course, its creator was someone like the terrible-tempered Abbot Samson of Bury St. Edmunds, who, secure in his power within his banlieu, raised the dam of his fishpond and new mill at Babwell and flooded out virtually every riverside landowner (including the monks), observing that his fishpond should not suffer for the benefit of the monks' meadow.[36]

But the most important part about the action of nuisance—whether by assize or viscontiel writ—may well have been that it applied only to free tenements, and could be brought only *against* the one committing the nuisance—not, for example, a man's heir or an abbot's successor—and only *by* the one who held the free tenement at the time the nuisance was committed. In any other case, the plaintiff was obliged to use an action *quod permittat*, asking that defendant permit him to exercise a right or that he, plaintiff, be permitted to abate the nuisance.[37] These were very severe limitations on the scope of the assize, and make the reported number of cases even more impressive.

One sort of injury, however, was not an actionable nuisance in either court, whether it involved a water mill or a windmill or a horse mill. Assuming that the builder of a new mill had a right to make it, one could not sue solely for loss of business. The leading case here, from Hilary Term 11 Henry IV (1410), is the *Prior of Lantony's Case* and on its facts has nothing to do at all with mills.[38] The prior was bringing an action of trespass on the case because the right of appointing masters for the Grammar School at Gloucester had always belonged to him and now another master had raised a school there. Competition had forced the prior's masters to cut their fees sharply, thereby causing the prior economic loss. So he sued for damages. He lost. The reason the case is important for mills is because in explaining why the prior took nothing by his writ, Justice Hankford of the Court of Common Pleas observed that "If I have a mill and my neighbor raises another mill, by which the profit of my mill is diminished... [because] others who used to grind at my mill [go there] by which my toll is reduced, it is damage without actionable injury." In other words, there was no cause of action.

It is dictum; that is, it did not really settle this case, but it was quoted over and over as the foundation for similar holdings, like one in Michaelmas Term 22 Henry VI (1443). There another prior, the prior of St. Neot's in Huntingdonshire, brought an action against a miller who had built a new mill within the vill and charged less than the prior's miller did, thereby enticing away the prior's customers. This time it was Justice Paston who remarked at some length that an action would not lie for a new mill on another branch of a stream even if it meant that an older mill thereby lost profit.[39] The rule survived the Middle Ages and is even quoted in William Sheppard's *Actions upon the Case for Deeds* from 1663.[40]

The rule protecting competition assumes that the maker of the new mill has the right to raise it. But he might well not have had that right. The very creation of a new mill might be actionable under some circumstances. Both lay and ecclesiastical lords often held charters or grants from the Crown or from pious laymen securing to them the right to have the only mill in a vill, or a manor, or providing that no one else could create a mill there without their consent. In 1242, when the prior of Davintry produced charters and demanded why Walter son of Simon of Davintry had raised a mill to the injury of the prior's mill already existing there, against the grants of Walter's ancestors, he lost only because Walter was able to explain that it was not a new mill, it was the repair of a pre-existing lawful mill which had burnt down before he came of age.[41] The defense of the pre-existence of a mill—or the right to a mill—was apparently decisive if proved, although it could be complicated by other factors and a prudent plaintiff might also throw in an allegation of physical damage.[42] Or, of course, one could use self-help under some circumstances; Bracton noted that "Things so [wrongfully] erected... to the wrongful nuisance [of another] may be immediately demolished and thrown down... while the misdeed is still fresh,... if the plaintiff is able to do so."[43] There is certainly case law to that effect. Nonetheless, it might have been wiser to rely on the courts; a man who did not might face an action for novel disseisin or trespass and cases show that despite the theory, self-help was not always viewed benignly by the judges.[44]

A happy solution, of course, was simply to terrify the defendant into removing the offensive mill, as did the wrathful, violent, and amazingly profane Abbot Samson of Bury St. Edmunds. In 1191, Herbert the Dean, a man of some standing, had erected a windmill to grind his own grain and when Samson heard it he ordered his carpenters to tear it down. When Herbert came to explain, Samson replied, among other things, "By the face of God, I will never eat bread until that building be overturned... you ought to know that neither the king nor his justiciar may... build anything within the jurisdiction of the monastery without the leave of the abbot and the house... Nor is this without harm to my mills... for the burghers will go to your mill and grind their corn at their pleasure, while I cannot lawfully hinder them since they are free men. Depart! Depart! Before you come to your house you will hear what has come to pass in the matter of your mill." The Dean promptly rushed home to destroy his mill so that when the abbot's carpenters arrived there was nothing to overthrow.[45]

III

This of course leads to the second great source of mill litigation: suit to a mill, *secta ad molendinum*. Simply put, it meant that the king or, more commonly, an ecclesiastical or lay lord had the right to compel a given group of people to grind their grain at his mill and to pay toll for it. The lord's right grew out of the institutions which have been called manorialism and feudalism, the latter a term now in some disrepute. Commonly, he would assert the right, based in custom and enforceable in his manor court, to make all his unfree tenants (villeins) grind their grain at his mill. He might also claim a further right to oblige free men to do so, a claim that had to have a further basis. If they held land from him, such men might owe suit as a condition of tenure, or even if they did not, they might owe it by express grant or by ancient and uninterrupted use. Action against villeins would have been by presentment in the manor court, or in more than one case by some strongarm action by the lord. Against free men, there was more often the action *secta ad molendinum*, usually brought before the perambulating justices; it in turn spawned counterclaims and suits demanding the right *not* to grind at the lord's mill, or to grind there free of toll.

Just as not all millponds flooded their neighbors' fields, all mills were not seignorial. Recent histories have traced a large number of free mills, held by knights or even peasants, and have found that even where a large landholder like an abbey theoretically had the right of suit to its mill, it could not always enforce the right on widely scattered holdings.[46] Those situations, of course, do not lead to actions demanding *secta ad molendinum,* and there is no mention of them in legal records.[47] But enough cases exist to suggest that the right to compel suit to a mill was widespread, that it was prized because it could be, and often was, very valuable, and that it was vigorously defended. Statements about the amount of multure that was claimed vary widely, probably because the actual amounts did, too. A statute titled *Statutum de Pistoribus etc. (*Statute concerning Bakers) of uncertain date—but certainly from late in the thirteenth century—provided that the toll of a mill should be taken according to custom and the strength of the watercourse, either the twentieth or the twenty-fourth part, by the king's measure.[48] But the statute does not seem to have been effective. A case from 1302 reported in the Year Books alleged that defendant had paid toll of the twentieth vessel.[49] At Wakefield in the first half of the fourteenth century the multure was one measure in 16 from the first of August until Christmas and one measure in twenty for the rest of the year.[50] At Assheton-under-Lyne in 1422, a custumal spelled out that tenants would pay toll of the sixteenth vessel on corn they either grew or dried with the lord's fuel; other corn would be charged at the rate of the twenty-fourth vessel. Elsewhere the custumal draws a difference between tenants at will, who pay toll of the sixteenth vessel, and the free tenants who owed soke to the mill, who "shall mill as their charters will and as they have been accustomed of old time."[51]

Lords were not alone in protecting their revenues. There are several entries in the plea rolls about the king's concern for his mills.[52] Some towns and cities also had a monopoly on the right to a mill, frequently spelled out in a municipal charter or bylaws. Cases with towns as plaintiffs were usually brought in borough or other local courts; the by-laws of medieval towns and boroughs frequently provide that suits concerning matters arising within the borough and its precincts are not to be taken outside the borough except in default of justice. At Bridgewater, provisions made in the thirteenth century ordain that a burgess who did so was to be fined 12d; at Newcastle-upon-Tyne in the late twelfth century no penalty is specified, but pleas initiated in the borough were to be tried and concluded there (except pleas of the Crown) and no burgess defendant was to plead in a suit outside the borough except in case of default of justice by Newcastle courts. Customs and by-laws could require, as at Lynn in 1432, that all residents were to grind at the common mill on pain of forfeiture of the grain ground elsewhere; on the other hand, they could provide, as at Newcastle-upon-Tyne, that any burgess could have his own handmill if he wished.[53] The prohibition against milling outside the town could address not only those who ground their wheat outside the town but those who bought wheat, presumably ready-ground, outside the town's mills.[54]

The most numerous and completely reported cases are those involving both lay and ecclesiastical lords and their tenants. Reading manor court rolls, it is sometimes very difficult to determine who is free and who is not, because both free and unfree men might owe suit; suit, then, is not a useful guide to individuals' status. The Custumal of the manor of Amberle of 1257 shows that both freeholders and villeins—one of whom was obliged rather mysteriously to "grind one quarter of corn for the dogs"—gave money at Midsummer and Michaelmas, which was paid for the mill of Fitelworth. There is no further explanation.[55] And on the barony of Manchester, freeholders obliged to grind at the mill along with the villeins were men who held substantial properties by homage and fealty, such as Sir Henry de Trofford, who held land in Ancotes and Charlton.[56]

The impression one gets from a manor like Walsham le Willows is that enforcement of suit of mill was sometimes pursued somewhat halfheartedly. Fines were low (typically 3d) and hardly a deterrent. Indeed, at Walsham le Willows one tenant, John Mann, was fined threepence in June 1340 and twopence in November 1343, because he continued to mill away from the lord's mill. Half a century later, another man, listed as a villein, received a fine of threepence in January 1398, because he had not ground his corn at the lord's mill for two years. He was fined twopence for the same at a court the following September.[57] The amercement begins to look almost like a license: in effect, one paid the small amount to be able to grind elsewhere.

But that was not always the case. Amercements could be both higher and more rigorously imposed, and suit to a mill was a festering issue on many manors, particularly those belonging to bishoprics and great abbeys. There were good reasons for resenting it. A mill might not be convenient to a tenant's croft. Carrying grain or loading it onto an animal took time, and once one was at the mill there might be a wait. On a number of manors, the lord had the right to have his grain ground first, no matter whose corn was already in the hopper, or how many were waiting.[58] More usually, the lord's grain was to be ground next after the grain then in the hopper, as a defendant recited in a 1244 trespass action.[59] Still, to a tired man next in line with his heavy grain sacks the added wait must have been galling. Moreover, millers were known to take too much multure, to give back less than the amount they should, and to use weights weighing more than their stated value.

The easiest way to avoid such problems was to boil grain into a pottage and eat it instead of bread, and the poorest did do that.[60] But the more usual practice was to grind the grain for one's family at home in a handmill, or quern.[61] And it is the quern which provoked some of the most serious altercations, both in and out of the lawcourts, particularly between ecclesiastical lords and their tenants in the thirteenth, fourteenth, and fifteenth centuries. The abbots of Peterborough, Ramsey, Bec, Vale, St. Albans, Bury St. Edmunds, and the monks and priors of smaller convents like Embsay Priory all figure in the struggle over handmills.[62] The most colorful was the contest at St. Albans, which spanned two hundred years, and involved litigation in the king's courts. Opposition to forced use of the abbot's mill is mentioned in a court book of 1250 at the manor of Abbots Langley.[63] The first reported skirmish, in 1274, involved both the abbot's fulling mill and his grist mill, and included a demand for the right to have handmills for grinding grain. It opened with a sudden raid by the abbot's bailiff and his men to seize the upper stone of existing handmills. At least some of the men of St. Alban's could claim to be free, and the royal courts were open to them as they were not to villeins. As the St. Alban's chronicler, Thomas of Walsingham, puts it, conspiring to persecute the monks "with a new fervor and burning furor" they hastened to the court of the lord king to seek a writ. They got it—to judge from the pleadings, it must have been a writ of trespass *de bonis asportatis* (goods taken away)—and the case was heard at the Cirencester assizes. The abbot's bailiff responded to the charges that his men had acted lawfully: the handmills were to the prejudice of the liberties of the abbot, and plaintiffs, his tenants, were obliged to grind at his mill. Sworn recognitors agreed. The abbot was exonerated and the plaintiffs fined, after which they, and the other townsmen, made a formal submission to the abbot. He graciously agreed that the miller would have to swear fealty and that if there were later complaints against him made by the better men of the town, he would listen.[64]

That did not mark the end of either the tenants' or the abbot's attempt at legal proceedings; in the early fourteenth century, the townsmen again rebelled and apparently once again set up querns without authorization. The abbot obtained a commission of oyer and terminer, on his complaint that named men "and others" who ought to do suit to his mill had erected handmills and then resisted his bailiff when he tried to take "diverse chattels" (*i.e.*, millstones) as distraint.[65] The resulting proceedings against one of the men, Robert de Lymbury, and the abbot's triumph, are set out with gusto in the *Gesta Abbatum Monasterii Sancti Albani*. The tenants, not to be deterred, at one point obtained a royal writ forbidding the abbot to molest them in enjoyment of their liberties and got a charter of liberties from the king. A subsequent abbot was made of sterner stuff, however, and after several years of legal action against them, the townsmen gave in, relinquishing their royal charter.[66] When the abbot's men once again seized the millstones and carried them off to the abbey, the abbot used them to pave the cloister courtyard outside his parlor. In 1381, at the time of the Peasants' Revolt, the townsmen invaded the cloister and "lifted up the millstones... laid there as a memento and memorial of the ancient agreement between the *villatos* and the monastery in the time of abbot Richard." Smashing the stones, they divided them up "as the bread that has been blessed is distributed and bestowed upon the Lord's people in the parochial churches. This was done so that when the people saw those fragments they would recall that they had once prevailed over the monastery in this cause."[67] But when the revolt was over, the abbot once again asserted his rights. Nor did the conflict end there; as late as 1455 the then abbot was busy suppressing an unauthorized horse mill.[68]

St. Alban's is an extreme case, perhaps the most extreme, but there were others and monastic houses were certainly not the only lords who acted to suppress querns. The king's mills were sometimes protected the same way. In 1356, Edward III confirmed the Customs of the Mill of Dee, in Chester; the mill belonged to the king and one of the customs provided that no one in the city should have handmills to its prejudice.[69] And as late as 1541, when Henry VIII held the Manor of Teynton, Oxfordshire, which had previously belonged to Tewkesbury Abbey, the manor court roll includes the entry that all tenants shall grind their grain at the customary mill and shall not use handmills for the future under penalty of 6s 8d for each of them.[70]

In the plea rolls, actions about suit to a mill take two forms. In one, the tenant is the plaintiff and the lord is the defendant because he has used a legal form of self-help, distraint: he has taken his tenant's animal or animals and the tenant has brought an action of replevin demanding their return. The response is that the lord was simply distraining for nonsuit to his mill as he had a right to do, or that he had intercepted the tenant's horses and grain on the way to another mill, as he also had a right to do.[71] If he could prove that right, the distraint held until the tenant made the required suit. More often, the lord is plaintiff, alleging his right by grant or custom, and the defendant denies that he owes suit. He and his ancestors never made suit and if they had ever ground at the mill, it was only at their own will. Or the grant on which plaintiff relies was only of a mill and did not include suit. Or tenants owed suit while they were villeins but they are now free and therefore no longer owe it. The first defense would usually have gone to a recognition, with a group of men sworn to tell the truth. When John of the Mill (Johannes Molendinarius) sued Martin de Fletham and his wife Agnes because they kept a manual mill and, he claimed, they owed suit to his mill because of the tenement they held from the Abbot of Westminster, he lost because twelve jurors said on oath that the ancestors of Agnes never owed suit to the mill.[72] The defense that the grant of a mill to a miller did not necessarily include suit to it was also taken seriously; in a suit by the prior of Lancaster against John son of Peter, the plaintiff showed a charter to prove his seisin but the Year Book report says "The charter said 'the mill' only," not mentioning *secta*. There is no reported decision, as is so often the case in Year Book reports.[73] Pleading one's freedom as a bar to suit was understandably less successful since suit to a mill was not confined to unfree tenants.[74]

Other suits involved the right to grind without multure. The claim to free grinding was fairly widespread; lords seem to have frequently included it on their own behalf in leases to millers, and it appears in many custumals.[75] Breach of the right could lead to a *quod permittat*, asking that the defendant permit the plaintiff to grind free of multure[76]—or even a writ of trespass, if a miller took multure without the right to do so.[77] It could also lead to violence, as in the case of Bartholomew de Stivekeye, who one day in 1244 was attached to answer Hugh de Stivekeye *quare*, wherefore he went to Hugh's mill and raised the sluices and broke the mill and took away the iron and beat Hugh's miller. Bartholomew explained that he had done no such thing, he was simply distraining by the iron and the sluices, taking them away to force Hugh to do what he ought. The mill and milldam were on Bartholomew's land and therefore he like his ancestors had the right to free grinding of grain and malt, and the miller had been unwilling to grind them for him.[78]

Finally, there are suits—quite a few of them—in which a plaintiff sued to compel the defendant to allow his villeins to do suit to the plaintiff's mill. In most cases the data are tantalizingly incomplete and suggest various possible backgrounds for the complaint. Sometimes the relationship between the parties is spelled out, as when in 1236 the Abbot of Hereford brought an action against Matthew Hoclere, asking that Matthew permit his men of Herting to make suit to the abbot's mills because he, the abbot, was in seisin of that suit on the day Matthew's father died. As heir to his father, Matthew would have been bound to the arrangement.[79] But other entries are more cryptic: Fabian de Nesse sued the Abbot of Ramsey in a plea that the abbot permit his villeins of Burwell to make suit to Fabian's mill, which they ought and used to do. But he did not pursue his suit, and so there is no explanation for it.[80] Was there a grant from the abbey? Was it custom? Had Fabian's ancestor been seised of the right? Had it been carved out of a grant to the abbey? And why did Peter de Vallibus believe that John de Thorenburg ought to let his villeins in Thorinburg do suit to Peter's mill, which he said they ought and were accustomed to do? Again, there are no records of the pleading; John did not appear, and that is all known about it.[81]

IV

Many of the issues mentioned here involved millers raising mill ponds, diverting water, suing recalcitrant tenants, and so on, often acting as agents of the mill owners from whom they held. But millers were litigants in a lot of other cases, and usually they were unwilling litigants. That is, they were defendants. People did not like millers, free or villein; that is clear from medieval literature like Chaucer's "Reeve's Tale". Millers, they said, were thieves, lazy, undependable, careless of their neighbours. They shut their mill and floodgate beyond reason, inundating meadows and destroying bridges.[82] They took a gift to let strangers cross the millbridge to go to the mill without paying toll.[83] They ground wheat and exported it in the fishing season at Yarmouth (it is not specified whether the complaint was about the miller's dealing in flour or about his timing).[84] They undermined river banks and made purprestures (illegal encroachments) on the town walls.[85] One who did not pay what he owed for taking a mill at farm caused his pledges to incur damages when the lord looked to them for the money.[86] Another, who had taken a lease on a horse mill, just abandoned both lease and mill and left without paying the rent due.[87] A miller drove the lord's cart carelessly, presumably when carrying flour.[88] Another received women strangers, who did great damage in the fields in summer and fall.[89] Millers failed to repair their millponds, causing damage.[90] One was alleged to have beaten the chaplain's pigs, and the matter went to the verdict of four named men.[91] They got into brawls and hit other people.[92] Rather more to his credit from our point of view if not his lord's, one miller refused to testify under oath in the manor court to inform on those who milled away from the lord's mill; he was fined for contempt.[93]

And of course millers lied and cheated and stole. That is the substance of most of the complaints. John Bundeley, the miller at the Ramsey Abbey manor of Niddingworth, had unsealed measures; they were heavy and he was fined sixpence and told to mend his ways.[94] The servant of Andrew the Miller in Norwich stole 18 pounds of flour.[95] In a post-medieval example, Thomas Fermour, gentleman, with two water mills on the manor of Somerton, took excessive toll and was fined fourpence in 1568.[96] The highly independent Richard the Miller at Hemingford in 1294 ground badly except at his own will and did not send out the mill's boat for the grain of those who complained.[97] And so many took too much toll or conveniently miscounted; John Bundeley received three bushels of grain and could find only two.[98] The miller at Elton in 1294 detained a ring of barley and was fined sixpence.[99] Almost every manor court roll has at least one entry complaining about a miller's dishonesty. After all, their bad reputation was secure enough that even at St. Alban's the abbot promised to hear complaints about his miller from the more respectable men of the town.

Why were millers apparently so prone to dishonesty? Perhaps because so many mills were held at farm; annual rents were often high, and the difference between the rent and the multure was the miller's income, which could be quite small. Or perhaps because with one exception, at York in the fourteenth century, millers apparently had no guild, so that there were no self-policing professional controls on conduct.[100] In most places it would have been almost impossible for them to form a guild; many millers were villein and most millers, even freemen, did not own their mills; they held them at farm or in many cases simply worked for an employer.[101] Frequently they did not work in close proximity to each other—indeed, lords' rights to exclude competing mills often guaranteed that they would not.

A statute of 1266 with the suggestive title of *The Judgment of the Pillory* deals not only with brewers and bakers, but also with millers.[102] Their measures are to be gathered together by twelve lawful men of the town and, presumably once tested, are to be inscribed with the name of the owner. Bakers who offend thereafter are to be fined or put into the pillory; the assumption must be that millers would suffer the same punishment.[103] It is understandable that the trade most closely linked to milling was baking—in fact, in some places millers may have been part of the bakers' company[104]—and only bakers seem to have attracted as much derision. The poet John Lydgate, who was born in the fourteenth century and lived into the middle of the fifteenth, wrote a satiric verse, no doubt much appreciated by his contemporaries, summing up the general attitude. Entitled "Against Millers and Bakers", its three verses suggest that the pillory is the natural abiding place for both; its last verse reads in part "Let mellerys and bakerys gader hem a gilde, / And alle of assent make a fraternite; / Under the pillory a litil chapell bylde, / The place amorteyse, and purchase liberte", so that all of their number could claim the pillory as their shelter.[105]

Life is no doubt easier now for riparian owners—or at least they are less likely to find their land flooded or starved of water by a neighboring miller's activity. It is a lot easier for someone wanting to bake a loaf of bread; one can go to any supermarket and the flour is sealed tidily into bags of uniform weight. Life should also be much easier for modern-day millers, the cereal companies, since shareholders may vote "no" at the annual meeting, but they cannot put their directors in the pillory. The contrast is in many ways instructive. As much as any institution, medieval mills reflect ideas of the period in which they thrived in their construction and their use. Concepts about limits on how a person could use his own land, and laws and customs crystallizing those concepts; the fine balancing of interest among competing parties shown in many court cases; understandings (and misunderstandings) about the relationship between the free and the unfree, the lord and the tenant, the great man and the lesser—all find illustration in the voluminous records of medieval mills and milling.

Notes

[1] Here cited as *YB* with the appropriate regnal year, term, and folio number. I have used the "Vulgate" or "Maynard" folio edition of the *Year Books* (London, 1678-80) except where otherwise indicated.

[2] H.C. Darby, *Domesday England* (Cambridge: Cambridge University Press, 1977), p. 361. Not every county of England was included in the Domesday survey. Richard Holt found the Darby estimate a good calculation (*The Mills of Medieval England* [Oxford: Oxford University Press, 1988], p. 8) but more recently has given a figure of 6500: Richard Holt, "Mechanization and the Medieval English Economy," in Elizabeth Smith and Michael Wolfe (eds.), *Technology and Resource Use in Medieval England: Cathedrals, Mills, and Mines* (Aldershot: Ashgate, 1997), pp. 139-57.

[3] Compared with physical injury and *secta ad molendinum* (suit to a mill), suits ostensibly about ownership are not common, although ownership was undoubtedly involved in many other cases.

[4] The St. Albans dispute is discussed below; the 1302 suit is printed in Alfred J. Horwood (ed. and trans.), *Year Books of King Edward the First, 30-31 Edward I*, Rolls Series 31.3 (1863; rpt. New York: Kraus, 1964), p. 254 [hereafter *YB of Edw.I: 30-31 Edward I*]. There are cases which mention fulling mills incidentally, such as a trespass action in 1221 in which plaintiff

complained of the carrying away of chattels including the timber of a fulling mill: *Curia Regis Rolls of the Reign of Henry III: vol. 10: 5 and 6 Henry III* (London: HMSO, 1949), p. 73.

[5] A subvariety of the water mill was the tide mill, dependent on the tide to enable the miller to grind and thereby necessitating shifting and frequently inconvenient working hours since the time of high tide is not constant. It was probably a tide mill that caused the havoc at Dover recorded in Domesday Book: at the entrance to the harbor there was a mill "which wrecks almost all ships through its great disturbance of the sea" and thereby did great harm to the king and his men: Philip Morgan [ed.], *Domesday Book: Kent* (Chichester: Phillimore, 1983), p. 1a. Despite their limited usefulness and the danger of their destruction by the sea, tidal mills survived through the medieval period. Several are still in working order, such as one at Eling, in Hampshire, rebuilt long after the Middle Ages. I am grateful to the Rev. Jason St. John Nicolle for drawing my attention to it.

[6] Tim Sistrunk, "The Right to the Wind in the Later Middle Ages," ch. 6 in this volume.

[7] Dorothy Willis (ed.), *The Estate Book of Henry de Bray, c.1289-1340*, Camden Society, 3rd ser. 27 (London: Royal Historical Society, 1916), pp. 50, 51, 56-57.

[8] Jean Gimpel has calculated that the monks of Glastonbury Abbey spent £11 12s 11d building a new post windmill, farming it out for a yearly rental of £3 and an entry fee, giving them a handsome return on their capital: *The Medieval Machine* (1972; rpt. New York: Penguin 1976, 1977), p. 27. There is a thorough examination of the profits of milling in Holt, *The Mills of Medieval England*, ch. 5. He sets out cash rents for different areas of England and shows that they were highest in the north, probably because the level of multure charged for grinding was highest there. Adam Lucas discusses the cost of repairs to both water and wind mills in "The Role of the Monasteries in the Development of Medieval Milling," ch. 4 of this volume.

[9] In a case heard in King's Bench at Easter Term, 1507, Henry Scropp, knight, claimed that Thomas Leventhorp had diverted the water of a river so that the fish in Henry's millpond died—he claimed the astounding number of three thousand roches, ten thousand of "the fish called the millers' thumbs" (a bullhead bass), and two thousand eels. He asked £40 damages but a jury awarded him ten: *Scropp v. Leventhorp*, London, National Archives, KB 27/983 mem. 70. The bullhead bass probably got its nickname from a perceived resemblance to the splayed thumb characteristic of millers. The case is mentioned in J.H. Baker (ed.), *The Reports of Sir John Spelman, vol. II*, Selden Society 94 (London, 1978), p.233, n.10.

[10] It had some value, judging from an entry in the custumal of Stretham, Sussex in 1374. The villein miller was obliged to scour the watercourse from the mill to a path toward Bramber Castle, but in return got grass on either side of the watercourse as far as an ox standing in the middle of the water could reach with his mouth. The value, of course, would have depended on the width of the watercourse: W.D. Peckham (trans. and ed.), *Thirteen Custumals of the Sussex Manors of the Bishop of Chichester*, Sussex Record Society 31 (Cambridge: W. Heffer & Sons Ltd., 1925), p. 119 [hereafter *Sussex Custumals*].

[11] S.C. Ratcliff and D.M. Gregory (trans. and ed.), *Elton Manorial Records 1279-1351* (Cambridge: Roxburghe Club, 1946), pp. 52 (flax), 110 (willows).

[12] A[dolphus] Ballard (ed.), *Seven Somerton Court Rolls, 22 Edward IV to 1573*, Oxfordshire Archaeological Society Transactions 50 (Oxford, 1906), p. 11.

[13] *The Case of the Thorns*, YB Mich. 6 Edw. IV, p. 7, pl. 18. The case did not involve willows; they were used as an example of when an act done lawfully might lead to an action.

[14] Statute of Westminster II, 1285, ch. 46 (*The Statutes of the Realm* [London: George Eyre and Andrew Strahan, 1810-1828], I:94). In the action of novel disseisin, a plaintiff claimed that he had been wrongfully and without judgment deprived (disseised) of his free tenement or common of pasture.

[15] Hugh Preest's account of the mills of Aylington, 1296-97, includes the entry "In 18 oaken boards bought about the Ascension of the Lord for mending the wheels. 3s": *Elton Manorial Records 1279-1351*, p. 52.

[16] There were specific writs for such cases, such as *de reparatione pontium vel stagnorum dirutorum ad nocumenti liberi tenementi* (concerning the repair of bridges or dams destroyed to the injury of the free tenement of plaintiff). They ordered a sheriff to cause defendant to make repairs, adding that if defendant did not do so he was to be before the justices to explain *quare* (why).

[17] *Extracta Rotulorum de Halimotis tentis apud Manerium de Kaysho, tempore Regis Henrici, filii Regis Iohannis... anno R.R. H. xxii*, in H.M. Cam, M. Coate, and L.S. Sutherland (ed.), *Ada Elizabeth Levett, Studies in Manorial History* (Oxford: Clarendon Press, 1938), pp. 196, 312.

[18] Warren Ortman Ault (ed.), *The Court Rolls of the Abbey of Ramsey and of the Honour of Clare*, Yale Historical Publications 9 (New Haven: Yale University Press, 1928), p. xx [hereafter *Court Rolls of the Abbey of Ramsey*].

[19] For example, a 1305 case of beasts taken for failure to do service of repairing the stank of the mill at "N" whenever there was a breach in it: Alfred Horwood (ed.), *Year Books of King Edward the First: 32-33 Edward I*, Rolls Series 31.4 (1864; rpt. New York: Kraus, 1964), p. 378.

[20] Custumal of Busshopeston, *Sussex Custumals* (note 10), p. 96.

[21] Ray Lock (ed.), *Court Rolls of Walsham le Willows, 1351-1399*, Suffolk Records Society 45 (Woodbridge, Suffolk: Boydell Press, 2002), p. 188.

[22] *Court Rolls of the Abbey of Ramsey*, p. 271.

[23] *YB of Edw.I: 30-31 Edward I* (note 4), p. 476. But at the same term, in a writ of waste involving a mill, Justice Bereford declared that if defendant said that the post and other timbers were carried away by an inundation and could aver it (assert it as a fact), he should not answer for the waste: *YB of Edw.I: 30-31 Edward I*, p. 480. And in another waste action at the same term, the defendant pleaded that a dam at the mill attached to another's land was washed away and could not be re-erected without permission of the landowner but that there was no (actionable) waste to the mill, while the other side argued the contrary and presumably there was trial on the issue: *YB of Edw.I: 30-31 Edward I*, p. 448. The difference in result probably lies in the form of action brought.

[24] All that is said here refers to free tenements. Tenants holding in villein tenure were obliged to rely on manor courts, where offenses by tenants against the lord or others within the manor were dealt with by presentment. Despite his personal status, a free man holding land in villein tenure would also have been remitted to the manor court if he attempted to bring suit concerning it elsewhere. Manor court rolls are full of presentments for various offenses: one has falsely raised the hue and cry, another has withdrawn himself from the lord's mill, a third has overburdened the common pasture with his cows, the miller has taken excess toll, a householder has put a dung heap in front of his house, and so on.

[25] Certainly the treatises called *Fleta* (later 13th century) and *Britton* (very late 13th century) make that distinction, and at least one early text of *Brevia Placitata* specifies that the mill in a viscontiel writ of nuisance is a windmill. *Fleta* reads "There are however some things done that cause a nuisance for which an assize will not be given, for cognizance belongs to the sheriff and they are to be pleaded in the county court... [examples include] sheepfold, windmill [*molendino ventricio*], sluice, bakehouse"; H.G. Richardson and G.O. Sayles (ed. and trans.), *Fleta*, Selden Society 89 (London, 1972), IV: ch. 1. *Britton* says "Some nuisances however are determinable by sheriffs in county courts and not by assize, as in the case of... windmills": Francis Morgan Nichols (trans.), *Britton* (1865; rpt. Holmes Beach, Florida: W.W.Gaunt, 1983), II: ch. xi,14. See the writ and commentary in G.J. Turner and T.F.T. Plucknett (eds.), *Brevia Placitata*, Selden Society 66 (London: Quaritch, 1951) pp. cxix, cxx, 203. Cases begun in county court could, however, be removed to the central courts by the writ of pone, available to the defendant for cause and to the plaintiff with no restrictions. For a historian, the bifurcation is unfortunate because only a handful of medieval county court rolls still exist. One of the two I have seen has an entry about a plea *captionis ferri molendini ventrici*, taking the iron of a windmill, but the circumstances are not specified: County Court, Lostwithiel, Cornwall, 7 Edward III, in William Alfred Morris, *The Early English County Court*, University of California Publications in History 14.2 (Berkeley: University of California Press, 1926), p. 192. The best modern treatment of county courts is Robert C. Palmer, *The County Courts of Medieval England, 1150-1350* (Princeton: Princeton University Press, 1982), which notes that rolls from the later 14th century include no cases of either nuisance or suit to a mill (p. 226).

[26] That date is traditionally assigned to the (lost) Assize of Novel Disseisin. Nuisance was an offshoot of novel disseisin; it involved doing injury without intruding into land or claiming possession of it. See Janet Loengard, "The Assize of Nuisance: Origins of an Action at Common Law," *The Cambridge Law Journal* 37.1 (1978): 144-66.

[27] The Statute of Westminster II (1285), ch. 24, provision *In consimili casu* attempted with limited success to widen the scope of the assize, but the distinction between viscontiel writs and writs for the assize was finally ended only in 1382 by statute of 6 Richard II, I, ch. 3 [*Statutes of the Realm* (note 14), I:83 and II:27]. It provided that all writs of nuisance commonly called viscontiel writs could, at the election of the plaintiff, "be... made... in the nature of old times used or else in the nature of Assises."

[28] *Fleta*, IV: chs. 1, 27. Bracton, *On the Laws and Customs of England*, the earlier thirteenth-century treatise on which *Fleta* is based, speaks of a servitude imposed by law by which one is prohibited from doing on his own land what may damage a neighbour. Servitude is a Roman law concept, but the Assize of Novel Disseisin would have been such a law: George E. Woodbine (ed.), *Bracton on the Laws and Customs of England*, trans. with notes by Samuel E. Thorne (Cambridge, Mass.: Belknap Press of Harvard University Press, 1977) [hereafter *Bracton*], III: f.232.

[29] Doris Mary Stenton (ed.), *Rolls of the Justices in Eyre: Rolls of Pleas and Assizes for Lincolnshire 1218-1219 and Worcestershire 1221*, Selden Society 53 (London: B. Quaritch, 1934), p. 475.

[30] *Liber Assisarum*, 32 Edward III, p. 194, pl. 2 (1359). The *Liber Assisarum* is printed as part of the Vulgate edition of the *Year Books* (London, 1679).

[31] *Curia Regis Rolls of the Reign of Henry III: vol. 15: 17-21 Henry III* (London: HMSO, 1972), p. 287.

[32] The bank case is *Liber Assisarum*, 21 Edward III, p. 74, pl. 1. The house case is *Smeteborn v. Holt*, YB Hil. 21 Edward III, p. 2, pl. 5. In 1348, Johanna Smeteborn brought an assise of nuisance against one Holt and his wife, Clarissa. Smeteborn had a water mill and claimed a right of way to it; the Holts had built a house across the way, creating a detour of two leagues. The women were sisters; at their father's death his holdings were divided between them, Clarissa getting the land and Johanna the mill, with the agreement that she should have the right of way. Most of the Year Book entry deals with whether the assize is the appropriate action in such a case—by the mid-fourteenth century there was a great deal of wrangling about procedure—but in the end, the assize was granted.

[33] *Brevia Placitata* (note 25), pp. cxx, 28.

[34] *Articuli ad Novas Narrationes* (London: William Rastell, 1534), p. 283.

[35] The Statute of Westminster II ch. 46 would not have applied since the right of common was not involved.

[36] Jocelin de Brakelond, *Chronicle of Bury St. Edmunds*, online through the *Medieval Sourcebook* at *http://www.csudh.edu/oliver/smt310-handouts/jocelin/jocelin.htm*. The entry is dated 1200. The text is also available in print: Antonia Gransden (ed. and trans.), *Chronicle of Bury St. Edmunds, 1212-1301* (London: Nelson, 1964).

[37] *William de la Souche v. Ralph de Bracy* in 1302 illustrates the action even more clearly: the writ reads, "Command Ralph de Bracy that justly etc. he permit William de la Souche to lead back the flow of a certain water in Millisbray into its due and ancient course, which water... Ralph unjustly and without judgment has diverted to the hurt of the free tenement of Matilda, whose heir he is..."; *YB of Edw.I: 30-31 Edward I* (note 4), p. 40. In *quod permittat* the cost of remedying the nuisance fell on the plaintiff.

[38] *Prior of Lantony's Case*, YB Hil. 11 Hen. 4., p. 47, pl. 21. The case is included as 1410.021 in the online Index and Paraphrase of Printed Year Book Reports, compiled by David J. Seipp at *http:// www.bu.edu/phpbin/lawyearbooks/search.php*.

[39] *Prior of St. Neot's Case*, YB Mich. 22 Henry 6., p. 14, pl. 23.

[40] William Sheppard, *Actions upon the Case for Deeds* (London: R.I. for Samuel Speed, 1663), p. 127.

[41] Alexandra Nicol (ed.), *Curia Regis Rolls of the Reign of Henry III: vol. 17: 26-27 Henry III* (London: HMSO, 1991), p. 197.

[42] A note on a case apparently between two millers as late as 1600 shows plaintiffs complaining that defendant broke a sluice and diverted water which had always flowed to their mill so that they lost profits amounting to twenty pounds. The defendant replied that their mill had not always existed, that he himself had a mill there, and that damage had been done to him to the value of 40 marks. Each produced witnesses, but the note ends there; San Marino, Calif.,Huntington Library, MS HM48946, Commonplace Book c. 1600, p.66.

[43] *Bracton* (note 28), III: f. 233.

[44] For example, the prioress of Nuneaton, having brought a writ of nuisance for a mill-pond heightened, was found to have cut it down herself. Both parties to the suit were fined, the defendant for raising the pond and the plaintiff prioress for cutting it down: Doris Mary Stenton (ed.), *Rolls of the Justices in Eyre, Gloucestershire, Warwickshire and Staffordshire, 1221, 1222*, Selden Society 59 (London: B. Quaritch, 1940), p. 174. In that situation, the justices may have viewed the action essentially as contempt of court. The issue is clearer in a Michaelmas 7 Richard II (1383) case: Peter brought a writ of trespass against the prior of "M" because

the prior had broken down his mill pond. The prior pleaded abatement, arguing that he had by grant a pathway next to Peter's pond and Peter had enlarged the pond, blocking the way. The court was unsympathetic to the argument, pointing out that the prior could have had a writ of covenant, an assize of novel disseisin, or a justification in an action of trespass: Maurice Holland (ed.), *Year Books of Richard II: 7 Richard II* (Cambridge, Mass: Ames Foundation, Harvard Law School, 1989), p. 55. Other cases do seem to condone self-help: see the involved case in *YB* Mich. 9 Edward IV, p. 34 pl. 10 (1469).

[45] Jocelin of Brakelonde, *Chronicle of Bury St. Edmunds* (note 36). The entry is dated 1191.

[46] Holt, *The Mills of Medieval England* (note 2), ch. 3.

[47] The windmill/watermill distinction mentioned above refers to the assize of nuisance, so the type of mill had no effect on venue in the action of *secta ad molendinum*.

[48] *Statutum de Pistoribus etc.* [*Statutes of the Realm* (note 14), I:202 at 203]. The date is uncertain and is given as 51 Henry III or 13 Edward I.

[49] *YB of Edw.I: 30-31 Edward I* (note 4), p. 146.

[50] Ray Lock (ed.), *The Court Rolls of Walsham le Willows, 1303-1350*, Suffolk Record Society 41 (Woodbridge, Suffolk: Boydell Press, 1998), p. 17.

[51] John Harland (ed.), *Three Lancashire Documents of the Fourteenth and Fifteenth Centuries*, Chetham Society o.s.74 (Manchester: Chetham Society, 1868), pp. 95, 109. Holt discusses multure at length in *The Mills of Medieval England*, ch. 5.

[52] W. Illingworth and G. Rose (eds.), *Abbreviatio Placitorum* (London: Record Commission, 1811), p. 47 (the burgesses of Ipswich found pledges about a milldam unjustly raised to the nuisance of the mill of the Lord King outside the city) and p. 151 (inquiry whether it would be to the injury of the Lord King or the detriment and nuisance of his town, Shrewsbury, if he allowed the burgesses of the town to raise a mill or two in the waters of the Severn.)

[53] The provisions for Bridgewater are transcribed in T. Bruce Dilks, "The Burgesses of Bridgewater in the Thirteenth Century," *Proceedings of the Somersetshire Archaeological and Natural History Society* 63 (1917): 55-56; the customs of Newcastle are transcribed in Charles Johnson, "The oldest version of the customs of Newcastle-upon-Tyne," *Archaeologia Aeliana*, 4th ser. 1 (1925): 170. The documents are on line together with custumals and by-laws of other English towns, most of them newly translated by Stephen Alsford, the manager of the web site at the Canadian Museum of Civilization in Quebec, at *http://www.trytel.com/~tristan/ towns/florilegium/flor*oo.*html* The Lynn documents were gathered from a number of sources, identified by the compiler. It appears that the mill at Lynn, built to provide a new source of revenue for the borough, could not remain profitable without coercion of the burgesses to patronize it.

[54] An example is Norwich: William Hudson (ed.), *Leet Jurisdiction in the City of Norwich*, Selden Society 5 (London: Bernard Quaritch, 1892), pp. 13, 28, 40 (Leet Rolls of 1287/8, 1288/9, and 1290/1, respectively).

[55] Custumal of Amberle, *Sussex Custumals* (note 10), pp. 47, 50, 56.

[56] Warren Ortman Ault, *Private Jurisdiction in England*, Yale Historical Publications 10 (New Haven: Yale University Press, 1923), p. 314. Richard Holt has suggested that by the thirteenth century suit to a lord's mill "was occasioned only by a tenant's villein status": Richar Holt, *The Mills of Medieval England* (note 2), p. 52. But the curia regis rolls and those of the justices in assize would indicate otherwise.

[57] *The Court Rolls of Walsham le Willows, 1351-1399* (note 21), pp. 204, 205.

[58] A provision in the custumal of the manor at Ashton-under-Lyne reads that when the lord's corn comes to the mill, "he shall put all men out of their grist and take their corn out of the hopper if there be any therein and his corn shall be ground next before all men": *Three Lancashire Documents of the Fourteenth and Fifteenth Centuries* (note 51), p. 109.

[59] *Hugh de Styvekey v. Bartholomew de Styvekey et al.*, in Paul Brand (ed.), *Curia Regis Rolls of the Reign of Henry III: vol. 18: 27 to 30 Henry III* (London: Public Record Office, 1999), p. 255.

[60] Or otherwise attempted to evade paying multure: the 13th-century treatise called *The Court Baron*, a handbook on how to hold a court and deal with various issues, gives an example headed "Of toll subtracted from the lord's mill." The steward is informed by the bailiff that William Long came at a specific time to his lord's mill to grind a specified amount of grain; the miller ground it and put it in sacks, and William "bethought himself of an evil trick and felonious device not permissible," collected the sacks, and rode off without paying toll. William denied that he had done such a thing and explained that his conduct was due to negligence and not to spite the lord. He offered to make amends and was told to find gage (a pledge or surety) for them: Frederic William Maitland and William Paley Baildon (eds.), *The Court Baron*, Selden Society 4 (London: Bernard Quaritch, 1891), pp. 33, 52.

[61] Occasionally, the use went beyond that. In an entepreneurial spirit, William Bigge and William Druladen had set up millstones in their houses on the manor of Ogburn (a manor of the Abbey of Bec), Wiltshire, and were grinding for other tenants, no doubt at a rate lower than at the lord's mill since they were convicted in the manor court of "taking toll and multure to the great damage of the lord as regards the suit to his mill": F.W. Maitland (ed.), *Select Pleas in Manorial and Other Seignorial Courts. Vol. I: Henry III and Edward I*, Selden Society 2 (London: B. Quaritch, 1889), p. 47.

[62] There is a good discussion on some of the cases involving handmills in Holt, *The Mills of Medieval England* (note 2), esp. pp. 40-44.

[63] Levett, *Studies in Manorial History* (note 17), p. 204.

[64] Thomas of Walsingham, *Gesta Abbatum Monasterii Sancti Albani*, ed. Henry Thomas Riley, Rolls Series 28.4.1 (1867; rpt. Kraus, 1965), I: 410-423.

[65] *Calendar of Patent Rolls Edward II (1313-1317)* (London: HMSO, 1898), II:65. I am grateful to Professor Andrew Lewis for drawing my attention to this document.

[66] Henry Thomas Riley (ed.), *Gesta Abbatum Monasterii Sancti Albani*, Rolls Series 28.4.2 (London: Longmans, Green, Reader, & Dyer, 1867), II: 149-54, 157-63, 240-60.

[67] John Taylor, Wendy C. Childs, and Leslie Watkiss (trans. and ed.), *The St Albans Chronicle (The Chronica maiora of Thomas Walsingham)* (Oxford: Oxford University Press, 2003), pp. 443, 457.

[68] Henry Thomas Riley (ed.), *Chronica Monasterii S. Albani. Registra Quorundam Abbatum Monasterii S. Albani, qui Saeculo XVmo Floruere. Registrum Abbatis Johannis Whethamstede*, Rolls Series 28.6.1 (London: Longman & Co. and Trübner & Co., 1872), pp. 198-202.

[69] Richard Bennett and John Elton, *The History of Corn Milling* (London: Simkin, Marshall & Co., 1898-1904), I: 212. The document is headed "Customs of the Mill of Dee used from a time when memory runneth not to the contrary." The citation is given as London, British Library, Harleian MS 2081, fol. 168.

[70] Nathaniel J. Hone, *The Manor and Manorial Records* (New York: E.P. Dutton, 1906), p. 179. Sometimes, however, handmills were licensed, even on one of the St. Albans manors: in 1332 at Codicote, Stephen le Bray gave a penny a year for a manual mill in his home, while in the same year one John Dolitel, who held only a cottage at Codicote, had a license from the lord for a handmill for a rent of twopence a year: *Redditus et consuetudines de Codicote*, 1332 in Levett, *Studies in Manorial History* (note 16), pp. 352, 359. On some manors, customary tenants owed an annual fee for license to mill wherever they wished: at Hatfield Chase in Yorkshire, for example, the sum was one penny halfpenny: L.R. Poos and Lloyd Bonfield (eds.), *Select Cases in Manorial Courts, 1250-1550: Property and Family Law*, Selden Society 114 (London: 1998), p. 137.

[71] *YB of Edw.I: 30-31 Edward I* (note 4), p. 64. The grant from Cecilia de Rumilly to the monks of Embsay Priory expressly provided for forfeiture of the grain and sack to the monks and of the horse to her should a tenant attempt to use another mill. The charter is set out in its entirety in Bennett and Elton, *History of Corn Milling*, I: 211.

[72] *Curia Regis Rolls*, vol. 17 (note 41), p. 424. An action of suit to a mill could apparently be made by anyone who was the beneficiary of it; John of the Mill held the mill from the abbot in fee farm of £4 a year and it appears that the multure would have been his. John could not have brought an assize of nuisance both because the mill was not his free tenement and because it had been held in the Staffordshire Eyre of 6 Henry III (1266) that novel disseisin would not lie because suit to a mill was not a free tenement. An assize of nuisance would have been subject to the same bar: Anthony Fitzherbert, *La Graunde Abridgement* (London: Richard Tottell, 1577), f. 76. More often, the tenant was not successful when he denied owing *secta ad molendinum*, as in the case of Peter de Cokenesse who was summoned to answer the prior of Trentham about suit to a mill and said that his ancestors and he had never made suit (an inquisition found otherwise): *Curia Regis Rolls*, vol. 17, p. 286.

[73] *YB* Trinity 34 Edward I in A.V. Horwood (ed.), *Year Books of the Reign of King Edward the First: 33-35 Edward I*, Rolls Series 31.5 (London: Longman & Co and Trübner & Co., 1879), p. 228.

[74] As in *Curia Regis Rolls*, vol. 17, p. 88.

[75] See, for example, the *Estate Book of Henry de Bray* (note 7), pp. xxvii and 56-57: the mill and pond each render a sum and the free toll remains in his hands; also Custumal of Busshopeston, *Sussex Custumals* (note 10), p. 88: the bishop is to grind without toll all manner of corn consumed in the manor or issued from the granary for his needs. At Ashton-under-Lyne, it was stipulated that the lord ground without multure, paying the miller "but as his lyst if he likes": *Three Lancashire Documents of the Fourteenth and Fifteenth Centuries* (note 51), p. 109.

[76] Cases illustrating the writ are given in William Huse Dunham, Jr. (ed.), *Casus Placitorum*, Selden Society 69 (London: B. Quaritch, 1952), p. 69 and *Articuli ad Novas Narrationes* (note 34), p. 282.

[77] *YB* Mich. 41 Edward III, p. 24, pl. 17. Palmer has also noted viscontiel writs concerning the right to mill free of multure: *The County Courts of Medieval England, 1150-1350* (note 25), p. 179.

[78] *Curia Regis Rolls*, vol. 18 (note 59), p. 255.

[79] London, National Archives, Just. 1/775, mem. 10d. (York, 20 Henry III [1280]).

[80] *Curia Regis Rolls*, vol. 17, p. 418; *Curia Regis Rolls*, vol. 18, p. 305.

[81] *Curia Regis Rolls*, vol. 18, p. 348.

[82] Isaac Herbert Jeayes (trans. and ed.), *Court Rolls of the Borough of Colchester* (Colchester: Colchester Town Council, 1938), II: 94.

[83] "And they say that Stephen le Mouner is not suitable for the lord's profit because, for a gift conferred upon him, he permitted strangers doing suit at the mill to pass over without toll"—he was fined 3d in 1300 and the next year he was removed from the mill as unfit: *Elton Manorial Records 1279-1351* (note 11), pp. 95, 104.

[84] Leet Roll of 49 Edward III, 1374/5, *Leet Jurisdiction in the City of Norwich* (note 54), p. 65.

[85] Leet Roll of 49 Edward III, 1374/5, *ibid.*, p. 11.

[86] Rolls of Domainal Courts of Ramsey Abbey with View: Cranfeld, February 1294 in Ault, *Court Rolls of the Abbey of Ramsey* (note 18), p.233.

[87] Account Roll of the Manors of Bicester Priory, Oxon., temp. Henry VI in Hone, *The Manor and Manorial Records* (note 70), p. 208.

[88] Domainal court at Cranfield, February, 1294, in Ault, *Court Rolls of the Abbey of Ramsey*, p. 234.

[89] Domainal court at Hemmingford, January, 1294, *ibid.*, p. 220.

[90] *Seven Somerton Court Rolls, 22 Edward IV to 1573* (note 12), p. 11, involving two separate mills in 1483.

[91] Honor Court of the Abbot of Ramsey, in Ault, *Court Rolls of the Abbey of Ramsey*, p. 46.

[92] Abbey Court of Ramsey at Houghton, *ibid.*, p. 258.

[93] *Court Roll of Walsham le Willows 1303-1350* (note 50), p. 264 (1343), although the roll has a marginal note, "Condoned"; presumably the fine was not levied.

[94] Domainal Courts of Ramsey, in Ault, *Court Rolls of the Abbey of Ramsey*, p. 225.

[95] Leet Roll of 49 Edward III, 1374/5, *Leet Jurisdiction in the City of Norwich* (note 54), p. 65. Other millers stole 12 pounds out of three bushels and five pounds out of one bushel—each was fined a mark: Leet Roll of 1390/1, *Ibid.*, p. 74.

[96] Court Baron of Elizabeth Fermour, widow, held October, 1568, in *Seven Somerton Court Rolls* (note 12), p. 22.

[97] Domainal Court of Ramsey Abbey at Hemingford, 1294, in Ault, *Court Rolls of the Abbey of Ramsey*, p. 220.

[98] Roll of the Domainal Courts of Ramsey, *ibid.*, p. 189.

[99] *Elton Manorial Records 1279-1351* (note 11), p. 44.

[100] Bennett and Elton, *The History of Corn Milling* (note 69), III: 111, 114.

[101] That seems to have been taken for granted in London: the early fifteenth-century *Liber Albus* includes a provision that if a miller was convicted of fraud, the mill-horse was to be attached until the owner of the mill came to redeem it. Assuming the miller had disappeared, the owner either produced him or paid half a mark. If the miller did appear, he was punished and the mill owner was obliged to make good the fraud on pain of having all persons forbidden to attend his mill. See Henry Thomas Riley (trans.), *Liber Albus* (London: Richard Griffin & Co., 1861), III: pt. 2, f.215b (p.307). The reference given is to Letter Book A, f. 113.

[102] *The Judgment of the Pillory, made 51 Henry III and Anno Dom. 1266* [*Statutes of the Realm* (note 14), I:201].

[103] In London, the *Liber Albus* provisions dealing with fraudulent millers say that such miller shall be adjudged the punishment of the hurdle "like a baker": *Liber Albus*, III: pt. 2,

f. 215b (p.307) and IV: f. 318b (p.601). The punishment for bakers was later amended to the pillory: *Liber Albus*, IV: f. 331a (p.610), referring to Letter Book B, f. 35.

[104] Bennett and Elton, *The History of Corn Milling*, III: 111.

[105] *The Minor Poems of John Lydgate*, Early English Text Society o.s. 192, pt. 2 (London: Oxford University Press, 1934; rpt. 1961), p. 448. The source is given there as London, British Library, Harley MS 2215, leaf 157.

The Right to the Wind
in the Later Middle Ages

Tim Sistrunk (California State University, Chico)

In the bottom of Hell, when Dante likened the three heads of Satan to a windmill in the cold dusk, he touched on the ambivalence many late medieval writers felt about such an ingenious device that seemed to capture the wind for human advantage.[1] The wind, after all, was particularly emblematic of the profound workings of nature, mysterious and beyond the ken of mortals.[2] The invention of the windmill in the last decades of the twelfth century prompted a reconsideration of this resource and required new definition of its place in the human economy.[3]

This is especially noticeable in the work of the medieval lawyers. In fact, some of the earliest evidence of windmill use in Northwestern Europe was in the context of legal disputes. In general, it appears that the windmill was accommodated within the traditional seigniorial relationships concerned with watermills that had grown up over the centuries across the West. A jealously guarded privilege, the monopoly of milling services—called the "suit" or "soke" of mill in England—rested on control of access to water power and the traditional obligations tenants of various types owed their lords to use their mills. The windmill, however, presented alternatives to this entrenched system. It has been described as anti-seigniorial because it employed the wind as a motive force but the wind had never been bound by statute or custom.[4] Disputes occurred.

A famous example is the account by Jocelin of Brakelond of a conflict between the Abbot Samson of Bury St. Edmunds and Herbert, the rural dean of Norwich, sometime around 1191. The dean had built a windmill on his own land on the outskirts of Bury without the abbot's permission. Samson became enraged as the mill impinged on his monopoly of the milling soke of the region:

> [W]hen the abbot heard of it, his anger was so incensed, that he would scarcely eat, or utter a single word. The next day after hearing mass, he commanded the sacrist of the monastery to send his

carpenters to Haberdun without delay and break down the windmill altogether and carefully put the wooden materials in safe keeping. The dean, hearing this, came to the abbot and argued that he was allowed to build on his own freehold, and he asserted that the 'benefit of the wind' [*beneficium venti*] ought not to be denied to anyone. He tried to reassure the abbot that he only wanted to grind his own corn and would mill no one else's. The abbot's anger was not appeased, and he answered: 'I give thee as many thanks as if you had cut off both my feet; by God's face, I will not eat bread until that building is taken down.'[5]

The dean hastily dismantled his windmill before the abbot's men arrived.

Samson's bombast resolved his own dilemma, but from a certain perspective, dean Herbert had a credible legal argument. Late twelfth century juridical ideas were profoundly shaped by the interpretive writings of the university scholars who studied ancient Roman law and slowly began to apply it to contemporary circumstances. From this period and with growing confidence through the thirteenth and fourteenth centuries these jurists, together with their colleagues in the canon law faculties, came to forge a common juridical discourse, a *Ius commune,* that furnished universal principles and terminology to shape customary practices and fill the lacunae of an increasingly literate, urban, and complicated legal world.[6] Both civil and canon law jurists were familiar with the maxim of Roman law that certain gifts of nature should be shared by all people: "The sea, the shores of the sea, running water and the air" were, according to the ancients, "common to everyone by natural law."[7] Use of them was limited only by the rights that others had to them. If the air was everyone's, on what grounds had Samson denied Herbert the wind?

This question was clearly asked by other windmill builders and their overlords. Between 1191 and 1198, Pope Celestine III turned to the matter and attempted to end the debate. In a decretal addressed to the Abbot of Ramsey and the Archdeacon of Ely, the pope confirmed the duty of windmill builders to pay a tithe on the profits of their machines.[8] A certain knight had built a windmill on parish land and denied any continuing obligations to tithe, perhaps in the same manner that Samson's dean had. Celestine, in answer, quashed all argument with ecclesiastical censure and observed that everyone owed the traditional tenth on any proceeds that had been acquired licitly: "We command that the knight 'H' pay the tenth from that which the aforesaid windmill provided without diminution...."[9] Windmills would be treated no differently than less novel devices. The pope's determination became standard doctrine—a clear enunciation of principal made possible by papal authority—and his response was included in the official collection of decretals promulgated as the *Liber Extra* in 1234 by Gregory IX.

But how should this decree be understood? Could the wind really be compassed by legal prescriptions? Canon lawyers commented on Celestine's words and tied the case to other texts in ecclesiastical law directing the faithful to tithe, especially on the bounty of more traditional producers of income like watermills. The jurists uncovered what was implied by licit profit and they wove canon and Roman law sources together to support their discussion.[10] They did not deny that the wind was common to all. The Ordinary Gloss to the *Liber Extra*, composed 1240-43, addressed the wider issue in brief terms. The rationale behind Celestine's decision was admittedly doubtful, we are told. The wind is not born in one place but moves everywhere as a gift of God (*beneficio Dei*). Nevertheless, two arguments support the decretal. Windmills, like watermills, are constructed by their makers in a certain place and produce fruits that should support the Church. Thus the miller must tithe. A story from the Gospel of Matthew added further foundation to the pope's decision: as Jesus was crossing the Sea of Galilee, a storm threatened the boat in which he slept. When his disciples grew frightened, he awoke and rebuked the gale and the raging water. Thus the sea and the wind obey God.[11]

These contentions are fascinating. The first uses an old established technique in juridical discourse: an argument by analogy. The windmill is like the watermill. Obligations will attach to a mill utilizing the air as they do to any other type of building. The fact that the structure employed the wind was not juridically significant. The second declaration is not strictly a legal one at all. It is sustained by no allegations to the rest of the law, and there is no attempt to relate it to the then current descriptions of papal power or sovereign character. Nor do later jurists add much that was material in their commentary. Hostiensis, writing in 1250-51, expanded the details of this analysis, but not their basic purport. It seems, he wrote, that the knight should not have to pay the tithe because the wind is born of itself and applied through human artifice, not divine power. Still, it is more important to remember as Genesis teaches us that God created the waters and the air, and just as the hand, with the help of God, operates the watermill, so too the windmill by God's aid is engaged.[12] By and large, into the fourteenth century, the canonists merely repeated these justifications of the Ordinary Gloss with the elaborations of Hostiensis.[13] This is remarkable given the important issues it raised about the nature of papal authority over such a common resource and their typical prolixity on other such matters.

Their rather muted response to the decretal reveals a hesitance in binding the wind legally.

This contrasts with the juridical treatment of other aspects of the air, which came to be markedly objectified and securely tied to private property and its uses. When Celestine concluded the windmill case at the end of the twelfth century and the canonists set to work to explain its meaning in the early thirteenth century, the pope's remarks resonated with other ongoing discussions about the legal features of this element. The scholastic jurists learned from Roman law how to conceptualize the air as a dimension of land ownership. Weaving together the disparate passages of the ancient text, medieval lawyers clarified and in some ways modified its ideas when they applied them to their own questions. The Romans considered the air space above landed property as wholly attached to it. Owners could build as high as they wished, and others were prohibited from interfering or intruding into the air beyond their neighbor's boundaries. Waterspouts, beams, tree branches, and smoke all had to be removed or prevented.[14] The ancients mitigated these restrictions in various ways. If a neighbor's tree branches hung above your field, you could cut them off up to fifteen feet above the ground but generally not higher, as above this their shade did no harm to you.[15] Normal runoff from rain water was acceptable, and everyone was allowed the ordinary use of fire that might generate some smoke.[16]

Roman jurists may have had other limitations in mind when they perceived the air as an aspect of real estate, but medieval glossators summarized their notions in fairly absolute terms.[17] In the 1220s at the famous law school of Bologna, Accursius compiled over a century of medieval juridical interpretation about the entire codification of Justinian's law into the *Glossa ordinaria*. His gloss would be copied for centuries beside the ancient text as it was studied in universities throughout the West, and his work would serve as an authoritative beginning to all legal scholarship on civil law. When Accursius explained the Roman passages that dealt with the sky above someone's land, he struck a maxim that has been carried down into our own times: "The owner of the land ought to be taken to own right up to the sky [*ad caelum*]."[18] Modern commentators have been hesitant about this formulation. Some scholars have suggested that the Romans meant to distinguish the sky from the air. The air, after all, was a common benefaction of humankind. How then could a single landowner claim a slice of it into the heavens?[19] Medieval jurists, however, specifically equated *aer* and *caelum*, just as we saw the canonists connected God's creation of the *aer* with their discussion of the wind.[20] Of course, late medieval writers had no need to make our fine distinctions. They did not have to accommodate flying machines and their overflight permissions, or air rights transferred from one landowner to another to build a high-rise skyscraper, for instance.[21] These later issues that can reach into the firmament and draw so many legal questions to them redefined the rights to the wind in later centuries, but in the Middle Ages it was largely the windmill that provoked debate.

Medieval jurists seem as content as we are today to live with ambiguity. They recognized that the air was common to all, and they also learned from the Romans that, like other wild creatures, the birds of the air belonged to no one. Their ownership could be claimed only through capture. Like the fish in the sea or the animals of the field, they were naturally free until someone seized them.[22] Yet specific cases are harder than principled statements. A case brought before the English royal courts in 1364 turned partly on the difficulties of understanding the common and the private features of the sky. A hunter, Amaury le Botiller, let his falcon take a pheasant in flight over the warren of another landowner, the abbot of St. Peter's, Gloucester. The abbot sued for trespass as his property had been violated. The air above his estate had been invaded by another. The falconer was not harvesting the unclaimed bounty of the heavens, he was encroaching on private space. Amaury for his part seemed genuinely taken aback, asking whether he could be assigned wrong in such a case. We should note that twenty-first-century advocates have been hard pressed to resolve just this kind of question in our own day.[23]

Beside connecting the sky and the land, Justinian's laws also recognized the rights that others might develop to qualify the absolute ownership of one's air space. These prescriptive rights, or "servitudes", created burdens on the unfettered enjoyment of the air above a landowner's estate. Most typical of these was the right of one's neighbors to have some opening to light and the sky, or a little direct sun. An owner might be restricted from building so high as to obstruct such benefits.[24] These rights were different from the right to prospect or view, and different entirely from a servitude that one might gain allowing the discharge of a great deal of smoke into the neighbor's air. The scholastics thought this last servitude might be necessary to establish because, unlike water hurled from a window, smoke is naturally passive and rises without human direction. Generating smoke without malice might be countenanced, but such behavior could be prevented by state interdict.[25]

The glossators wondered *more* about a provision of the old law that seemed to establish a servitude to protect access to the wind. In 531, Justinian asserted that it was a "perfectly plain rule of law" that forbade someone from erecting a building next to a threshing floor and preventing the "proper and sufficient" use of the wind to separate the grain from the chaff.[26] This *lex* appears to be straight-forward. The emperor recognized a specific limitation on property use—a servitude that one cannot build so as to inhibit the wind from reaching the neighbor's yard and, interestingly, this comes about in a a context of *productive* use of the wind, just such a context as would arise with respect to windmills 700 years later. Justinian's compilers included the rule under a title about servitudes. Interestingly, medieval jurists doubted such a thing could be, in fact, a servitude. The twelfth-century glossator Hugo asserted that this was a special law to protect the fruits of threshing floors and, therefore, it did not really constitute a general servitude: that is, unless the land next to them was being used to thresh grain specifically. It was not a universal way to limit someone from using their own estate as they chose. Johannes Bassianus and Azo countered that the passage turned on the duly constituted servitude that one could not build too high beside one's neighbor. But they doubted that all the conditions of a proper servitude were met here. Mutual restraints of this type required that the *buildings* of both of the landowners be balanced or checked against each other, not really that the neighbor's edifice was limited by some space and the breeze next door. Accursius, for his part, believed the servitude was valid, however, and Vivianus, writing the standard summaries of the laws in 1256, would depict this rule as particularly defending the *beneficio ventis*.[27] The lawyers' analysis was certainly taken up in practice. A thirteenth-century grant awarding the grinding soke to a windmill in Lancashire included provisions for a plot of land beside it to winnow grain in the wind.[28] Apparently, such a designation of land use established a presumption that secured it in the future, as no neighbor could build later and block the wind. Noticeably, the windmill itself did not seem to require any such protection.

Jurists in the fourteenth century carefully preserved the debate among Hugo, Azo, and Johannes in their own commentaries while they limited Justinian's order even further. All the earlier glossators agreed that the ancient text dealt only with threshing floors, and none of them would add any remarks that implied that the *beneficio ventis* belonged to any other structure or locality. In 1314, Cino da Pistoia narrowed the shaky servitude's application even more by coloring the law as if it really applied only to places where the wind had limited access: perhaps the *area* was surrounded on three sides by a mountain, he wondered.[29] Bartolus of Sassoferrato and Baldus de Ubaldis later in the century wrote as if the rule plainly dealt with a winnowing floor that had only one entrance for the wind.[30] They did not expand its application at all.

Civil law jurists appear as uncomfortable as their canon law colleagues in fixing the wind itself within narrow legal confines. The fruit of a building might be taxed as Celestine commanded, or the use of the wind that was restricted by an enclosed entrance could be preserved as the civil lawyers noted, but beyond these, the wind was everywhere, unfixed, and of no certain origin. The force of the wind was so unpredictable that damage caused by it did not produce liabilities. Shingles blown by the tempest were not actionable, nor were ships cast about by sudden gusts, and even fires spread beyond control must be resigned to the *vis ventis*, *vis tempestatis*, or *vis divinum*.[31] In Wales in the late thirteenth and early fourteenth centuries, the wind was emblematic of the unattached quality of men who neither held burgages nor lands within a town, but who still enjoyed the liberties of townsmen. These men were called "burgesses *de vento*" and they avoided certain tolls, castle guard, labor services and other burdens by paying to claim town status while legally 'on the wind'.[32] The jurists also employed contemporary natural philosophical notions about the wind in ways that captured its ephemeral nature. Roman law allowed a guardian to pay himself from his ward's estate for the expenses he incurred. The ward was ordered not to sue his benefactor later on to recover his spent monies because the guardian could not have lived on nothing while caring for his charge. He could not, as the law put it, "live on the wind"—a rather poetic image about surviving without means. Accursius added his own descriptive accent in his gloss of the passage: no one can live on the wind, he knew, except a wolf. This was an idea posited by the twelfth-century Latin *Bestiary*. Lore of this type, we should recall, often discredited the wolf as rapacious and cunning and symbolic of the Devil who must, as we all know, inherit the wind.[33]

Natural philosophy also blended with juridical constructions to depict the more tangible aspects of the wind, though it always remained somewhat indefinable. The lawyers added air to the list of things that were corporeal in a legal sense. Corporeal things could be touched, willed away, owed, and owned, as land, a robe, a man, gold or silver. Some corporeal objects, however, were beyond the simple scope of these. As Henry de Bracton, writing in the 1220s and 30s in England, explained, some things because of mischance or other difficulties might have fallen into the depths of the sea, or might be fixed in the heavens like a star.[34] Although these were untouchable, they were still corporeal. "Smoke and air are also corporeal," he wrote, "for air is one of the four elements of which all bodies are composed and created. It is that which is exhaled from the body as wind and breath."[35] As one of the basic components of the material universe, then, the lawyers obviously saw the air as fittingly substantial and therefore at least potentially ownable.

Still, when they discussed circumstances that were by nature impossible to fulfill, they used the air to illustrate what they meant. Thus, someone making a promise to fulfill a debt might add a stipulation that was frankly inconceivable. The promissory might quip, for instance, that he would pay his bill if he touched the sky with his finger. This was an impossible condition that vitiated the accord.[36] No one can touch the sky; it might be corporeal, but it was further than the hand could reach.

Of course, the idea that the air was one of the quaternary elements of terrestrial matter conformed to late medieval theories of disease and health as well. Air and wind were thought to affect the qualities of the four Galenic humours, and medical practitioners recognized putrefying or infected air as a source of illness and epidemic throughout the thirteenth and fourteenth centuries.[37] These were Greek ideas that medieval physicians refined and systematized in their own work. The Romans certainly followed these notions, and their lawyers believed that the sewers and drains of their cities should be kept clean and repaired for the health and safety of their citizens. The glossators knew these ancient texts well.[38] Medieval lawmakers, kings, and city governments all turned consciously to regulate the air partly because of their concerns about community well-being. The Constitutions of Melfi promulgated by Emperor Frederick II in 1231 provide a famous example of imperial intervention. In order to preserve the healthfulness of the air, the emperor forbade anyone to soak hemp or flax in water within a mile of a *castrum*. No one should fail to dispose of filth or the cadavers of animals that make a stench, nor should the dead be buried less than half an ell beneath the soil.[39] City statutes across Italy reflect the same concerns. Soaking hemp and flax, a process called "retting," produced fumes that were "highly pollutive" to air quality, and not surprisingly many municipal regulations designated where such activities must be conducted.[40] In addition, animal waste, dung, and garbage should be carried away or thrown in rivers or canals, and specific jobs like tanning and butchering were confined to certain locations with constraints about how to slaughter, move, or clean their products.[41] Coal furnaces, smithies, and hearth chimneys were also circumscribed, for as we have seen, too much smoke might be fined or prohibited as nuisance.[42] In 1388, lamenting the dung and filth and other corruptions filling the lanes and waterways of the towns and boroughs of the realm, the English Parliament enacted a national urban sanitary act.[43] These were corrupting the air and promoting many maladies and intolerable diseases. Measures must be taken, it was adjured.

Thus, throughout the thirteenth and fourteenth centuries public authorities became involved in managing the air and through their concerns would add new dimensions to its legal definition. It is important to note that their habits brought the air under public control as well. Their solicitude for the health and beauty of their communities defined how this common resource might be managed. Significantly, particularly for later periods, the exercise of this authority by kings and cities might then be translated into a kind of sovereignty over the sky.[44]

Probably in the late fourteenth century, but definitely by 1408, Dutch farmers turned to the windmill to help them reclaim land from the sea. They would use the power of the air to pump water from their polderlands. Windmills came to be applied in a way that created a systematic relationship between land and air that had never been seen before. Windmills draining water spread rapidly across Holland. The freedom to set up such a windmill was called the *ius ventus*, the "right to the wind." The earliest extant document that mentions a windmill to pump water was a 12 June 1408 grant by Sir Adriaen van Raephorst, Lord of the manor of Zoeterwoude, to his nephew or cousin, Sir Floris van Alckemade.[45] In this charter, Sir Adriaen gave Floris the wind (*den wint*) of his manor so that he could build a windmill, though he reserved the right to take the wind back should he need it for his own watermill. This right to the wind seems to have been managed in the same manner, and defended just as fiercely as any older privileges had ever been. One case in 1391 pitted the Augustinian monks of Windsheim, not far from Zwolle, against a neighboring lord who accused the monks of usurping his wind, claiming that "The wind pertained to him alone." The bishop of Utrecht intervened and vehemently asserted his own prerogatives over the wind of the diocese, arguing that no one should presume to usurp the right to the wind there without his specific grant. He then awarded the monks their mill.[46] The language of the law had thus evolved to encompass the air more fully. When Dutch windmill builders depicted the meaning of their devices, they were relying on older ideas about private property and resource use and altering them again. Their "right to the wind" had gained definition from centuries of debate and application.

Still, as we listen to these lords claim to control the wind and argue with their competitors, we might feel a certain chill. We might wonder, as Dante did, whether these new machines had promoted a strange kind of clarity in describing and owning the wind.

———

Like their contemporaries, medieval lawyers saw the wind itself as enigmatic. The advent of the windmill in Western Europe provoked continual reappraisal of the legal meaning of this element. Their juridical depiction moves back and forth between ambiguity and vivid definition. The wind is free and no one should be denied its benefit, as it belongs to all in common. But one must tithe the fruits of the earth whether they were born of the power of the breezes or not. This responsibility was absolute though it meant nothing else about the wind. A landowner owned the air above his estate up to the heavens, so much so that it was uncertain whether another could take a bird in flight above him. This was true even though the fowl of the air were, like the wind, common to all. There were, of course, restrictions on the use one could make of one's own air space. A neighbor might have a servitude to limit you from blocking his light or view and, as Justinian's law suggested, he could keep you from obstructing his access to the wind as well. As we saw, medieval jurists narrowed this to a single case when a threshing floor was open on only one side. The wind, instead, was everywhere, moving, and not like water or a building subject to human direction. Its force, a divine act, was beyond control and no one could be liable for it. It was unattached like someone not fully part of the community, and ephemeral like the food of a wolf. In other ways, it was tangible, an aspect of one of the four elements of the creation, and corporeal, which had legal significance though this was not articulated fully. Tangible, but elusive, beyond the ability to touch. Monarchs and municipal governments did not fully define their sovereign rights to the air, but they made regulations to curb disease and stench. The wind was not exactly the object of the law; the nuisances that effected the public were. But no one went as far as the Dutch landlords who, inspired by the possibilities of their windmills, wove the disparate strands of older ideas together into a stunning rendition of the legal wind.

Notes

[1] Dante Alighieri, *Divina commedia, Inferno* 34.4-7. E.J. Kealey, *Harvesting the Air: Windmill Pioneers in Twelfth-Century England* (Berkeley: University of California Press, 1987), p. 191, has reproduced an early 14th-century illustration from the Holkham Bible which shows the devil tempting Christ, and among the symbols of the wealth of the world is a windmill, alluding to the Biblical tradition depicting Lucifer as "the prince of the power of the air" (Eph. 2:2). See also the recognition of the excitement generated by windmills by John Langdon, "The Birth and Demise of a Medieval Windmill," *History of Technology* 14 (1992): 54, n.1.

[2] Wind in the Bible was used in a variety of ways to depict the ephemeral nature of many things including false hope, Prov. 11:29, *Hos.* 8:7; idle thought, Eccl. 11:4; mystery, Eccl. 11:5, uncertain ideas, Eph. 4:14, and the religious life, John 3:8: "The wind blows were it will, and thou can not tell from where it comes, and where it goes; so is every one that is born of the Spirit."

[3] There has been much good work done on the invention and spread of the windmill in the 12th century. Unfortunately, there is not agreement about the dating of the earliest mills. Kealey, *Harvesting the Air*, pp. 59-78 and Bradford B. Blaine, "Mills," in *Dictionary of the Middle Ages* (New York: Scribner, 1982-89), VIII:394-95, have argued for a period early in the 12th century, while Richard Holt, *The Mills of Medieval England* (Oxford: Basil Blackwell, 1988), pp. 20-35, 171-75; *idem*, "Milling Technology in the Middle Ages: The Direction of Recent Research," *Industrial Archaeology Review* 13 (1990): 53-54 and John Langdon, "Water-Mills and Windmills in the West Midlands, 1086-1500," *Economic History* 44 (1991): 433; *ibid.* "The Birth and Demise," p. 54, n. 2, among others, have suggested some time in the 1180s. I have opted to follow the later dating as directly verifiable. For this reason, I have not treated the mills mentioned by Janet Loengard, "Lords' Rights and Neighbors' Nuisances: Mills and Medieval English Law," ch. 5 in this volume, which appear in a writ of Henry II in 1156-59 because the language employed about "higher" and "lower" mills is consistent with typical legal decriptions of watermills sharing a common river. See also Paul Bautiers, "The Oldest References to Windmills in Europe," The International Molinological Society, *Transactions of the 5th Symposium: France 1982, April 5-10* (St. Maurice: Fédération Française de Amis des Moulins , 1984): 111-21; Anne-Marie Bautier, "Les plus anciennes mentions de moulins hydrauliques industriels et de moulins a vent," *Bulletin Philologique et Historique (Jusqu'à 1610)* 2 (1960): 606-26.

[4] Robert Philippe, "Les premiers moulins a vent," *Annales de Normandie* 32 (1982): 113. Beside the legal cases discussed below that concern windmills, see Holt, *Mills of Medieval England*, p. 174, n. 18 for another early dispute.

[5] H.E. Butler (ed. and trans.), *The Chronicle of Jocelin of Brakelond, Concerning the acts of Samson, Abbot of the Monestary of Saint Edmund* (London: Thomas Nelson & Sons, 1949), pp. 59-60; and in revised version, T.E. Tomlins, *Monastic and Social Life in the Twelfth Century as Exemplified in the Chronicles of Jocelin of Brakelond* (London: Whittaker, 1844), p. 17.

[6] The literature on the rediscovery and application of the ancient Roman law together with the study of the canon law is extensive. See generally Charles Homer Haskins, *The Renaissance of the Twelfth Century* (Cambridge, Mass.: Harvard University Press, 1927), pp. 193-223; Robert L. Benson and Giles Constable (eds.), *Renaissance and Renewal in the Twelfth Century* (Cambridge, Mass.: Harvard University Press, 1982), esp. pp. 299-323; Harold Berman, *Law and Revolution: The Formation of the Western Legal Tradition* (Cambridge, Mass.: Harvard University Press, 1983), pp. 120-23; Manlio Bellomo, *The Common Legal Past in Europe, 1000-1800*, trans. Lydia Cochrane (Washington, D.C.: Catholic University of America Press, 1995). On the influence of Roman law on the law of the Church, see James Brundage, *Medieval Canon Law* (London: Longman, 1995), pp. 59-61 *et passim*; C.R. Cheney, *From Becket to Langton: English Church Government, 1170-1213* (Manchester: Manchester University Press, 1956), pp. 29, 44; Charles LeFebvre, "La glose d'Accurse, Le Decrét et les Décretales: (Vers le 'ius commune')," in Guido Rossi (ed.), *Atti del Convegno Internazionale di Studi Accursiani* (Milan: Giuffrè, 1968), I: 247-84.

[7] *Inst.* 2.1.1: "Et quidem naturali iure communia sunt omnia haec: aer et aqua profluens et mare et per hoc litora maris." The list of benefits that were common to all people was repeated in many places in the law, see *Dig.* 1.8.2.1; *Dig.* 43.8.3.1 and *Dig.* 47.10.13.7. Cf. Emil Friedberg (ed. and rev.), *Corpus iuris canonici* (Leipzig: B. Tauchnitz, 1879; rpt. Graz:

Akademische Druck-u. Verlagsanstalt, 1959), vol. I: *Decretum Magistri Gratiani*, D.1 c. 7.3: "communis omnium possessio et omnium una libertas, acquisitio eorum, quae celo, terra marique capiuntur."

The standard references to Justinian's *Digest* [*Dig.*] and *Institutes* [*Inst.*] are found in Theodor Mommsen (ed.) and Paul Krueger and Alan Watson (trans.), *The Digest of Justinian* (Philadelphia: University of Pennsylvania Press, 1985) and Paul Krueger (ed.) and Peter Birks and Grant McLeod (trans.), *Justinian's Institutes* (Ithaca: Cornell University Press, 1987).

[8] X 3.30.23, *Corpus iuris canonici*, II: 563-64. Mary Cheney, "The Decretal of Pope Celestine III on the Tithes of Windmills, JL 17620," *Bulletin of Medieval Canon Law*, n.s. 1 (1971): 63-66, identified the litigants, although Holt, *Mills of Medieval England*, p. 21, n.14, doubts her suggestion about the plaintiff's name. *Cf.* Kealey, *Harvesting the Air*, pp. 180-83, and 216.

[9] X.3.30.23: "mandamus, quatenus H. militum ad solutionem decimarum de his, quae de praedicto molendino ad ventum proveniunt, sine diminutione...." Friedberg notes the knight is variously identified as "M" and "H" in different manuscripts.

[10] The *Glos. ord.* to X.3.30.23 v. *de molendino* particularly referred to X.3.30.5 and to X.3.30.28, which outlined the responsibilities of tithing and allowed necessary expenses to be deducted before rendering what was due. The ordinary gloss may be found in *Decretales d[omi]ni pape Gregorii [noni]* (Paris: Johannis Cabiller, 1516). The *Glos. ord.* to X.3.30.23 v. *licite* gave examples of illicit gains like the profits of prostitution, simony, and acting. The commentaries of Hostiensis, *Summa aurea* (Lyon: Claudius Servanius, 1556), p. 100vb; Innocent IV, *Commentaria, apparatus in V libros Decretalium* (Frankfurt a/M: Minerva, 1968), p. 416a-b, and Joahnnes Andreae, *In quinque decretalium libros novella commentaria* (Venice: F. Franciscum, 1581; rpt. Torino: Bottega d'Erasmo, 1963), III: 143va, substantially expand these discussions.

[11] *Casus* to X.3.30.23: "Et potuit esse ratio dubitandi in isto textu, quia venti non nascuntur in loco, nec videntur moveri ex Dei beneficio, ideo videntur quod decima ex tali molendino ad ventum non esset soluenda. Sed contrarium dicitur quia et mare et venti obedient Deo, *Matth.* 8.[26-27]. Item quia terra in qua est tale molendinum subiacet oneri decimarum, unde sicut Ecclesia ex tali terra perciperet fructus si coleretur, ita debet consequi de reditibus aedificii ibi constructi per hoc capitulum et c. Commissum supra eodam [X.3.30.4]. Abb[as] sic."

[12] Hostiensis, *Summa aurea* to X. 3.30.23 v. *sine dimunitione* (Lyon, 1556), p. 100vb: "Videbatur autem militia quod non esset danda decimal de molendino ad ventum quasi venti per se nascantur et quasi ex artificio humano non ex diuina potentia hoc haberet. Sed contarium respondetur et merito, quia qui fecit aquam, fecit et aera, ut patet, *Gen.* 1, unde sicut, legitur Matth. 8: 'Mare et venti obedient ei.'... Sed et ita operatur manus et iuvat Deus in molendino ad aquam, sicut in molendino ad ventum, et immo talis dubitatio nulla fuit." Interestingly, in his gloss to v. *ad ventum* in the same passage, Hostiensis remarked that windmills were everywhere: "Sicut patet exemplum Marsilie et Arelate et in multis aliis locis."

[13] See, for example, Ioannis Andreae *comm.* to X.3.30.23, written from 1336-42, *In quinque decretalium* (Venice, 1581), III:140va.

[14] *Dig.* 8.2.(1).1(23). Smoke was prohibited at *Dig.* 8.5.8.5, and overhanging tree branches had been condemned since the law of the XII Tables: *Dig.* 43.27(26).2.

[15] *Dig.* 43.27(26).1.8, cf. *Glos. ord.* v. *pedes quindecim.* For the medieval ordinary gloss to Justinian's *Corpus iuris civilis* I have used (Lyon: Gabriel Carterius, 1593).

[16] Run-off was countenanced at *Dig.* 8.2.20, and moderate smoke from an ordinary hearth at *Dig.* 8.5.8.6.

[17] The Romans may have considered public space like a public right of way, or a sacred place like a tomb as somehow different from typical private land. They certainly distinguished the distance required between buildings on public and private land. 15 feet was mandated of the first, and only 10 of the latter "for the free circulation of the air" (*liberi aeris*), *Cod.* 8.10.9 and 11, found in Paul Krueger (ed.), *Corpus iuris civilis*, vol. 2: *Codex Iustinianus* (Dublin and Zurich: Weidmann, 1877). *Cf.* the *Glos. ord.* to *Dig.* 8.2.14(13) v. *imperatores* and v. *a vicina*.

[18] *Dig.* 8.2.(1).1(23) pr. prevented beams, roofs, or projections above one's land, because as Accursius explained in *Glos. ord.* to v. *quia coelum*: "Nota, cuius est solum eius debet esse usque ad coelum...." Accursius' language echoed the words of *Dig.* 43.24(23)22.(21).4 that prohibited extending a gutter or roof into the airspace above a tomb since the tomb included the ground with the remains and "omne etiam supra coelum." Accursius repeated his formulation in the *Glos. ord.* to *Dig.* 43.24(23).22(21).2 v. *tum soli quam coeli*: "Quia coelum quod supra aedes meas est, usque ad coelum liberum esse debet...."

[19] Taken altogether, the ancient texts are somewhat ambiguous. A very fine discussion is Francesco Lardone, "Airspace in Roman Law," *Air Law Review* 2 (1931): 455-67. See also Herbert David Klein, "Cujus est solum ejus est... quousque tandem?" *Journal of Air Law and Commerce* 26 (1959): 237-54; Lord McNair [Michael R.E. Kerr and Anthony H.M. Evans (eds.)], *The Law of the Air*, 3ᵈ ed. (London: Stevens and Sons, 1964), esp. pp. 393-97; John Cobb Cooper [Ivan A. Vlasic (ed.)], *Explorations in Aerospace Law: Selected Essays* (Montreal: McGill University Press, 1968), esp. pp. 55-81.

[20] Accursius was almost oppressively consistent in glossing the word *caelum* in various contexts, cf. *Glos. ord.* to *Dig.* 7.1.13(15).6 v. *caelum*: "Id est aerem"; *Glos. ord.* to *Inst.* 1.2 pr. v. *in caelo*: "Id est in aere"; *Glos. ord.* to *Inst.* 2.1.12 v. *caelo*: "Id est aere" and *Glos ord.* to *Dig.* 41.1.1.1 v. *caeloque*: "Id est aere."

[21] Flying machines raise interesting problems. If I own the sky above my land, shouldn't I be paid when an airplane uses my space? The writers cited in note 18 above all addressed this question in different ways: Lardone, 462-67 suggested that the Roman legal sense of equity would have allowed use even while recognizing that the air is the landowner's *ad caelum*; MacNair, pp. 393 and 396-97 described Accursius' maxim as tyrannical and absurd; and Klein, p. 237 claimed it had a doubtful birth, an arbitrary existence, and a disgraceful death, and he distinguished *aer* from *caelum* on pp. 241-42. H. Goudy in "Two Ancient Brocards" in Paul Vinogradoff (ed.), *Essays in Legal History* (London: Oxford University Press, 1913), 231-32 made the same distinction. John Cobb Cooper, *Explorations in Aerospace Law*, p. 70 (who ended up as president of Pan American Airlines), also argued that the Romans did not equate *aer* and *coelum* and seemed to assert that such questions were really moot anyway as the state had always given landowners their rights over the air (and by implication, the state could therefore manage the sky as it wished).

[22] The most important texts about this are *Inst.* 2.1.12-13 and *Dig.* 41.1.1.1, which are discussed by Charles Donahue, Jr., *"Animalia ferae naturae*: Rome, Bologna, Leyden, Oxford and Queens County, N.Y.," in Roger S. Bagnall and William V. Harris (eds.), *Studies in Roman Law in the Memory of A. Arthur Schiller* (Leiden: E.J. Brill, 1986), pp. 39-63. *Dig.* 47.10.13.7 recognized that the sea and the shores, like the air [*sicuti aer*], were common to all and that no one could be prohibited from fishing or fowling in them, unless he could be prevented from entering by another's land anyway. If an animal escaped, it regained its natural freedom, which Accursius depicted particularly in *Glos ord.* to *Dig.*41.1.5 pr. v. *effugerit*: "In aere libero, non sub cappa."

[23] Both parties claimed the pheasant had started from their own lands, although Amaury denied trespass. The verdict is not preserved: Morris Arnold (ed.), *Select Cases of Trespass from the King's Courts, 1307-1399* (London: Seldon Society, 1985), I: 270, case 22.4. This case and two others like it from the 16th and 17th centuries are mentioned in Granville L. Williams, *Liability for Animals* (Cambridge: Cambridge University Press, 1939), p. 137. In a suit that came before the Supreme Court of South Dakota in 2002 (*State v. Rumpca*), a hunter appealed his conviction for trespass for shooting a bird he had flushed from public land while it was flying over private land. The court upheld his conviction and the legislature of South Dakota responded with new legislation.

[24] Servitudes could also be imposed to prevent one's neighbor from enjoying these pleasures as well. See *Dig.* 8.2.16(15) where it is explained that the right to light means the sky must be visible, cf. *Glos. ord.* v. *id est* and v. *inferioribus locis* and *Dig.* 8.2.17(16) pr. and 1.

[25] At *Dig.* 8.5.8.5 the ancients prohibited a cheese maker from discharging smoke from his shop without a servitude. The authorities might place an interdict on this behavior anyway. See also *Dig.* 47.10.44 in which an action for insult is granted if a neighbor's smoke fumigates your living space above his, or he pours something on you below with evil intent. Bartolus, *comm.* to *Dig.* 8.5.8.5, did not like the standard description of this text in the Gloss, because it conflated throwing water at someone with the passive movement of smoke upward. Bartolus' comments may be found in his *Commentaria*, 9 vols. (Venice: De Tortis, 1516-29; rpt. Rome: Istituto giuridico Bartolo da Sassoferrato, Il Cigno Galileo Galilei, 1996), I: 199va.

[26] At *Cod.* 3.34.14.1 Justinian described his rule as "apertissimi iuris" that no one should build "ut idoneum ventum et sufficientem ad praefatum opus infringat."

[27] Accursius in the *Glos. ord.* to *Cod.* 3.34.14.1 v. *faciat* summarized past discussion: "Speciale in area secundum Hu[go] favore fructuum, ubi licet non sit constituta seruitus, tamen a lege videtur imposita.... Ioan[nes] et Azo dicunt quod hic fuit constituta servitus altius non tollendi (et ita ponunt casum) quae videatur non valere quasi non interesset, ut ff. de seruitu. verb. praed. l. Si aedes, et l. Nemo [*Dig.* 8.2.32(31) and *Dig.* 8.2.39(38)], sed tamen valet et interest." The *Glos. ord.* to *Dig.* 8.2.9(8) v. *actio* also notes that this rule was special to gain the *fructa* of the edifice.

[28] The grant of a windmill with the soke of the town of Ince was made to Stanlawe Abbey in 1230 and included the liberty to use soil to elevate the mill as necessary: Richard Bennet and John Elton, *History of Corn Milling* (1898-1904; rpt. New York: Burt Franklin, 1964), II: 240-42.

[29] Cino da Pistoia, *In Codicem et aliquot titulos primi Pandectorum tomi, id est Digesti veteris, doctissima commentaria* to *Cod.* 3.34.14.1, (Frankfurt a/M, 1578; rpt. Torino: Bottega

d'Erasmo, 1964), I: 177rb, identified Hugo as Bulgarus, who had also worked in the 12th century: "secundum Bul[garum] hic speciale fauore bladorum. Ioan[nes] et Azo dicunt quod hic fuit servitus constituta, et dubium erat, quia non videtur interesse, tamen interest…. Sed tunc ad quid consideratur ventus sufficiens et idoneus, cum modus, etc. supra eadem l. non modus [*Cod.* 3.34.12]. Item ad quid consideratur, an per communem locum ventus excludatur ab area per huiusmodi aedificationem? Dico ergo quod primus intellectus est verior. Et pone in casu quod area montus habebat a tribus partibus et per solam quartam poterat habere ventum." Jacobus Buttrigarius in his commentary written in the second and third decades of the 14th century merely noted that there were two readings of this Code passage: see *Lectura super Codicem* (Paris: J. Petit, 1516; rpt. Bologna: A. Forni, 1973), 110va.

[30] Bartolus' commentary to *Cod.* 3.34.14.1 v. *cum autem apertissimi*: "Et forte iste paragraphum non est alibi secundum unum lecturam quae dicit: Si area non potest habere ventum, nisi ex parte praedio vicino ipso iure servitus est imposita non altius tollatur et ventum impediat," in *Commentaria*, (n. 24) VII: 127rb and Baldus degli Ubaldi, *comm.* to *Cod.* 3.34.14.1, *In Corpus iuris civilis… commentaria* (Venice, 1577), V: 334va and b: "Si area non potest habere ventum nisi ex una parte et non potest alibi fieri per dominium praedii, ipso iure praedio vicini servitus est imposita per legem ne aedificando ventum impediat…. Non quod frumentum non praestat suam utilitatem nisi exspicis separetur. Notatur ventum necessarium ad triturationem frumenti auferri non posse et tenet hic lectura Hug[o] quod speciale est hic. Non autem teneas lectura Ioan[nes] et Azo quod servitus esset constituta, quia tunc non fieret hic mentio de situ loci et frustra loqueretur hic de moderamine idonei venti, si servitus non esset constituta."

[31] If someone held something by loan or lease they were not responsible for damage caused by *vis tempestatis* at *Dig.* 19.2.15.2, or by *vim divinam* at *Dig.* 19.2.25.6. Roof tiles dislodged by the violence of wind or an act of God did not create liabilities if the building itself was not faulty at *Dig.* 39.2.24.4, 9, 10 and *Dig.* 39.2.43 pr. No fault accrued when ships became entangled by the *vis ventis* at *Dig.* 9.2.29.3 and fires spread by "subita vis venti" were forgiven at *Dig.* 9.2.30.3, when there was no intention or negligence.

[32] Southern and middle Welsh burgesses *de vento* are discussed by R.A. Griffiths (ed.), *Boroughs of Mediaeval Wales* (Cardiff: University of Wales Press, 1978), pp. 149-50, 306, 312 and Maurice Beresford, *New Towns of the Middle Ages: Town Plantation in England, Wales and Gascony* (New York: Frederick A. Praeger, 1967), pp. 65 and 225.

[33] Accursius was typically laconic in his gloss of the Roman passage that opined that no one could live on the wind, *Glos. ord.* to *Cod.* 5.50.2.2 v. *vento*: "Ut lupus." On the doubtful character of wolves see T.H. White (ed. and trans.), *The Bestiary: A Book of Beasts* (New York: G.P. Putnam's Sons, 1971), pp. 56-61.

[34] Corporeal things are discussed at *Inst.* 2.2 and *Dig.* 1.8.1.1, though Bracton is directly quoting the civilian lawyer Azo in this passage: S.E. Thorne (ed. and trans.), *De legibus et consuetudinibus Angliae* (Cambridge, Mass.: Selden Society and Harvard University Press, 1968), 2: 48. Frederick William Maitland provided the parallel writings of both of these jurists on these issues in *Select Passages From the Works of Azo and Bracton*, Seldon Society Publications 8 (London: Bernard Quaritch, 1895), pp. 128-30. Exactly when or if, Henry de Bracton actually wrote the famous treatise is still debated, though generally it is believed to have been written in the 1220s and 30s with material added into the late 1250s. See Paul Brand, "The Age of Bracton," in John Hudson (ed.), *The History of English Law: Centenary Essays on 'Pollock and*

Maitland', Proceedings of the British Academy 89 (Oxford: Oxford University Press, 1996), pp. 65-89, and J.L. Barton, "The Mystery of Bracton," *Journal of Legal History* 14 (1993): 1-142.

[35] *De legibus*, 2:48: "Item corporales res sunt fumus et aer. Est enim aer unum ex quatuor elementis ex quibus omnia corpora constant et creantur. Illud idem etiam est quod assumitur et remittitur a corpore, sicut flatus et anhelitus." The *Glos. ord.* to *Dig.* 1.8.1.1 v. *ius obligationis* wondered about the difference between incorporeal things, like obligations or rights to use, and breath: "Intransitive lege, id est ius quod est obligatio et sic de aliis. Sed de quibusdam dubitatur, scilicet de fumo, aere et anhelitu hominis. Sed dic corporalia. Sed quid de angelis bonis et malis et anima? Dic incorporalia licet de his nihil ad nos."

[36] Touching or not touching the sky with a finger was an illustration the Romans developed for an impossible condition: *Dig.* 45.1.7-8; *Dig.* 28.3.16 *in fine*; *Inst.* 3.19(20).11. The glossators repeated it often and systematized all the ways such a condition was impossible as when it violated law, nature, or turpitude, *cf. Glos. ord.* to *Dig.* 45.1.7 v. *concipitur*; *Glos. ord.* to *Dig.* 45.1.8 v. *Et Marcellus*; *Glos. ord.* to *Inst.* 2.20.36(37) v. *impossibilis conditio*.

[37] Nancy Siraisi, *Medieval and Early Renaissance Medicine: An Introduction to Knowledge and Practice* (Chicago: University of Chicago Press, 1990), pp. 123, 128-29; Lynn Thorndike, *A History of Magic and Experimental Science, Fourteenth and Fifteenth Centuries* (New York: Colunia University Press, 1934), 3: 4, 245, 303-4, 306, 314, 327-28, 332, 433, 532, 534, 556; Andrée Guillerme, *The Age of Water: The Urban Environment in the North of France, AD 300-1800* (College Station: Texas A.&M. University Press, 1988), p. 107.

[38] See, for instance, *Dig.* 43.23(22).1.2 v. *minanter*.

[39] *Constitutiones Regni Siciliae "Liber Augustalis"* (Naples, 1475; rpt. Glashütten: Detlev Auvermann, 1973), 73v; James M. Powell (trans.), *The Liber Augustalis or Constitutions of Melfi Promulgated by the Emperor Frederick II for the Kingdom of Sicily in 1231* (Syracuse: Syracuse University Press, 1971), p. 132.

[40] Guillerme, *The Age of Water*, p. 98. A cursory glance at city statutes in Italy in this period reveals law makers' particular concerns about this activity. Ronald E. Zupko and Robert A. Laures, *Straws in the Wind: Medieval Urban Environmental Law—The Case of Northern Italy* (Boulder: Westview Press, 1996), pp. 86-87, mention restraints in Verona (1276), Bassano (1295), and Ferrara (1287), cf. p. 65. Roberta J. Magnusson, *Cities, Monasteries and Waterworks after the Roman Empire: Water Technology in the Middle Ages* (Baltimore: The Johns Hopkins University Press, 2001), p. 154 refers to Viterbo's special pools. Other provisions limiting retting are Severino Caprioli (ed.), *Statuto del Comune di Perugia del 1279* (Perugia: Diputazione di storia patria per l'Umbria, 1996), 1:447; Antonio Menichetti (ed.) *Statutum Comunis et Populi Civitatis, comitatus et districtus Eugubii [1338] con le aggiunte del 1376* (Gubbio: Patruzzi, 2002), p. 68v; Ubaldo Morandi (ed.), *Statuto del Comune di Montepulciano (1337)* (Florence: Le Monnier, 1966), p. 363; Francesco Cognasso (ed.), *Statuti civili del Comune di Chieri (1313)* (Pavia: Pinerolo, 1913), p. 71; Gina Fasoli and Pietro Sella (eds.), *Statuti di Bologna dell'anno 1288* (Vatican City: Biblioteca Apostolica Vaticana, 1939), 2:140.

[41] Zupko and Laures, *Straws in the Wind*, esp. pp. 73-87. Examples of the putrid or fetid qualities of prohibited activities are noted in various statutes including Perugia (1279), I:18, 198, 199, 217; Mahmoud Salem Elsheikh (ed.), *Statuto del Comune e del Popolo di Perugia del 1342 in volgare* (Perugia: Diputazione di storia patria per l'Umbria, 2000), 3:355, 380;

Bologna (1288), 2:137, 172-73; Claudia Storti Storchi (ed.), *Lo Statuto di Bergamo del 1331* (Milan: Giuffrè, 1986), p. 99; Gubbio (1338), pp. 75v and 76r, and Dina Bizzarri (ed.), *Gli Statuti del Comune di Torino del 1360* (Torino: M. Gabella, 1933), p. 121. See also Ernest L. Sabine's remarks about air pollution in "Butchering in Mediaeval London," *Speculum* 8 (1933): 339, 342-44, 349-50, and *idem*, "Latrines and Cesspools of Mediaeval London," *Speculum* 9 (1934): 311, 317.

[42] William Te Brake, "Air Pollution and Fuel Crisis in Preindustrial London, 1250-1650," in Terry S. Reynolds and Stephen H. Cutcliffe (eds.), *Technology and the West: A Historical Anthology from Technology and Culture* (Chicago: University of Chicago Press, 1997), pp. 85-86 collected references to Edward I's attempts in the late 13th and early 14th centuries to alleviate the harm caused to the air and health of Londoners by sea-coal burning. Peter Brimblecomb, *The Big Smoke: A History of Air Pollution in London Since Medieval Times* (London: Methuen, 1987), pp. 5-16 is especially useful. The famous 1377 complaint of Thomas and Alice Yonge against the noise and smoke of Stephen atte Fryth's forge is found in Helena M. Chew and William Kellaway (eds.), *London Assize of Nuisance 1301-1431: A Calendar* (London: London Record Society, 1973), pp. 160-61.

[43] The act (12 Rich. II c.13) is translated by G.G. Coulton, *Social Life in Britain from the Conquest to the Reformation* (Cambridge: Cambridge University Press, 1918; rpt. New York: Barnes & Noble, 1968), pp. 330-31, which was cited by Jean Gimpel, *The Medieval Machine: The Industrial Revolution of the Middle Ages* (New York: Penguin Books, 1976), p. 87, n. 16.

[44] Severino Caprioli (ed.), *Statuto del Comune di Perugia*, I: 198, are typical in describing anti-pollutive measures as "*utilius*," an important concept in public authority pronouncements.

[45] The spread of windmills to drain peat areas in the Netherlands is discussed in G.P. van de Ven (ed.), *Manmade Lowlands: History of Water Management and Land Reclamation in the Netherlands*, 2[d] ed. (Utrecht: Uitgeverij Matrijs, 1994), esp. pp. 104-7. A copy of this early grant of the *ius ventis* is reproduced by Wim Bosman, "The Origin of the Drainage Windmill," in The International Molinological Society, *Transactions of the Fifth Symposium: France 1982, April 5-10* (St. Maurice: Fédération Française des Amis des Moulins, 1984), p. 142, and in A. Bicker Caarten, *Middeleeuwse watermolens in Hollands polderland: 1407/08-rondom 1500* (Wormerveer: Uitgeverij Noord-Holland, 1990), p. 51.

[46] Johannes Busch, *Chronicon Windeshemense und Liber de reformatione monasteriorum*, ed. Karl Grube (Halle: Otto Hendel, 1886), p. 294. The lay lord claimed the "ventum in Zallandia ad se pertinere" and the bishop responded: "Neminem vivencium in vento illo dominacionis nostre ius aliquod competere novimus nisi nobis dumptaxat et ecclesie nostre Traiectensi." It should be noted that it is not clear that the windmill the monks gained was used to pump water.

PUBLIC AND PRIVATE URBAN HYDROLOGY: WATER MANAGEMENT IN MEDIEVAL LONDON

ROBERTA MAGNUSSON (UNIVERSITY OF OKLAHOMA)

Whereas most works on wind and water in the Middle Ages tend to focus on mills themselves, it is worth taking a step back to bring a larger panorama into view. The water mills associated with medieval cities were situated within complex hydraulic networks that were themselves the products of natural forces and human engineering. Thanks to the intensive and ongoing work of historians and archaeologists in London, a detailed picture of the city's medieval hydrology is beginning to come into focus. What is becoming apparent is that London did not have an integrated water management program as much as it had a somewhat incoherent multitude of management schemes: some private, some ecclesiastical, some public. While the citizens were creating physical and social structures for water control, climatic changes and rising tide levels in the Thames estuary ensured that the hydraulic interface between nature and society remained dynamic.

The Romans founded the city of Londinium on the northern shore of the River Thames, on the external curve of one of the river's many meanders, and built a timber bridge (or probably three consecutive bridges) across the river.[1] The site was well provided with water. The channels of the Thames and its tributaries cut through the sands and gravels of post-glacial river terraces, which overlay the impermeable London Clay. The gravel terrace deposits are capped in turn by a bed of permeable brick earth, and form a substantial groundwater reservoir. The walls of the Roman city enclosed two hills flanking the marshy valley of the Walbrook, which bisected the city and was itself fed by a network of smaller streams. Outside the walls lay other tributaries, such as the River Fleet immediately to the west. Where the stream beds cut through the terrace gravels, freshwater springs gushed forth.[2] The Thames was tidal at this point, which permitted ships to take advantage of the incoming tide to sail upstream against the current and the prevailing westerly winds, as well as hasten their outward journeys on the ebb tide.

While it is not yet possible to reconstruct the overall hydrology of Londinium in detail, archaeological excavations indicate that Roman engineering had
a considerable impact on the natural flow regimes. Fragments of Roman embankments, timber revetments, pilings, and quays have been uncovered along the
Thames waterfront, which was located some 50 to 100 meters north of today's
riverbank.[3] Timber revetments were also employed to canalize the Walbrook,
while its smaller streams were either lined and incorporated into artificial drainage networks, or filled in. Marshlands in the Walbrook valley were reclaimed
by raising the ground level with dumps of gravel and clay. British precipitation
proved to be a match for Roman culverts, however, and the construction of a
stone defensive wall around the city probably contributed to the creation of a new
extramural marshy zone to the north.[4] Portions of this Roman urban infrastructure remained long after the legions had departed, and would continue to influence London's topography and hydrology for centuries. The moor north of the
walls was still boggy at the end of the Middle Ages, while within the walls the
reclamation zone in the upper Walbrook valley became a swampy marsh as the
Roman drains silted up.[5] It is not known how long the Roman bridge remained
in use, or if it remained passable at all in the sub-Roman period.[6]

The level of the Thames was changing. During the Roman period, high tides
in the river had averaged two to four meters below the present level, the range between high and low water levels was far less than it is today, and river levels were
falling.[7] At some point in the post-Roman era, however, a new marine transgres-
sive phase commenced, and the river level began to rise. The abandoned Roman
waterfront structures were eroded and then partially buried under silts and clays.
As the level of the Thames continued to rise, the channel of the meandering river
cut northwards, until the water was washing up against the southern face of the
Roman defensive wall. Whether or not it had ever defended the city against barbarian raiders, the Roman riverside wall did protect the city from the advancing
river, acting as a barrier against further erosion for several centuries. Memories
of the old riverside wall still lingered in the twelfth century, when William Fitz-
Stephen recalled that it had existed but had finally succumbed to the force of the
river. Recent archaeological work has confirmed both the existence and the erosion of the wall, which lay along the line of Thames Street, and which influenced
the layout of Saxon streets along the waterfront.[8]

Roman Londinium was virtually, if not completely, abandoned during the
early Middle Ages, while a Saxon settlement known as Lundenwic developed
along the waterfront some 3km upstream of the Roman site, in the present-day
area of the Strand. In the mid- to late ninth century, however, Lundenwic it-

self was apparently abandoned, probably due to the threat of Viking raids (although environmental changes in the riverfront may also have played a role).[9] The area within the old Roman walls was re-occupied; streets and property divisions were laid out. This intramural resettlement was followed by developments along the waterfront in the late Saxon and early Norman periods. A new timber bridge was built near the alignment of the old Roman bridge piers—the construction date is uncertain, but the bridge was standing by the early eleventh century.[10] London was once again starting to become a busy port. Three public quays were built: Aethelredshithe (later Queenhithe) upstream from the bridge, and Billingsgate and St. Botolph Wharf downstream. Beach markets were established near the mouth of the Walbrook, at Vintry, and at Dowgate.[11] Not all ships would have docked at the public quays. Archaeological excavations have revealed that at least some of the late Saxon foreshore was reinforced with timber, stone, and clay, creating sloping hard-standings where boats could be beached.[12] At New Fresh Wharf near Billingsgate, remains of a late Saxon wooden jetty and walkway were uncovered. The sloping timber and clay river embankments were not of uniform construction, and were built in segments that corresponded to later property divisions, suggesting that they were the work of private individuals.[13]

The rapid expansion of London in the High Middle Ages seems to have coincided with a relatively stable interlude in the natural hydrology of the Thames Basin. At around the time of the Norman conquest, the previously rising water level of the Thames apparently stabilized. It has been possible to reconstruct London's water levels with a high degree of precision by measuring the levels of decay zones in timber waterfront structures, while the structures themselves can be closely dated thanks to dendrochronology. Due to the alternate wetting and drying of the timbers, the base of the zone of the most rapid decay in waterfront structures will coincide with the level of the mean high water neaps (the lowest high tides).[14] The analysis of the decay zones in London's surviving medieval waterfront timber structures suggests that river levels remained fairly constant from the eleventh to the fourteenth centuries, even though sea levels were rising relative to the level of the land and causing alluvial deposition in the riverbed.[15] The climate too was relatively stable, at least until the end of the thirteenth century. This so-called Medieval Warm Period was characterized by mild and moderate weather patterns. However, the onset of the Little Ice Age in the early fourteenth century triggered a new era of extreme and unpredictable climatic fluctuations, and by the fifteenth century the level of the river seems to have begun rising again.[16]

The twelfth and thirteenth centuries witnessed intensive economic growth, a rising population (peaking at perhaps 80,000 around 1300), and the establishment of a semi-autonomous city government. It is in this period that documentary and archaeological evidence for London's water management becomes more abundant. Modern redevelopment in much of the area south of Thames Street has provided the opportunity for an intensive and sustained waterfront research campaign, initiated in 1973 by the Department of Urban Archaeology and then placed under the ægis of the new Museum of London. Thanks to a large and growing number of excavations, and to prompt publications which carefully integrate archaeological results with documentary research, London's shoreline has become one of the best known waterfronts in medieval Europe.[17] Archaeologists and historians are also shedding light on water management practices within the rest of the city.

———

Property boundaries divided the medieval city into a myriad of individual water-management cells. Each tenement plot was, in effect, its own hydrological microsystem. The owners (or tenants) of each property had to provide sufficient water for their domestic and perhaps industrial needs as well as to dispose of sewage and other wastes. Many of London's original tenements were probably typical of medieval urban plots, characterized by long strips of land running back from a narrow street frontage.[18] The main building would front onto the street, while the rear of the property would be given over to an open yard or garden, and perhaps smaller outbuildings such as sheds or privies. Some tenements had their own wells, which were sunk into the water-bearing gravels. Londoners who did not enjoy the luxury of a private well would have to depend on rainwater cisterns, carry water in from an outside source (such as a public well or the river), or purchase water from one of the city's professional water-bearers.[19] Most houses were constructed of timber, lath, and daub, which rendered them vulnerable to seepage, so it was essential to protect them against structural damage from precipitation and flooding.[20] Roof gutters terminating in spouts would eject water away from the vulnerable walls out onto the streets and into the yards in back of buildings. Ground-level drainage channels and soakaway pits were also used to channel away and dispose of precipitation runoff.[21]

Back yards served as waste disposal repositories, and were honeycombed with pits. The pits might be lined with timber or wicker, and by the fourteenth century stone-lined pits that could be emptied out and reused were becoming common. Analysis of the fills of these medieval pits reveals that the dividing line between "rubbish" and "cess" pits was, in practice, somewhat blurred. The pits beneath privies were often used for the disposal of household garbage and other wastes, while the fills of rubbish pits typically contain some intestinal parasite remains associated with human feces (perhaps carried there in medieval chamber pots). Although cess and rubbish pits were generally shallower than wells, they were often dug down to the level of the porous gravels, so that liquid wastes would drain away. Hence there was a danger that their contents could contaminate the groundwater supply.[22]

As the city's population density increased, tenement plots were subdivided and open yards built over.[23] Wells and cesspits which had formerly served a single tenement were often subdivided as well to jointly serve neighboring properties. Then as today, less open ground meant greater storm runoff, and an increased likelihood of street flooding. The more closely houses were packed together, the greater the likelihood of friction at the tenement boundaries. According to London custom, each property holder was supposed to "bear his own water in his own ground."[24] However optimal as a water management strategy from the individual's point of view, this often involved directing his unwanted water and wastes away from his own house and yard, onto the public street or into his neighbor's property. Inadequate maintenance caused problems for careless property owners and their unfortunate neighbors, as water cascading from broken gutters or muck from overflowing cesspits flooded cellars and rotted timber walls. Partible gutters, wells, and latrines were also ready sources of conflict, especially when costly repairs or cleaning were required.

Damaged structures led to damaged relationships between neighbors. Quarrels over nuisances were such a source of concern to city officials that they provided a public drainage network, issued building codes and ordinances, and allowed citizens to seek judicial remedies in the city courts. Citizens were not to cast water or slops out of their windows, but they were permitted to dispose of liquid wastes in the public kennels, open channels which ran down the centers of the streets and which ultimately drained into the watercourses.[25] According to tradition, the Assize of Buildings was issued during the term of London's first mayor, Henry FitzAilwyn (*c.*1189-1212), and sought to allay "the contentions that at times arise between neighbors," by regulating gutters, eavesdrop, latrine pits, and other potential nuisances.[26]

Private citizens could seek legal redress against hydraulic damages and noxious neighbors. Nuisances affecting the public streets were usually dealt with at the neighborhood wardmote. Assize of Nuisance complaints between private parties were heard in the city's central Court of the Hustings or Mayor's Court. The courts employed masons and carpenters as viewers, who would examine the alleged nuisance, take measurements, and give a mix of legal and practical advice to help litigants find solutions to their problems.[27] The Assize of Nuisance rolls of the fourteenth and fifteenth centuries record hundreds of conflicts between neighbors over water-related nuisances, while the Viewers' Certificates show little sign that the quarrels caused by London's private water management schemes were abating in the sixteenth century.[28]

The inhabitants of riverside tenements had ready access to water for domestic or industrial uses, and often employed the watercourses for waste disposal. It was common for tenements along the Walbrook and Fleet to have latrines that projected over the riverbanks, and gutters draining into the streams.[29] These were generally tolerated, although the pollution and obstruction of the rivers with excessive rubbish and dung led the city to issue periodic sanitation ordinances.[30] Tenement holders along the banks of the Walbrook, for example, were supposed to keep rakes to clear noxious flotsam out of the stream.[31] Tradesmen who required large quantities of water, such as tanners and dyers, were concentrated along the banks of the watercourses. London's butchers had been given their own wharf on the Fleet, which they used as a site for cleaning entrails—a noxious practice which occasioned such vociferous complaints from nearby residents that the king and city were forced to intervene.[32]

The Templar mill situated near the mouth of the Fleet was blamed for obstructing navigation and occasioned another long and bitter legal battle.[33] Some London households had mills and millstones (though many of these may have been hand-mills), but most of the mills associated with London were situated in the city outskirts, along nearby streams, or across the river in Southwark. Tidal impoundment mills were located along the Thames, although the river's strong current and large tidal fluctuations made it difficult to harness as a power source. Other tide mills lay along the mouths of the more tractable smaller tributaries. Tide mills, with their discontinuous action, were insufficient to meet the milling needs of the growing city, however, and Londoners came to depend on the power supplied by watercourses further afield. Ordinary water mills lay along the non-tidal upper reaches of the secondary streams such as the River Lea, 7km to the east. The corn mills clustered along the Lea were of particular importance to the city's bakers, and Londoners were using fulling mills there by the late thirteenth century.[34]

Waterfront properties were particularly vulnerable to erosion and flooding. In the Walbrook Valley, the marshy zone within the city walls was comparatively

Figure 1: **Thirteenth-century timber waterfront revetment, old Billingsgate;**
Museum of London Archaeology Service.

dry by the thirteenth century, thanks to piecemeal reclamation efforts that included cutting drainage channels and raising ground levels by means of dumps
of clay. The Walbrook and its tributaries were confined to narrower channels and
became gradually bridged over, until it finally became an underground stream.[35]
It appears that the transformation of the boggy, low-lying areas within the town
walls to land suitable for building was the end result of multiple private water
management initiatives, rather than any kind of public, centralized planning.[36]

About 90% of the Thames river frontage was in private hands.[37] Archaeological excavations have revealed that most of the land between Thames Street
and the modern riverfront was reclaimed in the period between the eleventh
and fifteenth centuries, as successive riverside wharfs and revetments pushed the
Thames shoreline back some fifty to one hundred meters[38] (Fig. 1). By the sixteenth century, this land reclamation had increased the area of intramural London by as much as one-sixth.[39] At many sites, such as Trig Lane, the waterlogged
remains of multiple medieval revetments survive. As each timber revetment decayed, a new one was built further out into the river, and the space behind it was
filled by tips of rubbish and soil. Wooden stairs and small lanes flanking the
properties provided residents with access to the river.[40]

Waterfront scholars have advanced several reasons to explain the proliferation of these private revetments. The creation of a sound frontage against the

force of the river may have been the chief motivation of tenement holders, with the consequent extension of their property a welcome but secondary consideration. In the Eyre of 1244, the city acknowledged the customary right of London citizens to protect their lands against "the sea ebbing and flowing night and day" by extending their frontages *towards* the current (although private quays extending out *into* the current could be considered illegal encroachments).[41] Silting and sanitation may have been other concerns. The Thames was the legal or illegal dumping place for every kind of refuse, and further filth washed in from the polluted tributaries and street kennels.[42] If a property owner's revetment did not project as far into the river as his neighbors' frontages, silt and refuse from the river would accumulate in the resulting backwater, becoming a foul-smelling nuisance at low tide.[43] Ships did sometimes unload their cargoes at private wharves, but the provision of deep-water docks does not seem to have been a primary motivation for the construction of most of London's private revetments. Indeed, the public quays such as Queenhithe, Dowgate, and Billingsgate lagged behind as inlets as the rest of the river frontage advanced.[44]

The process of river reclamation, then, was piecemeal and for the most part private. For the individual owner or occupier, it was easiest to protect his property by installing a new (and sometimes even prefabricated) revetment further out into the river when the timber of the old one decayed. As revetment construction techniques improved, the Thames frontage became more stable. By the fourteenth century, timber revetments were fabricated in two parts, so that only the decayed upper portion had to be replaced.[45] Property owners began replacing their old timber revetments with more permanent stone revetments in the fourteenth and fifteenth centuries, and the reclamation process gradually drew to a close.[46]

In their management of London's watercourses, the mayor and aldermen found themselves trying to balance the competing interests of different groups of citizens without antagonizing the king. City regulations governing the Thames and its tributaries were focused on the issues of shipping (essential for London's economic base), fishing, the maintenance of flow, and sanitation. In the period between the twelfth and fourteenth centuries, London acquired jurisdiction over the stretch of the Thames upstream as far as Staines, and downstream to Yantlet Creek near the estuary, for a total distance of some 120km.[47] Ships that were liable to pay customs were to offload their cargoes at the proper public quays and obey city market regulations.[48] Smaller vessels could berth directly at the quayside, but larger ships would have to anchor in the river and offload into lighters.[49] Water bailiffs surveyed fishing nets to ensure that they were of legal dimensions, and removed weirs that interfered with navigation.[50] City officials issued numerous sanitation ordinances in an attempt to keep the street kennels, watercourses, and docks clean, and were on occasion spurred to greater efforts by royal indignation at the "corruption" and "abominable stenches" that the proliferation of urban wastes generated.[51] The mayor and aldermen also protected river access for "the poor common people." Public streets leading down to the river terminated in wharves and stairs, where citizens could draw water or launder clothes. By the fourteenth century there seems to have been pressure to ensure public access to the waterfront through lanes which may have had private origins.[52]

The public structure that had the most impact on the hydrology of the Thames was London Bridge (Fig. 2). A series of timber bridges had spanned the Thames on roughly the same alignment since Roman times, but in 1176 construction of a new stone bridge commenced.[53] The work was directed by chaplain Peter of Colechurch, who also appears to have been responsible for raising money for the ambitious project through the formation of bridge fraternities. Many citizens of London and London's first mayor, Henry FitzAilwyn, were among the charitable benefactors who provided financial support.[54] Custody of the bridge passed to Bridge Wardens, who ran the administrative unit known as the Bridge House. The wardens were elected by and served the City of London (apart from a nearly disastrous interval of mismanagement in the mid-thirteenth century when custody of the bridge and its revenues was taken over by Henry III and Queen Eleanor of Provence).[55]

To protect the vulnerable bridge piers against the scouring effects of current and tides, Peter of Colechurch had surrounded each pier with a starling, a boat-shaped platform of piles, rubble, and reinforcing timbers. The Bridge House accounts show that regular maintenance of the starlings was one of the top priorities of the Bridge Wardens.[56] The starlings worked brilliantly in terms of protecting the piers—the medieval bridge would serve London until it was replaced in the nineteenth century—but they were bulky and had a major impact on the hydrology of the Thames. The flow of water was so restricted that the bridge acted as a partial dam, raising the level of the river upstream at Queenhithe nearly half a meter within a few years. Complex patterns of sedimentation and scouring developed in the riverbed due to the bridge's impact on the river's flow regime. The partial damming of the water (and perhaps a reduced salinity) on the upstream side of the bridge resulted in the buildup of ice during severe winters, while the starlings blocked ice floes from passing easily under the bridge. A drawbridge permitted large ships to pass through the bridge, while smaller ves-

Figure 2: View of old London Bridge from the south by
Anton van den Wyngaerde (d. 1571);
Guildhall Library, Corporation of London.

sels negotiated the rapids between the arches, an adventure known as "shooting the bridge" that resulted in many fatal accidents.[57]

During the thirteenth and fourteenth centuries, many London religious houses and the city itself began to exploit the freshwater springs in the outskirts of the city by building piped water systems. London's conduits fit within a much broader framework of technological diffusion. The construction of aqueducts, pipes, and fountains was taking place throughout Western Europe in the High Middle Ages. In Britain, piped water systems had been reintroduced in the mid-twelfth century, and were usually associated with palace or monastic sites.[58] Although London's religious houses were not among the earliest adopters of the technology, an unusually high number of them did eventually build piped water systems. The best known systems belonged to the Franciscans and the Carthusians. The Greyfriars' system was built in the mid-thirteenth century. The friary register contains a detailed topographical description of the course of the pipeline, and the conduit houses have been examined archaeologically.[59] The Charterhouse conduit was constructed in 1442, and a famous waterworks plan provides a very detailed record of the system's various components. Some of the smaller religious houses and hospitals were fed by branch pipes from the larger systems.

Medieval monastic waterworks were carefully planned and well integrated systems that served small, cohesive communities. Springs could provide an adequate supply of clean water for a convent with a few dozen monks, but could not supply a city of 80,000 inhabitants. London's civic water system did not seriously reduce the city's reliance on rivers and wells, but it did provide an additional (and cleaner) source of water for at least some residents. London was not the first medieval city in Europe to build a water system, but it was the first in Britain to do so. The inspiration does not seem to have come from the local monasteries—indeed, work on the civic system may have started before any of London's monastic systems were built. The royal plumbing at Westminster Palace may have provided the inspiration. The palace had been provided with some sort of conduit and fountain since 1170, but Henry III installed a new water system there in 1234.[60] Gilbert de Sanford, acting at the request of the king, granted the springs and waters in his fief in Tyburn to the city and citizens three years later.[61] Hydraulic expertise was still quite rare in the early thirteenth century, so it is tempting to speculate that one or more of the craftsmen who installed the Westminster system served as engineering consultants for the city. The water was conveyed from the conduit head by means of subterranean pipes to the Great Conduit, a public fountain in Cheapside. In the fourteenth and fifteenth centuries more springs

Figure 3: **Cheapside in 1585 by Ralph Treswell (c. 1540-1616)**;
Guildhall Library, Corporation of London.
The Little Conduit is the structure abutting the east end of the church of St. Michael le Querne.
The view depicts the pipes which fed the enclosed cistern, and the tankards of the water-bearers.

and additional distribution points were incorporated into London's conduit system, which would continue to function until the Great Fire of 1666.[62] The conduits served tradesmen, such as brewers and fishmongers, as well as ordinary citizens who drew water there for domestic use.[63] (Fig. 3) By the fifteenth century some citizens even had private pipelines, which tapped water (legally or illegally) from the public mains.[64]

Water management in medieval London, then, was a jumbled mix of private, ecclesiastic, and public initiatives. The very complexity of the picture makes it difficult to assess the overall effectiveness of these attempts, but a few observations may nonetheless be hazarded. Private hydraulic microsystems could have a large collective impact. In London, the riverfront revetments are the most obvious example. Since London was on the external side of a river meander, a natural flow regime should have produced erosion along the northern foreshore and the accumulation of sediments along the southern, inner shore of the curve. The

riverside revetments, however, reversed the expected pattern, creating a significant zone of reclaimed land along the north bank, and deflecting the currents so
that they eroded the Southwark shoreline instead, to the point that the tide "carried away bodies buried in the churchyard."[65] They also seem to have provided
the city with a fairly effective flood barrier. Medieval chronicles record severe
flooding in Westminster, Lambeth, Southwark, and Barking, but most of the
documented floods within London's walls appear to have been the result of inadequate street drainage during heavy rains (or on occasion burst conduit pipes),
not overflowing river banks.[66]

The only public work to have a comparable impact on Thames hydrology was
London Bridge, but that impact was not necessarily a positive one. The bridge's
disruption of the river's flow regime was not as severe in the Middle Ages as it
would be by the end of the sixteenth century, by which time rubble from a col-
lapsed arch, and the insertion of corn mills and a wheel-driven water pumping
station in several other archways, had reduced the river to one-sixth of its natural
width.[67] Nevertheless, it was already a hazardous impediment to shipping, and it
became even more of one after 1476, when structural problems made it too risky
to raise the drawbridge.[68] When large ships could no longer pass through the
drawbridge, upstream quays like Queenhithe decayed, while the suburbs below
the bridge developed into London's main docklands.[69]

The city government does seem to have been reasonably effective at miti-
gating the social friction that ensued when private microsystems clashed. The
courts and viewers provided legal outlets and practical remedies for hydraulic
disputes between neighbors. Public kennels linked private drains into more coherent drainage networks. In general the city does seem to have been responsive
to complaints about hydraulic abuses, and to have made a real effort to strike a
balance between the needs of different citizens when resolving disputes over access to water.

Public authorities were, however, less successful at finding satisfactory solutions to the problem of water pollution. The waste disposal practices of private
citizens were not easily controlled, in spite of royal and city ordinances. Public
sanitation measures like the provision of extramural laystalls and the employment of municipal rakers probably did reduce the amount of filth that ended up
in the rivers, but watercourses remained convenient and popular dumping sites
for urban wastes. Most medieval pollutants were organic materials that decom-
posed fairly readily. Fluvial pollution must have been a serious problem in the
smaller watercourses of the Walbrook and the Fleet, but the Thames was large
enough to be essentially self-purifying. The rubbish on its riverbanks was un-

doubtedly stinking and insalubrious at low tide, but there is no indication that
the volume of organic matter in the river was tipping the oxygen balance to create anaerobic conditions.[70]

Medieval monastic water systems were precocious examples of integrated,
centralized water management, and such evidence as we have for London's ecclesiastic waterworks seems to fit this broader pattern as well. The city too built a
freshwater conduit system that was technologically advanced for its time, and it
was one of the few cities in Britain to do so. The conduits provided water that
was far cleaner than river water, but they could never provide it in sufficient
quantity to eliminate (or probably even seriously reduce) the citizens' reliance on
the river and wells. The scale of the medieval city was too large for the scale of
medieval hydraulic technology. London's city government could regulate, supplement, and even loosely link its citizens' private water management schemes,
but it was not capable of replacing them with anything approaching a cohesive
and integrated water management system.

Notes

[1] Bruce Watson, Trevor Brigham, and Tony Dyson, *London Bridge: 2000 Years of a River
Crossing*, MoLAS Monograph 8 (London: Museum of London Archaeology Service, 2001),
pp. 28-51.

[2] Derek Keene, "Issues of Water in Medieval London to c.1300," *Urban History* 28
(2001): 162, 171.

[3] Peter Marsden, *Ships of the Port of London: First to Eleventh Centuries AD*, English
Heritage Archaeological Report 3 (London: English Heritage, 1994), pp. 24-28; Gustav
Milne and Chrissie Milne, *Medieval Waterfront Development at Trig Lane, London*, London
and Middlesex Archaeological Society Special Paper 5 (London: London and Middlesex Archaeological Society, 1982), p. 2.

[4] Catharine Maloney, *The Upper Walbrook Valley in the Roman Period*, Council for British
Archaeology Research Report 69 (London: Museum of London: Council for British Archaeology, 1990), pp. x, 119.

[5] Maloney, *The Upper Walbrook Valley*, pp. 123-24.

[6] Watson, *et al.*, *London Bridge*, p. 51.

[7] *Ibid.*, pp. 25-27; Marsden, *Ships of the Port of London: First to Eleventh Centuries*, pp.
23-24.

[8] Charles Hill, Martin Millett, Thomas Blagg, and Tony Dyson, *The Roman Riverside
Wall and Monumental Arch in London*, London and Middlesex Archaeological Society Special
Paper 3 (London: London and Middlesex Archaeological Society, 1980), pp. 2-3 and 71-73;
Tony Dyson, *Documents and Archaeology: The Medieval London Waterfront* (London: Museum
of London, 1989), p. 24.

[9] Alan Vince (ed.), *Aspects of Saxo-Norman London*, London and Middlesex Archaeological Society Special Paper 12 (London: London and Middlesex Archaeological Society, 1991), 2:418-19.

[10] Watson, *et al.*, *London Bridge* (note 1), pp. 52-60.

[11] Peter Marsden and Caroline Caldwell, *Ships of the Port of London: Twelfth to Seventeenth Centuries AD* (London: English Heritage, 1996), p. 21.

[12] Brian Hobley, "The London Waterfront—the exception or the rule?" in Gustav Milne and Brian Hobley (eds.), *Waterfront Archaeology in Britain and Northern Europe*, Council for British Archaeology Research Report 41 (London: Council for British Archaeology, 1981), pp. 3-7.

[13] Ken Steedman, Tony Dyson, and John Schofield, *The Bridgehead and Billingsgate*, *Aspects of Saxo-Norman London*, London and Middlesex Archaeological Society Special Paper 14 (London: London and Middlesex Archaeological Society, 1992), 3:8, 102-4.

[14] Milne and Milne, *Medieval Waterfront Development at Trig Lane* (note 3), p. 61.

[15] Steedman, *et al.*, *The Bridgehead and Billingsgate*, pp. 120-21; Marsden and Caldwell, *Ships of the Port of London: Twelfth to Seventeenth Centuries*, p. 37.

[16] Brian Fagan, *The Little Ice Age: How Climate Made History 1300-1850* (New York: Basic Books, 2000), p. 80.

[17] For a recent overview of London's waterfront research, see Gustav Milne, *The Port of Medieval London* (Stroud: Tempus, 2003).

[18] John Schofield, *Medieval London Houses* (New Haven: Yale University Press, 1994), p. 28.

[19] John Schofield, *The Building of London From the Conquest to the Great Fire*, 3rd ed. (Stroud: Sutton, 1999), p. 97. For a recent study of London's water-bearers, see Ted Flaxman and Ted Jackson, *Sweet & Wholesome Water: Five Centuries of History of Water-bearers in the City of London* (Cottisford: E. W. Flaxman, 2004).

[20] Schofield, *Medieval London Houses*, p. 118.

[21] *Ibid.*, p. 118.

[22] Vince, *Aspects of Saxo-Norman London* (note 9), 2:13-16; Milne and Milne, *Medieval Waterfront Development at Trig Lane* (note 3), p. 87.

[23] Schofield, *Medieval London Houses*, p. 59.

[24] Janet Senderowitz Loengard (ed.), *London Viewers and their Certificates, 1508-1558*, London Record Society 26 (London: London Record Society, 1989), pp. lii-liii.

[25] Henry Thomas Riley (ed. and trans.), *Memorials of London and London Life in the XIIIth, XIVth, and XVth Centuries* (London: Longmans, Green & Co., 1868), p. 389.

[26] Henry Thomas Riley (trans.), *Liber Albus: The White Book of the City of London* (London: R. Griffin, 1861), pp. 276-86; Schofield, *Medieval London Houses*, pp. 4, 32-34.

[27] Helena M. Chew and William Kellaway (eds.), *London Assize of Nuisance 1301-1431: A Calendar*, London Record Society 10 (London: London Record Society, 1973); Loengard, *London Viewers*.

[28] Chew and Kellaway, *London Assize of Nuisance*; Loengard, *London Viewers*.

[29] Riley, *Memorials of London*, pp. 478-79.

[30] Ernest Sabine, "City Cleaning in Mediaeval London," *Speculum* 12.1 (1937): 19-43.

[31] Riley, *Memorials of London*, p. 23.

[32] *Ibid.*, pp. 214, 339-40; Marjorie Blanche Honeybourne, "The Fleet and its Neighborhood in Early and Medieval Times," *London Topographical Record* 19 (1947): 53-54; Ernest Sabine, "Butchering in Mediaeval London," *Speculum* 8.3 (1933): 335-53.

[33] Honeybourne, "The Fleet and its Neighborhood," pp. 45-47, 52.

[34] Bruce M.S. Campbell, *et al.*, *A Medieval Capital and Its Grain Supply: Agrarian Production and Distribution in the London Region, c. 1300* (Lancaster: Institute of British Geographers, Historical Geography Research Group, 1993), pp. 79-80; Nicholas J. Barton, *The Lost Rivers of London* (London: Phoenix House, 1962), pp. 84-90; Martha Carlin, *Medieval Southwark* (London: Hambledon Press, 1996), pp. 53-57; K. G. T. McDonnell, *Medieval London Suburbs* (London: Phillimore, 1978), pp. 73-75 and 84-86; Keene, "Issues of Water in Medieval London" (note 2), p. 165.

[35] Maloney, *The Upper Walbrook Valley* (note 5), pp. 79-81; Barton, *The Lost Rivers of London*, pp. 22-23.

[36] Keene, "Issues of Water in Medieval London," p. 162.

[37] Dyson, *Documents and Archaeology* (note 8), p. 20.

[38] Hobley, "The London Waterfront—the exception or the rule?" (note 12), p. 7.

[39] Schofield, *Medieval London Houses* (note 18), p. 6.

[40] Milne and Milne, *Medieval Waterfront Development at Trig Lane* (note 3), pp. 14, 62-63.

[41] Helena M. Chew and Martin Weinbaum (eds.), *The London Eyre of 1244*, London Record Society 6 (London: London Record Society, 1970), pp. 133-34; Riley, *Liber Albus* (note 26), p. 409.

[42] Riley, *Memorials of London* (note 25), pp. 295-96, 299.

[43] G. Milne, "Medieval Riverfront Reclamation in London," in Milne and Hobley, *Waterfront Archaeology* (note 12), pp. 33-36; Milne and Milne, *Medieval Waterfront Development at Trig Lane*, pp. 66-67.

[44] Milne, "Medieval Riverfront Reclamation in London," p. 34.

[45] Gustav Milne, *Timber Building Techniques in London c.900-1400*, London and Middlesex Archaeological Society Special Paper 15 (London: London and Middlesex Archaeological Society, 1992), p. 79.

[46] Milne, "Medieval Riverfront Reclamation in London," p. 33; Mary D. Lobel and W.H. Johns (eds.), *The City of London from Prehistoric Times to c.1520*, The British Atlas of Historic Towns 3 (Oxford: Oxford University Press, 1989), p. 53.

[47] Keene, "Issues of Water in Medieval London" (note 2), pp. 167-68.

[48] Riley, *Liber Albus* (note 26), pp. 209-17; Marsden and Caldwell, *Ships of the Port of London* (note 11), pp. 38-40.

[49] *Ibid.*, p. 38.

[50] Betty R. Masters, "The Mayor's Household before 1600," in Albert E. J. Hollaender and William Kellaway (eds.), *Studies in London History* (London: Hodder and Stoughton, 1969), pp. 101-2.

[51] Riley, *Memorials of London* (note 25), pp. 223-24, 279-80, 295-96, 298-99, 356-58, 367-68, 389, 435-36, and 478-79.

[52] *Ibid.*, pp. 648-49; Dyson, *Documents and Archaeology* (note 8), pp. 18-24.

[53] Watson, *et al.*, *London Bridge* (note 1), chapters 4-8.

[54] *Ibid.*, p. 83.

[55] Patricia Pierce, *Old London Bridge* (London: Review, 2001), pp. 41-45, 58-61, and 84-90.

[56] Vanessa Harding and Laura Wright, *London Bridge: Selected Accounts and Rentals, 1381-1538*, London Record Society 31 (London: London Record Society, 1995).

[57] Watson, *et al.*, *London Bridge*, pp. 162-63.

[58] Roberta J. Magnusson, *Water Technology in the Middle Ages* (Baltimore: The Johns Hopkins University Press, 2001), p. 6.

[59] Charles L. Kingsford, *The Grey Friars of London*, British Society of Franciscan Studies 6 (Aberdeen: The University Press, 1915), pp. 48-51, 158-61; Philip Norman, "On an Ancient Conduit-head in Queen Square, Bloomsbury," *Archaeologia* 56.2 (1899): 251-66; Philip Norman and Ernest A. Mann, "On the White Conduit, Chapel Street, Bloomsbury, and its Connexion with the Grey Friars' Water System," *Archaeologia* 61 (1909): 347-56. There is also a great deal known about some other town water systems, *e.g.*, Bristol; see Julian Lea-Jones, "The History and Devlopment of a Thirteenth-century Lead Water Conduit: The Carmelites' Friary Pipe, Bristol, England," in Robert Bork, *et al.*, (eds.), *De Re Metallica: The Uses of Metal in the Middle Ages*, AVISTA Studies in the History of Medieval Technology, Science, and Art 4 (Aldershot: Ashgate, 2005), pp. 219-45.

[60] Valerie Horsman and Brian Davison, "The New Palace Yard and Its Fountains: Excavations in the Palace of Westminster 1972-4," *The Antiquaries Journal* 69.2 (1989): 279-97.

[61] Reginald R. Sharpe (ed.), *Calendar of Letter-Books: Letter-Book A* (London: John Edward Francis, 1899), pp. 14-15.

[62] Keene, "Issues of Water in Medieval London" (note 2), pp. 174-76; Derek Keene and Vanessa Harding (eds.), *Historical Gazetteer of London Before the Great Fire*, vol. 1, *Cheapside* (Cambridge: Chadwyck-Healey, 1987), no. 105/36.

[63] Magnusson, *Water Technology in the Middle Ages*, pp. 139-45; Keene, "Issues of Water in Medieval London," pp. 176-79.

[64] *Ibid.*, p. 175; Magnusson, *Water Technology in the Middle Ages*, p. 32.

[65] Watson, *et al.*, *London Bridge* (note 1), p. 72; Carlin, *Medieval Southwark* (note 34), pp. 231-32.

[66] Andrew Saint and Gillian Darley, *The Chronicles of London* (New York: St. Martin's Press, 1994), p. 31; John Richardson, *The Annals of London* (Berkeley: University of California Press, 2000), pp. 31, 52, 70; Carlin, *Medieval Southwark*, pp. 38, 231-32; Watson, *et al.*, *London Bridge*, pp. 60-65, 152-55; Riley, *Memorials of London* (note 25), pp. 374-75; Honeybourne, "The Fleet and its Neighborhood" (note 32), p. 49.

[67] Pierce, *Old London Bridge* (note 55), pp. 105 and 148-50.

[68] Watson, *et al.*, *London bridge*, p. 107.

[69] McDonnell, *Medieval London Suburbs* (note 34), pp. 95-99.

[70] Alwyne Cooper Wheeler, *The Tidal Thames* (London: Routledge & Kegan Paul, 1979), pp. 20-21.

MILLS AND MILLERS IN MEDIEVAL VALENCIA

THOMAS F. GLICK (BOSTON UNIVERSITY)
LUIS PABLO MARTINEZ (UNIVERSITY OF VALENCIA)

Study of the wheat-flour-bread cycle in medieval Valencia reveals patterns typical of peasant agricultural production systems. At two key steps of the cycle—the purchase of grain from the fields on which it was grown, and the conversion of grain into flour in water mills—the trade was conspicuously in the hands of a large number of impoverished agents and dealers, operating on scant profit margins on the order of only one to six percent, and who were constantly in debt. Such systems of peasant agricultural production and distribution have been studied in many societies around the world and have revealed remarkable similarities in all.[1] This particular system, involving an evil miller, lawsuits, and the Valencian Cathedral Chapter, offers an excellent case study in the wheat-flour-bread cycle of preindustrial Europe

Grains and their Provision

Mills and millers were part of an interlocked technological system that began in peasant fields of the Huerta ("irrigated plot; orchard"—hence the agrarian region) of Valencia. Sources distinguish diverse grades of bread flour in medieval Valencia, although it is not clear whether there was a distinction drawn only between the qualities of the grain or whether different varieties of wheat were used for each. In medieval Valencian documents, the generic terms for wheat were *blat* and *forment*. It has been widely supposed that in Islamic Spain only hard wheat (*Triticum durum*) was grown, ostensibly for semolina. Hard wheat, however, can be used for bread by sifting out the coarser flour and using only the finer flour, or by milling it twice, although this latter option is far less likely. After the Christian conquest of Valencia (1236-45), records survive of payments in kind made by wholly Muslim villages, apparently growing the normal roster of species that Christians cultivated, in particular, bread wheat (*Triticum aestivum*). In an age that lacked the technical capacity even to select seeds of the same variety for planting, much less standardize a species, one would expect considerable variation in closely related cultivars, each of which was susceptible to local adaptations by natural, if not human, selection.

There were three basic grades of bread in medieval Valencia: white (*pa de blanc*, also known as *pa de moflet* or *pa de rei*), the highest quality; golden (*pa de ros*), of a medium quality; and the inferior grades, generically known as *pa de pobre* (poor man's bread), which included different kinds of bread, like *pa de sedaç* (sieved bread) or *pa de mijans* (middling bread), the latter sometimes conflated with so-called "mixed bread" (*pa de mestall*). White bread was made of the highest grade wheat (*candeal* or *seixa*), whereas golden bread was made from *forment fort* ("strong wheat"), evidently a reference to hard wheat. The poorest quality breads were made with *forment fort*, mixed with inferior cereals (generically *blat moresc*, "Moorish wheat"), mainly spelt, but also millet. In times of extreme shortage, barley and oats were used to make the most inexpensive bread. Old or almost rotten grain was used to make biscuit (*bescuit*), bread cooked twice, particularly appropriate for long-term conservation, such as required by ocean navigation. Bakers (*flequers*) were specialized according to distinctions in the grade of bread they produced: *flequers de blanc*, *flequers de ros*, and *bescuiters*, for example.[2]

The main population centers of the Kingdom of Valencia, including Castelló de la Plana, Sogorb, Morvedre, Lliria, Valencia (city), Alzira, Xàtiva, Ontinyent, Alcoi, Alacant, Elx, and Oriola, all suffered from scant and irregular rainfall, with annual averages ranging from 200mm to 600mm, with sharp droughts in the summer months and the possibility of devastating floods in spring and autumn. Inasmuch as feudal lords collected agrarian taxes in kind (usually in wheat or other cereals), tax figures provide evidence of the cereal varieties grown in different places, and the distribution of cereals broadly reflects microclimates mainly differentiated by aggregate annual rainfall. Tax figures for 1268-69 from Pego, a valley to the south of Gandia with average rainfall of slightly over 800m (a privileged microclimate, given de Kingdom's climatic conditions), still inhabited wholly by Muslims some twenty years after the feudal conquest, are extremely detailed. Large amounts of wheat (*forment*) and barley (*ordi*) were grown, along with small supplemental crops of spelt (*espelta*—*Triticum spelta*, Ar. *sult)* and millet (*panis, dacsa*),[3] a roster that reveals the characteristic Mediterranean strategy of growing a variety of plants to ensure the survival of at least one crop even if the others did not reach harvest. The more diverse the water requirements of the crops harvested and the more varied their growing season, the lower the risk of losing the annual harvest.[4] On the other hand, the development of agriculture also depended on the development of irrigation systems that balanced the lack of rainfall by means of the diversion and control of surface waters.[5]

Durum wheat has a lower water requirement than *T. aestivum*, which is attractive for environments with summer drought; it could be sown in the spring. Bread wheat was normally sown in the fall but, according to Sallares, "soft varieties of bread wheat are the only type of naked wheat likely to have a chance of succeeding in practice if sown at the start of Spring, in areas with a true Mediterranean climate."[6] Ultimately, only paleobotanical evidence can resolve the issue. If one looks, for example, at results obtained from the excavation of a thirteenth-century *graner* at Vic, one finds a predominance of *T. dicoccum* (emmer), followed closely by *T. aestivum-compactum* (bread wheat), with a lesser incidence of *T. monococcum* (einkorn, Cast. *escaña*, the most primitive of wheat varieties).[7] The predominance of emmer is surprising; it may have been used as fodder. Such a split among three or more wheat species is normal for a Mediterranean microregion.

The minor grains mentioned in medieval records represent adaptations to very specific niches, rather than a reflection of consumption patterns or taste. Spelt does well under cold conditions. Barley is hardier than wheat, grows better than wheat on poor soils, and therefore its cultivation presents fewer risks. Much of it was presumably used for fodder (in which case it was harvested green), although it was used for couscous instead of durum semolina, particularly among Berbers.[8] Oats are not mentioned at all in these documents. Millet *(Panicum miliaceum)* is the least productive of traditional cereals, but it does comparatively well under dry summer conditions. It can be baked in small domestic ovens (called *fornet*s or *tenor*s, from the Ar. *tannur)*, without yeast, to make flat bread.[9] All these small-grained cereals had what might be termed shifting identities, with one variety easily mistaken for another—local races of pearl millet, common millet, and/or sorghum. All are sown in the spring, and their growing cycle is shorter than that of wheat.[10]

We know what kinds of cereals were grown in Christian Valencian villages of the late thirteenth century, because many were held feudally of the king in return for rent equal to one-third of the tithe *(terç delme)*. When Torró aggregated the 1263 *terç delme* figures from Borriana, Cullera, Alzira, Corbera, Gandia, and Ontinyent he found that twice as much oats was grown *(*53.8% of all cereals) as wheat (28.6%) and concludes that it was used to make poor man's bread *(pa de pobre)*, either by itself or mixed with other grains. Rice could also be made into flour for bread.[11] A letter sent 18 August 1374, by the magistrates *(jurats)* of the city of Valencia to the Governor and the city council of Mallorca states the importance of *blats menuts* ("small" or less significant cereals, identified as *paniços, dacses,* and *arrossos*) in the Valencian diet, mixed with *blats grossos* ("big" or important cereals, especially wheat, generically referred as *forments*).[12] The diversity in variety of cereals in part reveals consumption patterns, but it also reflects the willingness of cultivators—whether Christian or Muslim—to supplement wheat and barley—the primary staples—with varieties less attractive from the point of view of human consumption in order to make the maximum use of available niches. In medieval cereal culture, variety is everything.

Wheat was both dry-farmed and grown on irrigated parcels, the latter being vastly more productive. The city of Valencia imported its wheat both from abroad by ship and locally: from the southern kingdom of Valencia, drawing particularly from the wheat lands of the Xúquer river basin, currently known as "La Ribera"; from the mountain areas south of the Xúquer; to the southernmost reaches of the kingdom in the lower Segura river basin—Oriola and its huerta, known today as the Vega Baja del Segura. In the Ribera del Xúquer and Oriola, most wheat was irrigated, giving rise to impressive yields. Wheat was always grown under irrigation in the Lower Segura as the average annual rainfall there is only 200-300mm, under the minimum requirements for rain-fed cultivated wheat. Therefore wheat was always grown under irrigation there.

Valencia city was provisioned with cereals through different and complementary trade circuits. Italian (mainly Sicilian, but also Neapolitan and Sardinian), Berber, Castilian (Andalusian), and French grains reached the port (Grau) of Valencia aboard round ships and galleys of large capacity. Cereals from Aragon and Catalonia, as well as from Oriola in the south of the Kingdom, arrived at the Grau by means of small vessels.[13] Finally, grains from the mountain areas south of the Xúquer, the Xúquer basin, the Huerta of Valencia, the land frontier with Castile, and the north of the Kingdom, were driven to Valencia on the back of beasts of burden.

From their establishment, the Laws of the Kingdom (the *Furs*) focussed on the provisioning of the capital city, thus prohibiting the export of local grains and giving legal advantage to municipal agents in the acquisition of grain. Nevertheless, the subsistence crises of the fourteenth century forced the adoption of active financial policies by the city council, designed to guarantee a steady flow of grain to the public grain depot (the Almodí) and to control cereal prices. These policies included fixed or assured price contracts, interest-free cash advances (*prèstecs*) and subsidies (*ajudes*) to merchants, mechanisms that benefited the more prominent grain merchants and required the signing of public instruments or contracts. The system was completed by the distribution of small subsidies (*ajudes de menut*) to the smaller grain dealers who carried cereals from a distance of at least six leagues (33km) away from the city. The distribution of small subsidies did not require a prior contract.

The free sale of cereals in private depots called *alfòndecs* or *botigues* (or even *albercs*, households) and mills was never completely banned, although such prohibitions are recorded regularly throughout the fourteenth and fifteenth centuries.[14] Nevertheless, the system promoted the centralization of grain trade in the Almodí, where it was sold (and taxed) at controlled prices to bakers and direct consumers.[15] Municipal control of cereal trade in the city by means of its centralization in the Almodí was never fully achieved. The implementation of such a system (to support, in theory, the common welfare through controlling the price of staples, both wheat and bread) seems to have been spasmodic. In the event of subsistence crises, the city councilors ordered the closing of the small shops which were allowed to sell cereal under normal circumstances.

Internal trade within the Kingdom of Valencia, which interests us here, was in the hands of dealers specialized in wheat, called *formenters*. In the first quarter of the fifteenth century, 315 different individuals, 70% of whom are mentioned but once, held contracts to deliver wheat to the city from different areas of the Kingdom. Some scholars have taken this for the "scant professionalization of the internal wheat trade."[16] Professionalization is not the issue, however; rather, it is the small scale of business operations, and low level of capitalization, in this sphere. As we have seen, the large number of traders is just what we would expect to find in a peasant agricultural production system. Indeed, the number of such dealers in the Kingdom must have been much larger, because the 315 just mentioned were specifically persons holding subsidy contracts (*ajudes*) with the city of Valencia, not the only center of wheat consumption in the Kingdom, and representing relatively large amounts of wheat.

Although price control was still a major concern, corruption caused by the involvement of municipal officials with the beneficiaries of the system, as well as the interference of the king, created a spiral of over-importation of cereals and public indebtedness that increased the tax burden supported by the commoners. The public debt charged to finance the acquisition of grain was paid by means of taxes on consumption (including the grain whose acquisition was ordered by the city council), paid by those unable to procure grain from their own rural properties, as the richer peasants, artisans, notaries and lawyers, merchants, patricians, churchmen, and noblemen did.

Flour-milling

For most of the population of Valencia, the final stage of the wheat-flour-bread cycle was a highly dispersed bread market in the hands of an impoverished class of bakers (*flequers* and *flequeres*, often husband and wife) who had to purchase wheat at the Almodí at prices set by the city. They generally did not have their own ovens and could not have earned more than a pittance. We know something of their localization in the city from litigation in 1407, when 76 bakers of golden bread sued the city, claiming that the town officials have forced them to purchase rotten grain, a byproduct of the over-stocking of cereal promoted by the municipal grain system.[17] As a point of comparison, the number of bakers of white bread in the city was limited in 1334 to eight.[18] All but the wealthiest of *flequers* were constantly in debt, because all the wheat transactions in the Almodí had to be paid in cash. They were poorly organized as medieval trades went, had little bargaining power (they had no guild), and had a larger proportion of women (around one-third in 1407) than comparable trades in the city.[19] Juan Vicente García Marsilla's study on the development and evolution of the credit market in medieval Valencia ranks the *flequers* among the professions (generally speaking, craftsmen and small merchants) most susceptible to incurring short-term, high-interest debt (*mutuum*), which he interprets as capital loans to allow small, family-based enterprises to make necessary investments such as the purchase of grain or flour by bakers.[20]

Between the Almodí and the bakeries were the grist mills that turned wheat into flour. In 1238, the Christian conquerors found no less than 100 sets of millstones already at work in Valencia and its environs.[21] The water-mills of Valencia were carefully sited on irrigation canals serving the irrigated fields that comprise the huerta landscape.[22] Well known in Muslim times, grist mills located directly on the banks of the river and independent of the irrigation systems declined after the Christian conquest, as diversion of river waters for irrigation increased.[23] The overall design of the hydraulic system of the Huerta of Valencia reconciled the maximization of water use by peasants with the development of other, mostly urban-oriented uses such as supplying power to grist and industrial mills, delivering water to drinking troughs for livestock and public baths, and even fire-fighting and complex sanitation systems. Similar arrangements can be found in the other huertas of the Kingdom: no matter their extension, complexity was the rule in the design of hydraulic systems.

Urban mills had been implicated in commerce from the moment of the Christian conquest of the Valencian region in the mid-thirteenth century. The villages of the "four quarters of the Huerta" (the Huerta districts of Campanar, Algirós, Patraix, and Russafa) were in general regalian rather than seigniorial, and the cultivators (*hortolans*) were both free men and (if holding regalian land) also citizens of the city of Valencia as well as of their own villages. From 1283, the Laws of the Kingdom prohibited the banality of mills (that is, a feudal monopoly) wherever the king's writ ran (in regal lands only, that is): "Anyone may mill wheresoever he pleases."[24] Originally many of the Huerta mills had been fully regalian, that is, they were royal property, and the grantees paid high percentages of their profits to the crown as feudal rent (typically one-third). But by the second quarter of the fourteenth century virtually all the king's mills in the Huerta had been sold by the crown to private owners, along with royal jurisdiction. From then on, ownership of these mills was technically seigniorial by a kind of legal fiction: the fief of a *senyor de molí* consisted of the mill only (the building containing the machinery, plus the land making up the property). The keystone of profit for true feudal mills, banality, was not on the table, inasmuch as the mill's lord was unable to force anyone to mill at his establishment. Royal records from the fifteenth century again record mills paying tribute to the crown in exchange for the payment of fixed and quite reduced rents in cash (*cens*), along with certain restrictions (*fadiga* and *lluisme*)—these were, however, a handful of newly-built mills, the construction of which was allowed by the crown but required no royal investment in their construction.[25] And again, the new mills could not make use of feudal monopoly or banality at all.

Milling in the Valencian Huerta soon became commercialized. Already in the early fourteenth century we find mills run by groups of investors who leased them from their lords, contracted professional millers (*moliners*) and foremen (*sobrestants de molí*), and invested to ensure a flow of grain to their mills. Usually wheat came to the Huerta grist mills by three distinct mechanisms: (1) the mill manager or foreman (the *sobrestant*) bought it directly from the Almodí, or other grain depots (*alfòndecs, botigues*); (2) the Huerta farmers and landowners (indistinctly called *hortolans, casolans*, or *parroquians*) brought their own grain (generally by virtue of subsistence farming; note that wheat was normally irrigated in medieval Valencia); or (3) it was brought to the mill by bakers (*flequers*), who made possible the availability of bread to most of the city inhabitants. The three mechanisms responded to market economy patterns, with all their opportunities and risks.

However, mill owners or mill leasers frequently bound bakers to them through loan contracts in order to ensure profitability. Such contracts, though, were illegal, because the Laws of the Kingdom explicitly prohibited mill owners from extending credit to bakers. By giving loans to bakers, mill owners ensured the creation of a wide captive market, a sort of financial re-invention of banality. Bakers were contractually forced to mill at the creditor's mill, and by controlling bakers, millers controlled whole sectors of the urban bread supply. They also ensured an increase in profits, since the loan contracts established a discount (*quitació*) of one percent in the favor of the creditor beyond the milling tax (*moltura*) authorized (and limited) by the *Furs*. Moreover, the availability of surplus grain allowed mill owners to reinforce their control of bakers, because, as Enrique Cruselles has observed, *flequers* could obtain grain from them on credit, instead of paying for it in cash at the Almodí. Moreover, wheat accumulated in the hands of mill owners as a consequence of their activities was sold at much higher prices than permitted at the Almodí.[26] By bypassing the Almodí, credit to bakers allowed millers to exceed the profit limits fixed by the *Furs* as well as to undermine municipal tax and price control policies. This generalized survey of the Valencian wheat-flour-bread cycle can be clarified by examining a particular early fifteenth-century case.

An Evil Mill Owner

Enter Jaume Perfeta, the lord of a grist mill in the Huerta of Valencia who appeared repeatedly in litigation throughout the first three quarters of the fifteenth century. He was one of the few mill owners who personally ran his own milling enterprise, rather then leasing the mill out to lessees. He was unremittingly scurrilous, fulfilling and even using to his advantage the bad reputation that millers typically had throughout Europe. The material that the court records reveal, however, provides an interesting window on the complex world of flour production in the urban world of the later middle ages, where mills, although they were seigniorial in a strict legal sense, had already completed the transition to commercial operation. Perfeta first appears in archival documentation resident in Genoa in 1411 as a Valencian merchant involved in wool trade.[27] In 1413 he bought a mill with five sets of millstones on the Algirós branch of the Mestalla Canal from the previous owner, Joan Gascó. Gascó was a noble; Perfeta was not.

Valencian water mills made use of both vertical- and horizontal-drive waterwheels, according to their use.[28] Grist mills were equipped with horizontal paddlewheels propelled by a water jet produced by irrigation-canal water rushing down a chute under pressure. In the huerta, as well as in the other large irrigated areas close to the seashore with gentle slopes and large irrigation ditches (*séquies*), pressure was obtained by means of widening the irrigation canal just upstream of the mill's intake gates (one for each chute, disposed in a battery, perpendicular to the flow of water). In mountain areas, pressure was maximized by means of storing water in a tower or vertical penstock (*cup*) with one or two chutes opened at its bottom (an *arubah*-style horizontal mill). Small *cups* can be found in some huerta grist mills, like those in the *main canals* of Elche and Ontinyent.

Vertical wheels were found in fulling mills, paper mills, and rice-husking mills. The vertical wheels of these "industrial" mills were generally undershot, mounted directly on irrigation canals, if located in a huerta where the copious, steady flow of water offset the low mechanical efficiency of undershot wheels. In mountain districts they were usually driven by overshot wheels. There were at least eight fulling mills in the Huerta in 1527, and we know of the construction and operation of a paper mill in the mid-fifteenth century.[29] Rice mills were common from the time of the Conquest (mid-thirteenth century).[30] Irrespective of the point of impact of water on the wheel, vertical mills shared the same design: a vertical wheel, with a axle or tree (*arbre*) which powered a set of hammers.[31] Such a mill is described in a document of 1357: "the rice mill, with all its apparatus, that is, with its six hammers and with its tree and wheel, and its six basins."[32] And another of 1440: "a rice mill with its great wooden wheel, and a wooden tree, which does not run except with four hammers, to crush the rice."[33] These documents are particularly significant because the mills of the huerta have been widely supposed to have been uniformly horizontal.

Vertical and horizontal waterwheels could coexist in the same mill house (*casal de molí*), or milling complex. Bernat de Ripoll bought from the crown in 1348 "a flour, fulling and rice mill" (*un casal de molins de fariner, draper e arrocer*) close to the city walls and the river Turia.[34] The mill of Joan Gascó, purchased by Perfeta in 1413, is described as a "rice and flour" mill and, many years later, a former lessee of the rice mill declared he had been forced to give up the lease because Perfeta contiually jacked up the price. He recalled storing 800 bushels (*cafis*) of rice there and having seen "millstones, trip-hammers and other apparatus," with five millstones in the grist mill.[35] That is, the mill house contained a horizontal mill of five sets of millstones, each set with a power chamber (*cacau*) with a horizontal paddlewheel below it, and somewhere else in the building a vertical wheel, most likely undershot, that powered the trip-hammers that husked the rice. How dual mills worked in practice cannot be determined. But other mills are described as "grain or fulling" (*fariner o draper*) and there is a ruined mill on the Senia River with a horizontal rig and a vertical wheel in the same building.

Operating the two mills simultaneously would have been a difficult matter indeed, since horizontal and vertical mills have different water flow requirements. By the time the litigation started, however, Perfeta ws operating the *casal* as a horizontal grist mill only.

The man who would become the most hated mill owner of Valencia had acquired his mill by means of financial engineering.[36] Perfeta become a mill owner or "lord" in 1413, when on 29 April, he purchased from the knight Joan Gascó, lord of Alcàntera, and his wife the "mills, one-third of the tithe, and manorial house [*real*] with its orchards and appurtenances." The property was known as the mill or *real* of "en Gascó," but also its former owners' names: "Na Mallada", "Na Gostança", "Mossén Diago de Cetina", or "En Ponç de Soler".[37] Its sale price was high, because the milling compound was located directly in front of the city's Gate of the Holy Cross or Portal Nou, crossing the Turia river. The property was worth 59,000 solidi, Perfeta received a debt instrument amounting to 39,000 solidi, and his investment generated an annual interest of 3,000 solidi. Gascó and his wife were also the objects of prosecution by creditors, placing Perfeta in good bargaining position.[38] Gascó sold him the property for just 20,000 solidi, the difference between the real price and the debt owed on the property. Moreover, Perfeta did not have to pay this amount until the trial was resolved: until that time, he only had to pay the 1.900 solidi of annual interest that Gascó paid for four other debts. A positive end of the court matter would have meant the payment of the 20,000 solidi within six months after its resolution, and of the remaining 39,000 solidi five years later. If the result of the trial was losing the property, Perfeta would had remained free of any debt.

He immediately began to do business, giving credits to bakers, and negotiating with his wheat profits. He maintained his mercantile and seafaring activities a few years more. In 1418 he was elected (along with Pere Coll) judge in the conflict that pitted the merchants Mateu Bondia and Vicent Colomer against each other. In 1419, we find him as shareholder of a galley provisioned by the knights Joan de Vallterra, Nicolau Jofré, and Joan Pardo.[39] From this year on, he focused on the milling enterprise, supplemented by his participation in credit market (*censals* and *violaris*), real estate, and slaves. He began to be called *ciutadà* (citizen) in public documents instead of *mercader* (merchant), a symbol of his integration into the urban patriciate.[40] Notwithstanding his prosperous and honorable demeanor, he mendaciously denied in 1427 that he owed 20,000 solidi to Joan Gascó's widow, saying that it was she who owed that sum to him.[41] He first appears in litigation in 1419 and was continually in litigation for forty-five years, until 1464. Here, however, we will focus on one series of eight cases between

1446 and 1450, when Perfeta took on the owner of a fulling mill (the Cathedral Chapter of Valencia, no less!), and another series between 1462 and 1464 when he sued an heir of Joan Gascó.[42]

When Perfeta bought his mill, there was no other mill between his own and the divisor which divided the current between the Algirós and Rambla branches of the river. Later on, Martí Ferrada built a fulling mill on the intervening parcel. This mill paid a rent (*cens*) to the Cathedral Chapter.[43] There is no good description of Marti Ferrada's mill but we can infer that it had an undershot vertical wheel mounted directly on the canal, while Perfeta operated his horizontal mill, with one or more channels leading from the canal through his five power chambers and back out into the river. For some unstated motive, Perfeta wanted to buy the fulling mill and began a campaign to force its sale to him. He shut the intake gates (*barbacanals*) of his mill in such a way that the water, unable now to flow downstream, flowed back in a whirlpool in such a way that the fulling mill was unable to run.[44] This episode set off a public relations battle between Perfeta and the Chapter. Perfeta had ruined the fulling mill; the Chapter retaliated by cutting down some mulberry trees he had planted alongside the canal and, at the same time, blocked the main canal with slats, in such a way that more water entered the Rambla branch at the divisor, and not enough water was left in Algirós to run Perfeta's grist mill.

Next came a dramatic confrontation between Perfeta and the Chapter's lawyer, Pere Belluga, and at one particular moment, when Jeroni Orts, a presbyter of the Cathedral, appeared with a worker who was going to re-open Perfeta's closed intake gates, Perfeta threatened them: "I know why you have come," he said, "because I have a devil in a little bottle who told me everything, because you can't do anything or plan to do anything that I don't know about!"[*]

Hearing these words, the presbyter turned to some onlookers (who happened to include a notary!) and said: "you are witnesses of what Mossen Jaume Perfeta said and what you have heard him say." Subsequently the presbyter denounced Perfeta to the Inquisitor, as a result of which Perfeta was prohibited

---

*For a number of reasons—the peculiar noises emitted by mills, because of their operation at night, the general ill repute of millers, from accidents and deaths associated with mills, and because mills were a fire hazard (see, for example, the famous Bosch diptych of Hell, which includes a burning mill)—the folklore of all European countries identify mills with devils, demons, or indeed, the Devil himself. Here, Perfeta appears to have been manipulating a popular image of millers to frighten his adversaries despite the obvious risk that such an open statement carried: the suggestion of some mental disorder or an admission of open consorting with the Devil.

from holding mass in his mill—large mills had chapels for the use of their owners, employees, and perhaps neighbors.[45] Moreover, the inquisitor had displayed
posters (*cartells*) in certain places in the city charging Perfeta with being a "bad
Christian". Still and all, the Chapter sold him the mill, putting an end to the
affair.[46] Again, he bargained well: victory in his technological war allowed him
to purchase Ferrada's fulling mill for just 6,700 solidi, far from the alleged real
price of 11,000 solidi, and free of census to the Chapter.

Mill owners were frequently parties to suits because of the potential of dis-
rupting the flow of water upstream from their intakes. In order not to interfere
with the smooth functioning of agriculture, whose use of water was prioritized
over that by millers in the Huerta of Valencia, mills were preferentially sited at
the heads of canals, either close to the diversion dam (mills located on the main
canal—*séquia mare*), at the water divisor (mills placed on large secondary feeders
of the *séquia mare*), or at its very end (mills placed in *escorredors*, collectors of the
system drainage), all areas where there were no agricultural fields. The struggle
between the Cathedral Chapter and Perfeta was complicated by the fact that the
flow of water to downstream irrigators was impeded. In this case, both branch
canals were *corribles*, meaning that water legally had to flow through them, in
effect mandating that the intake and outflow gates of the mills or their bypass
canals (*almenares* or *derramadors*—standard on Huerta mills) were always open,
allowing water to flow uninterrupted when the mill was not in operation. The
vast majority of litigations involving mills were of one mill against another or of
a mill against the commons of the canal or its officers. Eventually, some secondary canals were designed only for milling, as for example the Axera branch of the
Rascanya canal system, both to minimize conflict between millers and irrigators
and also to make oversight of mill operations more efficient.

In 1463, Perfeta, now made a nobleman, sued a noblewoman named Elvira
de Ribelles, heir of Joan Gascó, before the Civil Justice of Valencia. This action
proved to be the Waterloo of the veteran litigator, who claimed that the original contract by which he had purchased the grist mill from Gascó was invalid
because his mill had failed through want of water. He now sought indemnifi-
cation from Gascó's heirs for a sale made forty-nine years before, now claiming
the mill was worth 156,000 solidi. The witnesses confirmed that the mill had
been ruined—*desparroquiat*, they said—not through lack of water, however, but
rather owing to the foul behavior of Perfeta himself. When the mill had been in
good condition (*ben aparroquiat e feya bones faenes*), as a miller formerly employed
by Perfeta testified, "even without counting the local folk (*casolans*) who milled
there daily," the mill handled between 30 and 35 sacks of grain daily, brought

there by between 20 and 23 *flequers* (the high number confirms that *flequers* were the middlemen described by Ward).[47]   On one memorable occasion, the mill was so filled with sacks that he had to bolt (*garbellar*—to sift ground flour into grades) the grain outside the mill.[48]

With the passage of the years, Perfeta's outrageous behavior set off the chain of events that led to the mill's ruin. He employed slaves (*catius*) of very bad repute whom he provided with only bread and wine. To procure other victuals (*companatge*), clothing, and shoes they were forced to steal.[49]   Second, he was very tough on the *flequers* whose debt contracts he held. The lawyer of Elvira de Ribelles argued that Perfeta "had written such unfavorable contracts with those who milled with him that most were impoverished, and finally he had many of them imprisoned in the common jail while others fled, lost all their goods, and did whatever they could so as not to die in prison."[50] The result was that *flequers* had ceased to patronize his mill.

Perfeta also stole wheat and flour from his own clients. In 1392, the city council of Valencia explained to their counterparts in Murcia that their system for the prevention of such frauds was based on the double control of weighing grain on its way from the city to the mills, and weighing the flour on the way back.[51]   Nevertheless, Perfeta persisted in his larcenous trade. One day, a client complained to the miller, a slave named Jacomet, "Brother, how come the sacks I bring to the mill are not full [after the milling]?" The slave replied, "My friend, I won't tell you a lie," and proceeded to explain that Perfeta had forced him to "steal your wheat, because it is pretty, and he ordered me to replace it with another not so good; in addition, he had me charge you [*molturar*] twice."[52] As if that weren't bad enough, the same witness added that "the millers there moistened [*banyaven*] the grain so that the flour would look fuller and prettier. Clearly the owner of the mill got the profit and not the owners of the flour, by reason of the weight."[53]

Unfortunately, the manuscript does not record the verdict. But the fact that at the end of 1462 we find Perfeta humiliated, imprisoned in the city jail (where he used to send indebted bakers), and promising to pay Lady Ribelles 3,000 solidi in the court of the Lieutenant Governor of the Kingdom, suggests that he was finally defeated.[54]

Perfeta was a master manipulator of a legal system—that of royal justice—which normally functioned quite well. In general, when a person litigates constantly, it is because the case is weak. The strategy is to hope that the opponent will tire of paying the transactional costs of litigation and quit, which is how Perfeta won against the Chapter, for whom it was less costly to sell the mill than it was to pay the lawyers. He was ultimately defeated by his own arrogance and to the wealth of lady Ribelles, on the one hand, and to the egregious lack of merit of his case, on the other, which led the court to impose heavy sanctions indeed.

Perfeta's case illuminates one phase in the long transition from the feudal or banal mill to a fully commercial model. It is an irony that Perfeta, when he demanded the exclusive loyalty of *flequers* to his own mill, was reinventing a kind of banality using a financial rather than a legal method. The market wasn't free but tied up in a web of contractual relations—some legal, many not—among mill owners, grain dealers, flour wholesalers, bakers, and others. Perfeta's objective was to create a captive market for his services (milling) and goods (flour). If municipal justice was unable to soften the straits of *flequers* who died in the common prison as victims of Perfeta's greed, then royal justice ultimately acted in the public interest. Curiously, some *flequers* obtained royal safe-conducts, protecting them from the tyranny of the insistent miller. Ultimately royal justice proved more sensitive than municipal government to the tribulations of ordinary citizens.

What Perfeta's Case Reveals about Peasant Production Systems

The case of the evil miller Perfeta may be unique in its relatively rich documentation, but certainly the type of miller represented here would have been common in many if not all preindustrial contexts. Understanding this context, and putting it into perspective using comparative material from a roughly analogous situation, allows us to draw conclusions about how peasant production systems functioned during the transition from fully rural to urban (or urban-controlled) industrial milling.

1. Theory

Peasant markets require the services of middlemen because peasant producers lack the time and skills to market their own produce commercially. These middlemen have very small margins of profit, lack cash, and must rely on credit to purchase the produce. This situation creates a distinctive social pattern, as described by Barbara Ward, the key theorist of peasant commercial production:

> In the vast majority of cases the creditor parties to such arrange-
> ments themselves have very little capital, and the number of debtors
> they can serve is therefore closely restricted. Furthermore, these are
> nearly all arrangements of personal trust made between individuals
> who are very well acquainted with each other, and there is a limit to
> the number of individuals any one creditor can know well enough
> to trust in this way, even if he had (as usually he has not) a relatively
> large stock of capital.[55]

Rather than personal trust, Perfeta used illicit contracts to control the milling and distribution of flour. In this sense, he took unfair advantage of the low profit margins that characterize peasant commercial production systems.

2. Peasant Commercial Wheat Production in Twentieth-Century Romania

A parallel may be seen in an unmodernized context from Romania. Boston University owns the business archive of a Romanian Jewish cereals dealer named Jacob Bercovici covering the years 1908-1914. Bercovici was a regional whole-saler based in Bacau whose network of middlemen (called "cerealists") included around 400 persons, nearly all of whom were Jewish. Cerealists purchased wheat from the farmers' fields. They typically had no office or store, just a shed in which to store grain and sacks. They worked for very low commissions (typically 1%) and were habitually strapped for money (to the extent that, for example, they would rent the grain sacks and then recover them after the sale was made). They were enmeshed in networks of short-term debt, both horizontally (via extended families or the Jewish community) and vertically (having borrowed from small-town dealers or from Bercovici himself; Bercovici was constantly in court seek-ing to recover bad loans). Part of the reason why Jews were so prominent in the wheat trade throughout eastern Europe has to do with the strength of extended family networks which made them ideal agents for a commercial system that could not function without the routine, low-level borrowing (*i.e.*, usury) that is a standard feature of peasant commercial production.[56] Small-scale middlemen can have access to credit only through a highly personalized credit system. "But if credit is to be advanced only to personal acquaintances, then there is a limit— and a fairly low limit—to the number of clients any one creditor can have."[57] The system of credit, then, accounts for the multiplicity of middlemen.[58]

3. Distribution of Wheat and Flour in Medieval Valencia

Ward's general thesis and aspects of the Romanian case are applicable to medieval Valencia. *Formenters* are the rough equivalent of Romanian cerealists. The wealthier *formenters* contracted with the city. Small dealers and agents (who resemble the Romanian cerealists) received *ajudes de menut*, and it can be inferred that *formenters* collected their cereal by means of small middlemen or agents.

Some inferences also can be made regarding the functioning of the urban inner circuit of grain transformation. *Flequers*, not as bakers but as purchasers of grain and flour, also display some congruence with Ward's model: most are very modest-to-poor artisans, operating on thin profit margins, and consequently chronically short of cash and carrying burdensome debts. To finance grain purchases, which had to be paid in cash, *flequers* borrowed money from mill owners. The standard contract took this form: "[Name], *flequer*, promises to owe [to the miller] ten pounds which he has borrowed from him, promising to return them, by milling at his mill. The mill owner ought to subtract 7 pence (*diners*) from each sack of white bread flour, as is the custom."[59] These loans were normal, even though they were illegal: the *Furs* (*Fueros*, the civil law code of the kingdom of Valencia) prohibited mill owners from lending to *flequers*. Under the terms of the contract the *flequer* had to mill at the lender's mill only; if he milled somewhere else, the issuer of the contract could demand full payment. So mill owners financed (though credit) the purchase of wheat by the *flequer*, and milled the grain (adding the milling fee to the principal of the loan). The contract could then be paid off when the *flequer* sold his flour or bread. In consequence, the loans created a kind of banality or monopoly.[60]

Concluding Observations of Systems of Peasant Commercial Production

The case of Valencia exemplifies the impact of urban demand on preindustrial economies. Production takes place in small, under-capitalized structures such as family farms, stores, and businesses. Any more complex arrangements imply the penetration of capital (usually, merchant capital) into the sphere of production. Moreover, the low level of technological development forced the capture of surplus through the aggregate of small-scale actions of these low-level merchants or commercial agents. The growth of cities both stressed the system through the indebtedness and impoverishment of *flequers*, for example, and fostered the trend of the multiplication of dealers and agents as the demand rose. The same credit/

indebtedness pattern can be found in other areas beyond cereal production and trade, as, for instance, in the acquisition in advance of wool by merchants associated with textile production.[61] In a figurative sense, the city has to extend its financial web in order to capture and even generate surplus from the hinterland, in order to survive and grow. The system generated opportunities for enrichment, as well as risks of indebtedness and bankruptcy.

Notes

[1] See Barbara E. Ward's classic article, "Cash or Credit Crops? An Examination of Some Implications of Peasant Commercial Production with Special Reference to the Multiplicity of Traders and Middlemen," in Jack M. Potter (ed.), *Peasant Society: A Reader* (Boston: Little, Brown, 1967), pp. 135-51.

[2] See Agustín Rubio Vela, "El consumo de pan en la Valencia bajomedieval," in *Ir Collóqui d'Història de l'Alimentació a la Corona d'Aragó: Edat Mitjana: Actes* (Lleida: Institut d'Estudis Ilerdencs, 1995), 1:153-83; and Juan Vicente García Marsilla, *La jerarquía de la mesa. Los sistemas alimentarios en la Valencia bajomedieval* (València: Diputació, 1993), p. 101; Josep Torró, *El naixement d'una colonia* (València: Universitat, 1999), p. 149, table 1. The oblique reference to "strong wheat" reflects the transition from a Muslim wheat regime based on hard wheat to a Christian regime based on bread wheat. Muslims used a smaller-diameter millstone for hard wheat than was common for bread wheat, explaining why some mills mentioned in the *Repartiment* of València had 8 millstones whereas others had but 5 or 6; see Sergi Selma Castell, "De la construcció islàmica al casalici modern: L'Evolució del molí hidràulic valencià," in Thomas F. Glick, Enric Guinot, and Luis Pablo Martínez (eds.), *Els molins hidràulics valencians: Tecnología, història i context social* (València: Institució Alfons el Magnànim, 2000), pp. 101-63 at 110-17.

[3] *Dacsa* is a Valencian Arabism for millet, and also a synonym of *panis*; see F. Corriente, *A Dictionary of Andalusi Arabic* (Leiden: Brill, 1997), p. 181 where he identifies *dacsa* as "common panic grass", that is, panis (Lat. *panicum*), which is millet. Cf. idem, *Diccionario de arabismos y voces afines en iberorromance* (Madrid: Gredos, 1999), p. 94, where he says it is spelt, which is erroneous. After the discovery of America, the word was applied to maize: J. Corominas, *Diccionari etimològic complementari de la llengua catalana* (Barcelona: 1991), III:9-10. To complicate matters even more, the Andalusis distinguished between pearled millet *(Pennisetum typhoideum;* Ar. *dukhn)* and common millet *(Panicum miliaceum),* which they called *banij,* the Mozarabism that was to evolve into Castilian *panizo*: Abd al-Malik b. Abi l-Ala' Ibn Zuhr, *Kitab al-agdiya. Tratado de los alimentos,* trans. García Sánchez, Fuentes arábico-hispanas 4 (Madrid: Consejo Superior de Investigaciones Científicas: Instituto de. Cooperación con el Mundo Árabe, 1992), p. 48. *Sorghum vulgare* (Ar. *dhura)* was also confused with *banij (ibid.,* p. 48, n.9). The three species are closely related.

[4] There is, to be sure, one circumstance that might have hastened a change in cultivars: feudal lords may have specified in which variety of wheat they wished their rents to be paid. There is, however, no record of them having done so.

[5] See *Aigua i paisatge. El territori valencià i els recursos hídrics* (València: Universitat, 2000).

[6] Robert Sallares, *The Ecology of the Ancient Greek World* (Ithaca: Cornell University Press, 1991), p. 329.

[7] I. Ollich and C. Cubero, "Paleocarpologia i agricultura a l'Edat Mitjana: l'excavació i estudi d'un graner medieval a Catalunya," in *Actas, III Congreso de Arqueología Medieval Español, Comunicaciones* (Oviedo: Universidad de Oviedo, 1989), pp. 73-85, table on p. 81:89 grains of *dicoccum* were found; 57 of *aestivum*, 27 of *monococcum*, and 9 of other wheat species.

[8] On barley as fodder, E. Ashtor, "Kamh," *Encyclopedia of Islam*, 2nd ed. (Leiden: Brill, 1997), 5:519-20. On its hardiness, B. Rosenberger, "Cultures complémentaires et nourritoures de substitution au Maroc (XVe-XVIIIe siècle)," *Annales ESC* 35 (1980): 477-503 at 484. On barley cousous, see A. Cour and Ch. Pellat, "Kuskusu," *Encyclopedia of Islam*, 5:527-28; for Tunisia and the Moroccan Rif and Sus see Paula Wolfert, *Mediterranean Grains and Greens* (New York: Harper Collins, 1998), p. 213; for Moroccan Berber couscous, *eadem*, *Couscous and other Good Food from Morocco* (New York: Harper & Row, 1973), p. 158.

[9] Sallares, *Ecology*, p. 362; Torró, *Naixement* (note 2), p. 157.

[10] Rosenberger, "Cultures complémentaires," p. 486.

[11] This and the following data from Torró, *Naixement*, p. 149, table 1.

[12] See Agustín Rubio Vela, *Epistolari de la València medieval* (València/Barcelona: Institut Interuniversitari de Filologia Valenciana & Publicacions de l'Abadia de Montserrat, 2003), document 82 (1:196-97).

[13] On the significance of cabotage (short-haul coastal shipping), see Peregrin Horden and Nicholas Purcell, *The Corrupting Sea* (Oxford: Blackwell, 2000), esp. pp. 140-141.

[14] See Nicolau Primitiu Gómez Serrano, *Contribució al estudi de la molineria valenciana mijeval* (1928; rpt. València: Universidad Politécnica, 2001), pp. 21-27.

[15] On provisioning of grain to Valencia, see H. Rausell, D. Guillot, M. Llop, and E. Belenguer, "Movimiento secular de las importaciones trigueras del siglo XV mediante las 'ayudas' de la ciudad de Valencia," *Estudis* 2 (1974): 4-95; García Marsilla, *Jerarquía de la mesa* (note 2), pp. 23-65, 95-144; José María Cruselles, "Producción y autoconsumo en contratos agrarios de la huerta de Valencia (siglos XIV y XV)," in *Actes, I Colloqui d'Història de l'alimentació a la Corona d'Aragó. Edat Mitjana* (Lleida: Institut díEstudis Ilerdencs, 1995), 2:61-78; and Enrique Cruselles, José María Cruselles, and Rafael Narbona "El sistema de abastecimiento frumentario de la ciudad de Valencia en el siglo XV: entre la subvención pública y el negocio privado," in M. Barceló and A. Riera (eds.), *XIV Jornades d'Estudis Històrics Locals: La Mediterrània, àrea de convergència de sistemes alimentaris (segles V-XVIII)* (Palma de Mallorca: Institut d'Estudis Balears, 1996), pp. 305-332.

[16] Rausell *et al.*, "Movimiento secular," p. 20.

[17] García Marsilla, *Jerarquía de la mesa*, pp. 113-18, map of bakery stalls on p. 113.

[18] Rubio Vela, "El consumo de pan" (note 2), p. 167.

[19] See García Marsilla, *Jerarquía de la mesa*, pp. 127-28. Oven owners charged a baking commission of 4% (p. 126, n. 53). In medieval Zaragoza, the commission of resale of bread

purchased from bakers was 6% (p. 121, n. 41). If *flequers* made 4% or less on the sale of bread (whose price was fixed by the city), that would be in line with the expectations of peasant agricultural production systems.

[20] *Vivir a crédito en la Valencia medieval. De los orígenes del sistema censal al endeudamiento del municipio* (Valencia: Universitat, 2002), pp. 39-55.

[21] Vicenç M. Rosselló, "Els molins d'aigua de l'Horta de València," in *Los paisajes del agua. Libro jubilar dedicado al profesor Antonio López Gómez* (Valencia/Alicante: Universitat de València, Universitat d'Alacant, 1989), pp. 317-45.

[22] See Thomas F. Glick and Luis Pablo Martínez, "La molineria hidràulica valenciana: Qüestions obertes," in Glick, Guinot, and Martínez (eds.), *Els molins hidràulics valencians* (note 2), pp. 29-99; Luis Pablo Martinez, "Molins i batans," in Miguel del Rey, *et al.*, *Alqueries. Paisatge i arquitectura en l'horta* (Valencia: Consell Valencià de Cultura, 2002), pp. 57-65.

[23] See Antoni Furió and Luis Pablo Martínez, "Assuts i molins sobre el Xúquer en la baixa edat mitjana," in *Actes, IV Congrés d'Arqueologia Medieval Espanyola* (Alicante, 1994), 3:575-86.

[24] See "De almaceris et molendinis, et quod quilibet possit ubique molere," in *Aureum Opus Regalium Privilegiorum Civitatis et Regni Valentie* (Valencia, 1515), folio 30v.

[25] *Fadiga* was the feudal right to deny the selling of the infeudated property by the holder of the *dominium utile* to a third party, or preferentially acquire it. *Lluisme* was a percentage of the price of the approved sale discounted by the feudal lord.

[26] Enrique Cruselles found that in the first half of the fifteenth century the mill owner Jaume Perfeta sold his wheat at more than 70 solidi per bushel (*cafís*), whereas the great grain merchants sold wheat at 20-40 solidi per bushel, and prices at the Almodí fluctuated between 30-50 solidi per bushel: Enrique Cruselles, *Hombres de negocios y mercaderes bajomedievales valencianos*, unpub. Ph.D. dissertation, Valencia, 1996.

[27] See Enrique Cruselles, *Los mercaderes de Valencia en la edad media* (Lleida: Editorial Milenio, 2001), p. 167.

[28] On the recent historiography of medieval Valencian mills, see Glick and Martínez, "La molineria hidràulica valenciana" (note 22). On *molins de cup*, watermills fitted with vertical penstocks, and their significance, see Miquel Barceló's important revisionist article, "The Missing Water-Mill: A Question of Technological Diffusion in the High Middle Ages," in Barceló and François Sigaut (eds.), *The Making of Feudal Agricultures?* (Leiden: Brill, 2004), pp. 255-314.

[29] In 1283, Peter III of Aragon granted Ramon Scorna a rice mill which was built within the precincts (*in medio*) of Scorna's grist mills. Two years later, the rice mill is described as "illo casali molendinorum... vocato molendium de arrocio in Orta Valencie et in loco vocato Campanar" (Archivo del Reino de Valencia [ARV], *Reial Cancelleria*, 614, ff. 81v, 91r).

[30] In 1453, the merchant Agostino Marchesano had already built "en l'Orta de Valencia, molt prop de la ciutat, la via de Campanar... hun molí en lo qual se fahia novament paper, ço qui era una notable introducció en aquest regne, e molt gran benefici e honor a la dita ciutat e cosa pública de aquella" (Archivo Municipal de Valencia [AMV], *Manuals de Consells*, A-35 ff. 313v-314r). For Huerta fulling mills, see ARV, *Batllia*, *Plets*, 162.

[31] Husking mills, for example, needed to be vertical mills, because that operation requires trip-hammers. In the account book of the rice mill built in 1511 by the town council of Sueca were recorded "lo procehit de les picadures," as well as the amount of rice *blanquejat* (bleached): see Antonio José Mira Jódar, *Las finanzas del municipio. Gestión económica y poder local. Sueca (s.XV-XVI)* (Valencia: Diputació, 1997), pp. 178-83, 229-33. Some mills identified as *arrocers* may, however, have been horizontal mills producing *rice flour* from already husked rice.

[32] Inventario del Molí Blanc, propiedad de Francesc de Falgueres: "Lo molí de arroç, amb tots sos arreus, ço és, ab ses sis maçes, e ab son arbre e ab sa roda, e ab ses sis piles" (ARV, *Protocolos*, 2.823, no pagination).

[33] Inventory of the rice mill of Francesc de Monpaho: "Moli arrocer ab sa gran roda de fust, e l'arbre axí mateix de fust, que no lavora sinó ab quatre maces, per a picar aroz" (ARV, *Protocolos*, 2.592, no pagination).

[34] ARV, *Reial Cancelleria*, 614, f. 156v.

[35] Testimony of Joan Davó, 28 June 1463: "Moles, maces e altres arreus que y eren" (AMV, *Procesos*, 22, f. 52v).

[36] Fitfy years later, the Borgias built up their estate in Gandia following a similar pattern, that is, taking profit of the problems caused to feudal lords by credit indebtment. See José Luis Pastor Zapata, *Gandia en la baixa edat mitjana: la vila i el senyoriu dels Borja* (Gandia: CEIC, Institut Alfons el Vell, 1992).

[37] ARV, *Governació*, 2.252 (*Litium*, 1434), 13, f. 27v; Archivo de Protocolos del Real Colegio-Seminario del Corpus Christi de Valencia [APPV], 1.015, no pagination. This parcel left a considerable paper trail: in 1378, Berenguer Vicent sold the "*real* de Diego López de Cetina" to the banker Pere Llonguet (Archivo de la Catedral de Valencia [ACV], *Pergamins*, 9.223); in 1384, Diego López de Cetina sold his *real* to Guillem Ramon, on behalf of Pere de Santa Eulàlia (ACV, *Pergamins*, 9.229); in 1385, Berenguer Vicent, canon and dean of Valencia's Cathedral, bought from Pere de Santa Eulàlia, on behalf of Guillem Ramon de Soler, the *real* called 'of Diego López de Cetina' (ACV, *Pergamins*, 9.211); Peter IV of Aragon granted to his courtier, Garcia López de Cetina who was married to Mallada Martínez d'Entença, one-third of the tithe from the *alqueria* or *real* "which belonged to Ponç de Soler" (ARV, *Reial Cancelleria*, 614, f. 141r and 148r).

[38] Aimeric de Centelles was the creditor who perceived annually 3,000 solidi; and the court trial was pressed by "la honorable dona na Mallada d'Entença," widow of "l'honorable mossén Nicolau de Vinatea" (APPV, 1.015, no pagination). This mill appears to be the property contested by Mallada d'Entença, also known as Mallada de Cetina, widow of Nicolau de Vinatea (and probably of Diego López de Cetina, former proprietary of the *real*).

[39] See Cruselles, *Mercaderes* (note 27), p. 217, n.102; Miquel Batllori (ed.), *Diplomatari Borja* (Valencia: Editorial 3 i 4, 2002), 1, doc. cxxxvii.

[40] See Cruselles, *Mercaderes*, pp. 318, 338, and García Marsilla, *Jerarquía* (note 2), p. 128, n. 57.

[41] "Lo qual dix que no tenia res de la dita dona... ans que ella ha ha [*sic*] tornar a ell" (ARV, *Governació*, 4.310 [*Manaments i empares*, 1427], 1, 24r-v).

[42] On various suits involving Perfeta, see Thomas Glick, *Irrigation and Society in Medieval Valencia* (Cambridge, MA: Harvard University Press, 1970), pp. 89-93.

[43] "Item, fa en Martí Ferrada sobre unes cases e molí draper contiguus situades en la partida de les Tendetes, XII lliures; ítem, fa lo dit en Martí Ferrada sobre VIII fanecades de terra campa situades prop lo dit molí, IIII lliures XVI sous" (ARV, *Mestre Racional*, 7.923 [*Manifest del bisbat de* València, 1448], no pagination).

[44] Reply of Elvira de Ribelles's lawyer to Perfeta's denunciation, 7 February 1464: Perfeta "donà orde e manera de alçar o tenir tancats tants dels seus barbacanals del seu molí que la aygua de aquell, no podent decòrrer a avall per la cèquia tenint tancats los dits barbacanals, que la aygua de la dita cèquia feya gran regolf e umflava, per manera que la dita aygua, no tirant avall, per causa del dit regolf e umflament de aygua lo dit molí pilater de Capítol qui stà molt a prop e damunt lo dit molí del dit mossén Jacme Perfeta qui fon e és primer en la aygua de la dita cèquia, no podia fer fahena ni son lavor, segons havia acostumat fer" (AMV, *Procesos*, vv 22, f. 28r-v).

[45] The association between mills and chapels—two centers of frequent pilgrimage, whether for material or spiritual reasons—is especially visible in the association between the Molí de Vera and the Ermita de Vera, two structures still to be seen in the Huerta of Valencia.

[46] Testimony of Jeroni Ortí, 3 August 1463: "E anant ell, dit testimoni, e lo dit porter vers lo dit mossén Jacme Perfeta, ans de plegar a aquell e de dir-lli cosa alguna lo dit porter ni ell, dit testimoni, lo dit mossén Jacme Perfeta dix a ell, dit testimoni: 'ja sé perquè veniu, que hun diable tinch en una ampolleta que m'o diu tot, que escasament féu res, e ho voleu fer, que ja u se yo!;' e hoynt ell, dit testimoni, les dites rahons, giràs a huns hòmens que allí eren, entre los quals hi era lo discret en Francesch Pelegrí, notari, e dix-los: 'vosaltres siau testimonis del que diu e haveu hoyt dir a mossén Jacme Perfeta!;' de que ell, dit testimoni, denuncià a aquell dit mossén Jacme Perfeta davant lo reverent inquisidor qui lladonchs era, de que fon provehit e vedat que no s'i digués missa en lo molí del dit mossén Jacme Perfeta, com se n'hi acostumàs de dir, en temps de entredit; e aprés, per relevar escàndels e inconvenients, per intervenció de algunes notables persones lo dit mossén Jacme Perfeta volch comprar lo dit molí draper ab les heretats de aquell, de que fon concordat vendre lo dit molí draper per lo dit capítol al dit mossén Jacme Perfeta, ço que jamés lo dit capítol haguera fet sinó per rahó del fer-hi lo dit regolf que lo dit mossén Jacme Perfeta <hi féu> pensant en destrohir lo dit molí" (AMV, *Procesos*, vol. 22, 167v-168v).

[47] Testimony of Joan Pérez de Peralta, 19 July 1463: "Lo dit molí del dit mossén Jacme Perfeta era ben aparroquiat e feya bones faenes; ho sab ell... per ço com lladonchs era lo seu moliner, e veya ell... que sens los casolans, que y molien molts, cascun dia hi molien de vint-e-dos a vint-e-tres flaquers ensús, qui almenys molien cascú hun sach cada dia, e n'i havia encara de dos e tres sachs cascun dia, que pujava la suma tota dels sachs que s'i molien, ab la molta aygua que y era, de trenta, trenta-dos, trenta-tres e trenta-cinch sachs ensús de forment cascun dia" (AMV, *Procesos*, vv 22, f. 79r-v).

[48] Testimony of Joan Roger, 21 January 1464: "lo dit mossén Jacme Perfeta tenia lo dit seu molí molt be aparroquiat axí de flaquers com de casolans; e lo qual dit molí veya ell... que era axí ben aparroquiat com molí que fos en la present ciutat de València e Orta de aquella, en

tant que lo dit molí en lo dit temps stava ple de sachs de forment, que per ésser o star lo dit molí ple de sachs de forment havia de garbellar lo dit forment defora lo dit molí, com no s'i pogués garbellar dins lo dit molí, per aquell ésser ple de forment, segons dit ha" (AMV, *Procesos*, vv 22, f. 204r-v).

⁴⁹ AMV, *Procesos*, 22, ff. 108r and 121v.

⁵⁰ Reply of lady Ribelles's lawyer to Perfeta's denunciation: "Diu que.l dit mossén Jacme Perfeta, lo temps que ha tengut lo dit molí, ha tant mal contractats los flaquers qui molien ab aquell e en lo dit molí que la major part de aquells se són fets pobres e a la fi los ha executats, en tal manera que noáls ha lexats béns alguns, et a la fi ne ha detenguts molts presos en la presó comuna, et altres qui se'n són fogits de la present ciutat per por de aquell, elegint més perdre los béns e tot ço que tenien que morir en presó" (AMV, *Procesos*, vv 22, f. 8r). On prison deaths, see also *ibid.*, f. 123v.

⁵¹ Testimony of Miquel de Vilagenís, *flequer*, 29 July 1463: "Gran temps ha en aquesta ciutat se té e s'usa pes dels blats de la farina que van a moler e tornen del molí, e d'aquest pes tenim casa appartada e hom salariat per cascun any, lo qual contínuament té son pes e dóna son dret a les gents e als moliners en aquesta manera: que quant lo blat va al molí, ell lo pesa e escriu en son libre lo pes, e quant torna de molí farina passa per lo pes, e lo pesador pesa la farina, e si la troba que sia d'aquel pes que ell escriu lo blat, bé està, e si no, tramet [e]l satg a penyorar al molí o a la casa que·l moliner té ací per tal com fall del primer pes e per les messions, e paga e satisfaga al senyor d'aquella farina de ço que li fal e de les messions que fetes hi haurà" (Rubio Vela, "El consumo" [note 2], p. 161, n.27).

⁵² "Compare meu sou, que no us vull anar ab falsia; you us dich que vos dieu veritat, però no us hi puch fer pus, però avís-vos que lo senyor (dient-ho aquell del dit mosén Jacme Perfeta) me fa levar del vostre forment, que és bell, e fa-us-hi metre altre forment sotil; hoc encara queáll me fa molturar dos vegades" (AMV, *Procesos*, 22, f. 108v).

⁵³ *Ibid.*, f. 109r.

⁵⁴ ARV, *Governació*, 4.324 [*Manaments i empares*, 1462], 6, 3r.

⁵⁵ Ward, "Cash or Credit Crops" (note 1), p. 138.

⁵⁶ The Bercovici archive is part of the collection of the Shtetl Economic History Project at Boston University. It consists of approximately 4000 documents in Romanian, 3500 of which have been translated and entered into a database, and several hundred more in Yiddish.

⁵⁷ Ward, "Cash or Credit Crops," p. 142.

⁵⁸ *Ibid.*, p. 141: Two essential features of the types of credit system under discussion are: (1) the creditors themselves are normally small men with very limited amounts of capital at their disposal; (2) credit is almost invariably given without security in the full sense, simply on the personal reputation of the debtor, or rather one should say on the personal knowledge of the creditor. These two facts between them account for the multiplicity of creditors and hence very largely for the multiplicity of small-scale middlemen and retailers.

⁵⁹ A document from 1326 in ARV, *Protocolos*, 10.408 (Aparici Lappart), fol. 215v.

⁶⁰ In feudal parlance, a banal mill was one whose feudal owner could bind his peasants to mill only at his mill, and nowhere else. However, even fully "feudalized," banal mills were market-oriented. The high profits accruing from a captive market, protected from competi-

tion, produced capital accumulation that could be used for commercial reinvestment. On the commercialization of feudal mills, see the discussion of the Bazacle mills by Germain Sicard, *Les moulins de Toulouse au Moyen Age* (Paris: Armand Colin, 1953).

[61] L.P. Martínez has also detected this pattern in medieval weapons production: in times of war, the Crown has to distribute cash advances (*acorriments*) among craftsmen for them to meet sudden increases of demand; see "Guerra, Estado y organización social d ela producción. La Corona de Aragón en guerra con Castilla, 1429-1430," *Anuario de Estudios Medievales* 23 (1993): 445-71.

John Ball's Revolutionary Windmill: "The Letter of Jakke Mylner" in the English Rising of 1381

David W. Marshall (Indiana University)[1]

> *Here lies an honest miller, and that is Strange*
>
> — Epitaph of a miller named Strange in Essex churchyard

As Terence Paul Smith writes, windmills "abounded in England from the twelfth century onwards."[2] Despite their ubiquity in medieval England and their recurrence in the archaeological, historical, and onomastic records, windmills seem to be sparse in the literary record. Watermills occur here and there, the best known of which is that tended by Symkin, the conniving miller of *The Reeve's Tale*, but windmills seem to turn quietly on their isolated mounds, unnoticed by writers of the period. Of the few references to windmills that we do have, perhaps the most intriguing is the allegorical one in "The Letter of Jakke Mylner," appearing in the *Chronicon* of Henry Knighton, the monk from Leicester who penned his work in the closing years of the fourteenth century. Knighton offers one of the four most complete chronicle accounts of the so-called Peasants' Revolt that shocked the ruling class of England in early summer of 1381, and he includes in his description five letters of the rising, including the Mylner letter. Mistaking the letter for a transcription of a speech, Knighton recounts "There were twenty thousand men in this miserable crowd, their leaders being Thomas Baker, the first mover and later the chief leader, Jakke Strawe, Jakke Mylner, Jakke Carter, Jakke Trewman."[3] Knighton concludes with the text of the letters, the first of which is Mylner's. The letter imagines a windmill of four sails that are capable of turning in either a clockwise or counter-clockwise direction. The windmill, the author cries, turns in the wrong direction, and so help is needed:

> Jakke Mylner asketh help to turne hys mylne aright. He hath grounden smal smal; the kings sone of heven he schal pay for alle. Loke thy mylne go aright, with the foure sayles, and the post

stande in stedfastnesse. With right and with might, with skyl and
with wylle, lat might helpe ryght, and skyl go before wylle, and
ryght before myght, than goth oure mylne aright. And if myght
go before ryght, and wylle before skylle; than is oure mylne mys
adight.[4]

Sails and Meaning

The Mylner letter, now attributed to the radical priest John Ball, assigns each
of the four sails an allegorical significance in order to make claims about social
problems and the means by which to fix them, as scholars have explained.[5] Yet
the Mylner letter remains largely unaddressed. Only Steven Justice has discussed the socio-economic implications of the metaphor, and that only briefly.
Moreover, the extent to which Ball may be invoking the mechanics of the windmill has been entirely left out of scholarly work on the letter.[6] For example, the
movement of rotating sails implies the reciprocal movements of gears and stones
within the mill structure that might have some implicit role in Ball's appropriation of the imagery. Additionally, we must deal with the pseudonym—Jakke
Milner. As the epigraph heading this essay reminds us, millers were rarely associated with virtue. And while Steven Justice has linked the letter to the disputes over milling rights in later medieval England, his brief mention seems to
be the extent of the discussion. These unexplored avenues and the limited explanations of the letter create gaps that need filling. In the following pages, I
will explore these problems to suggest that, in the letter of Jakke Mylner, the
hedge priest John Ball drew on associations implicit in windmills and millers
to unify a potentially disparate group and posit a moral basis for the insurgency
that swept across (particularly) south-eastern England in 1381. In the process,
Ball deployed a metaphor that evoked the oppression that the rebels of the rising
sought to abolish.

"The Letter of Jakke Mylner" is one of five letters appearing in Knighton's
chronicle amidst his account of the Peasants' Revolt of 1381. Together with letters attributed to Jakke Carter, Jakke Trewman, and two to John Ball, all the
letters are believed to be pseudonymously written and are suspected of being the
work of Ball, an excommunicated priest and one of three central leaders in the
English rising of 1381.[7] It was during this rising that, according to chronicle reports, tens of thousands of insurgents rose in Kent and Essex, with others joining
them from other London-area counties. As two armies moving from southeast

and northeast, the Kentish and Essex rebels converged on London on Thursday, 13 June and exacted demands in two separate meetings with King Richard II. On 15 June, Corpus Christi Friday, Wat Tyler, Ball, and Jack Straw led the masses to Smithfield for their second meeting with the King. Tyler rode to talk with the king and was killed when, according to the various chronicle accounts, he either scuffled with John Newton (one of the king's men), seized the bridle of the king's horse, or resisted arrest after insulting the king. Upon his death, the rebel masses were put to flight. Ball fled with Jack Straw, but was captured sometime later and executed at St. Albans on 15 July. The five pseudonymous letters are believed by Knighton and most of those who study them to be texts calling out rebels to join the rising and move with Ball and Tyler on London.

That much of "The Letter of Jakke Mylner" is fairly clear,[8] but in his *Historia Anglicana*, Thomas Walsingham may have best described the Ball letters when, concerning a sixth letter now titled "Letter to the Essex Commons", he writes that it is *aenigmatibus plenam*—full of riddles.[9] Ball's letters are built around an allegorical system that seems to pick and choose from a variety of sources, known and obscure. For example, in at least two of the letters we have references to William Langland's long, shifting allegory *Piers Plowman*, which explores the demands of spiritual living in the material world of the fourteenth century via a dreamer's journey through various epistemologies of spiritual knowledge, each represented by a different allegorical figure who talks with the dreamer's alter ego.[10] Those references in the Ball letters include mention of Piers (the noble peasant laborer), Ball's Essex text pseudonym 'Johan Schep' (associated with Langland's dreamer by both Konrad Burdach and Ann Astell), mention of *dowel* and *dobet* (part of a triad with *dobest* that Langland uses to examine virtue in the active life), and potentially Hobbe the Robber, whom Burdach sees as resonant of the lazy 'wastours' of the allegory.[11] Additionally, the letters deploy conventional sermon phrases that can be found in manuals for preachers of the day, particularly "mendicant preaching manuals like Grimestone's notebook or the *Fasciculus Morum*."[12] The effect on the letters is to produce a set of cobbled-together texts exhibiting a clear moral intent but an often obscure message.

Unlike its five siblings, the Mylner letter does not derive from either *Piers Plowman* or the medieval preachers' manuals suggested by Richard Firth Green for the other letters. Green does offer two potential sources for this text: first, he posits a potential, lost poem that constructs an allegorical windmill turned by the four sails, Right, Might, Will, and Skill. While not out of the question, closer to the mark, perhaps, is his suggestion that Ball took as his inspiration *The Sayings of the Four Philosophers*, a popular medieval work that appears in the

Speculum Christiani, a collection of religious treatises, sermons, and poems that found a broad audience in the fourteenth century. In the *Sayings*, a king consults four philosophers and asks "what cause tho myshaps fellen [more] in the peple in his tyme than in tymes of predescessours."[13] Within the answers given by the four philosophers, the pairing of "right" and "might" occurs, as well as "will" and the Middle English word "rede" ("counsel", or "a plan"), which based on other lines from the *Speculum* Ann Astell argues is corollary to "skill".[14] These answers are followed by series of quotations from church fathers such as Origen, Augustine, Gregory the Great, and John Chrysostom. If we wish to preserve the prospect that Ball was inspired by a now lost poem, then that missing work must have itself been founded on the *Sayings*.

The connection between the *Sayings* and the Mylner letter forms the basis of Astell's interpretation of the windmill allegory. Her reading positions the windmill as the allegorical representation of England, correlating to the king's realm in the *Sayings*. There, the first philosopher states that the problem in the kingdom is that "Myght is ryght" and the third claims "Wyl is rede" (or "skyl"). The premise of the philosophers, then, is that that which should be subordinate has become dominant: might trumps what is right, and will overcomes good counsel. The Mylner letter, according to Astell, applies the same assessment to England, calling on insurgents to rise together to turn the state of affairs around so that all is properly ordered. As she explains it:

> The "Might" of the wealthy can no longer be "Right," but neither can "Right" by itself be "Might." Rather, "Right," understood as social justice, must be furthered by "Might" in a show of armed resistance by the peasants: ...Thus, not only does Ball offer a fourfold diagnosis of the causes of misfortune in England, but also he rearranges those same four terms to define its cure. In so doing he echoes the answer of the first philosopher, "Might is right," even as he transforms it.[15]

To unpack Astell's compact explanation, Ball's allegorical use of the windmill follows the philosophers' assessments of the realm's (or for Ball, England's) ills in what the philosophers imply is an improper inversion of the two rhyme pairs. Ball asserts, with the philosophers, that "Ryght" must lead "Myght" and "Skyl" must direct "Wyl." The cure for those ills is located, then, in reprioritizing those word pairs so that proper order is created. Correcting this problem requires causing the windmill's sails to turn in an opposite direction that privileges right and skill. This argument sets a general strategy for reform that in the *Sayings* emerges from the series of exegetical quotations and in the Mylner letter from the reiterated formulations of the rhyme pairs.

Methodologically different from Astell, Steven Justice argues for the windmill not as allegory, but rather as metonym. Justice reads the Ball letters as "elliptical" expressions that "assume that their community of address, and its interests and purposes, sufficiently define the terms of... meaning and render them comprehensible to that community."[16] Thus, Justice positions "The Letter of Jakke Mylner" in relation to milling rights as a disputed issue in the period and one of the many concerns voiced by the rebel leaders. Observing that milling rights had long been a contested issue between landlords and tenants, Justice states, "With its 'post' and 'foure sayles,' Milner's letter claims a technology more ambitious than the peasant handmill: it imagines rebels possessing a mill of their own and the lordship that milling rights belonged to."[17] This argument resembles Astell's in so far as they are in agreement that the windmill's sails are used not just to define the problem, but to give moral justification to the violence that will be committed as a cure. Justice, however, resists analysis of the windmill as allegory, and instead situates it within a materialist approach that emphasizes the real-world connections that allegory often neglects. He suggests the corrected direction of the four sails is a call for "corporate discipline" in the revolt.[18]

Justice goes on to explain the significance of the windmill's grinding small and the atonement in Christ's sacrifice by connecting the occurrence of the line "He hath grounden smal smal; the kings sone of heven he schal pay for alle" to a similar, though he says "more elaborate version" in another of the Ball letters:

> Iohan the Mullere hath ygrounde smal, smal, smal;
> The Kynges sone of heuene schal paye for al.
> Be war or be ye wo;
> Knoweth your freend fro your fo;
> Haueth ynow, and seith "Hoo";
> And do wel and better, and fleth synne,
> And seketh pees, and hold you therinne;
> And so biddeth Iohan Trewman and alle his fellawes.[19]

Justice proposes that the grinding of the windmill's stones "figures the discrimination and judgment that separate 'frend' from 'foo,' so that in Milner's letter the turning of the mill 'aright,' the communal enterprise for which he 'asketh help,' is the location and execution of enemies, the mill grinding the largest grains down to equal size." Justice, then, finds in the windmill a representation of the peasant violence so labored over by the chroniclers of the Peasants' Revolt. He concludes his explication of Mylner's windmill by offering that the mention of Christ's redemptive sacrifice asserts the rebel position that "lords will be punished (and their victims rewarded) for the lordly oppressions represented metonymically by the restriction of milling rights."[20] For Justice, then, the windmill as a metonym draws its power from the reference to milling disputes and their positioning by Ball in a synecdochal relationship to the oppressions overall.

These explanations for John Ball's windmill go far in blowing the dust off a long-used millstone to reveal the bumps and grooves in its surface. Astell offers the general logic of the allegory and Justice (and, to a lesser extent, Astell) translates the letter into the living principles that motivated John Ball and the other insurgents in 1381. What distinguishes these two is their sense of *how* the windmill represents. The problem that creates the distance between them is the tendency (or belief in a tendency) of allegory to ignore the concrete circumstances in favor of the abstract principles. Despite these individual focuses, Astell and Justice step toward each other. In asserting the allegory in the letter, Astell states that she does not "wish to deny the sign value of the letters themselves as vernacular documents."[21] Justice, on the other hand, describes the windmill's four sails as "schematically allegorical."[22] Astell argues outright and Justice implies the possibility that both levels may function simultaneously or at least parallel to each other. But the allegorical and material readings can be linked further so that the abstract religious allegory can be read as a product of real material concerns. The windmill, as a practical technology, can be invested with allegorical significance that addresses the immediate material concerns of the rebels and that proposes equally material solutions.

As with any good reading of an allegory, Astell's and Justice's clarification of the sails and their meaning opens space for questioning other elements of Ball's windmill. Two significant issues need to be addressed to gain a better understanding of Ball's "Letter of Jakke Mylner" and his use of the windmill as allegorical focus. First, is the allegory limited to the sails of the mill, or can we uncover a fuller sense of Ball's trope by examining the mechanics behind the sails? Second, the associations of milling or millers with theft are exceedingly common and enduring, to judge by the number of proverbs and other sayings that lasted up through the nineteenth century. Given that association, how should we understand the moral tone of the letter? The explanation Astell and Justice have begun can be expanded by answering those questions.

Tail-Poles and Sacrificial Toil

In the "Letter of Jakke Mylner," Ball uses the image of a medieval post mill, as the reference to "the post stande in stedfastnesse" indicates, to call all those who are discontent to rise against a corruptly administered social hierarchy that alienates most of its members from economic benefits while it perverts the workings of justice. A compact structure, the post mill was a small, perhaps 18 foot square housing set on a post. Like a sailboat that moves best when the wind strikes the sails from the proper angle, windmills function most efficiently when the sails are positioned in the correct relation to the wind. If the sails fail to catch the wind, the millstones are stationary and cannot grind the grain into flour. Too much wind, or wind from the wrong angle, and the sails can be torn free or the whole mill could topple (a rare, but not unknown occurence). To make the mill function in all breezes, then, the sail structure and housing was built to rotate upon the post, maximizing efficiency and control.

While most students of Ball's windmill seem to conflate the first line of the Mylner letter's plea for "help to turne hys mylne aright" with turning the sails, a more likely alternative is that Ball requests assistance in turning the body of the mill itself. To rotate the millhouse (called a "buck") on the post, windmills of this type were equipped with a long tail-pole, which was used to gain leverage on the heavy structure. (The manuscript record offers an example in the well-known image of the windmill from the *Luttrell Psalter*, which depicts the pole jutting off to the left of the buck and the miller's dog perched on its end.) As Smith notes, the difficulty of turning the mill into the wind required great force, often provided by hitching horses to the end of the tail-pole.[23] Since the task of rotating the buck on the post required some force, to call for help in the task is only logical for Ball. Including a tail-pole on Ball's windmill also concretizes his allegory in a way that the other reading does not. It makes possible the image of rural laborers (and even more compelling, urban artisans with them) exerting themselves as they heave against the tail-pole, re-orienting the mill and allowing it to function properly. That image emphasizes a belief in the power of communal activity. What Ball identifies as a need are stout bodies capable of performing difficult labor. The reading that the call for help in "turning the mill aright" is a reference to the sails is viable, although only metaphorically, since people do not turn the sails of a windmill. That metaphor, however, restricts the letter's allegory to an abstract level that obscures the power of labor as a conceptual model for the rising.

The inclusion of a tail-pole connects Ball's "Mylner" letter to those letters that reference *Piers Plowman*: a rhetorical move that invokes ideas of sacrificial labor and mutuality, the ideological foundation of the three estates. Mutuality as a doctrine maintains that each member of society labors for the welfare of all other members. It is implicit in the theory of the three estates, in which knights protect clergy and commons, clergy prays for knights and commons, and commons labor to provide for knights and clergy. This idea leads to a theology of sacrificial labor and idealized images of the plowman that elevate the work of agricultural labor to a special status because the plowman humbly toils for the welfare of all.[24]

Mutuality surfaces in the relationship Ball draws between Piers and the rebels who here turn the windmill when in the letter of Jakke Cartere he directs Piers to "duelle at home and dyght ["prepare" or "cultivate"] us corne" while Jakke Cartere travels with the rebels to "dyghte youre mete and youre drynke." Translated to the events of the Peasants' Revolt, we might insert the peasant army moving on London and leaving comrades home to maintain order or continue the work of farming. The implication is that each labors to benefit the other, in an image that harks back to the trope of the rural laborer enacting a sort of sacrificial activity that is mutually reinforced by those for whom he works. The relationship is reciprocal and positions the rebels as representatives of a larger body of workers. The interesting upshot of this is that we glimpse a sense of imagined mass participation in the June rising: Ball sees members of the third estate (laborer or artisan) as united in a community that is brought together by belief in shared goals and a division of labor required to achieve those goals. If we follow an understanding of the windmill that infers a reference to turning the buck, the implicit image of shared labor becomes a point of connection among the letters.

Understanding the mustering call in relation to a windmill's tail-pole also explains the problem Ball identifies in his mill and permits an extrapolation into the area of the signified. If Ball's Jakke Mylner makes a plea for "help to turne his mylne" around, then the problem in terms of the allegory is that the mill is not situated to catch the wind in the sails properly. The multiple reformulations of the rhyme pairs suggest a further problem with the mill's operation. Ball writes "lat...skyl go before wylle, and ryght before myght, than goth oure mylne aright." This sentence states that good counsel should be made to direct acts of will and that force must be used only in support of righteousness. This order, claims Ball, is the ideal that turning the windmill needs to produce. Ball indicates, however, that the sails are actually turning opposite to that ideal direction so that strong wills act without good counsel and that might makes right. Mechanically, a backwards-turning sail structure does not appear to be outside the realm of possibility. Windmills functioned most efficiently facing into the wind, with the angle of the sails, like the folds on a pinwheel, catching the wind and being pushed in one optimal direction. If the wind were from abaft, or the mill was pointed in the wrong direction (like a misguided England, where the third estate is abused), then the sails could rotate backwards, Ball's wrong way. Although a windmill will rotate backwards, it is not ideal, and indeed, parts can break or bind in this situation, so it is one to be avoided.

Turning the mill buck, then, produces the change in sail direction so that, in Ball's words, the wind will make "skyl go before wylle, and ryght before myght." Clearly, turning the mill to rotate the sails appropriately is a curative move that effects a productive change in the mill. While Justice's Marxist/materialist approach discourages direct interpretation of the allegorical significance behind this image, Astell, as recounted above, explains that Ball's logic is that the revolution must overturn the practice of "Might" making "Right" by bringing "Right" to the fore by the use of "Might," and presumably, though she does not say so explicitly, motivated by a "Wyl" that is guided by "Skyl."[25] I would like to move the discussion of that curative away, however, from what Justice characterizes as being vengeful violence, reading the references to grinding small as an expression of the desire to execute foes in an act of revenge.[26] Astell notes in a more moderate form that in an ironic twist, Ball reiterates the current problem by promoting violence or "Might" as the restorative action.

Millers' Guilt and Angels' Wings

Emphasizing the violence implicit in the letters as vengeance loses sight of the limited extent of that violence during the rising. I do not wish to suggest that there was no violent activity in the Peasants' Revolt. Certainly there was, beginning with the 30 March attack upon Thomas de Bamptoun and his sergeants-at-arms in Fobbing, the act credited with inciting the rising.[27] And for sure, Archbishop Sudbury was beheaded at the Tower as a traitor, along with John Legge.[28] Outside of London, John de Cavendish, a prominent noble and justice in Suffolk, and John de Cambridge, abbot of Bury St. Edmunds, were beheaded and made to kiss in a grisly display of decapitated heads at Bury.[29] Beyond executions of the nobility, most chronicles agree that there was violence against the Flemings in London, and as Justice, among others, has shown, the

burning of manuscripts was calculated, not haphazard.[30] But if there was violence in the revolt and violence implicit in the taking up of arms, the chronicles
tend to render that violence as mindless and roll it into a coalesced picture of the
ignoble and beastly rabble.

We need only look so far as Walsingham's description of the execution of
Archbishop Sudbury to gain a vivid understanding of just how base the insurgents (whom Walsingham in a reductivist move refers to as *rustici*) were perceived
to be.[31] Walsingham describes Sudbury in beatified terms, rendering his execution a typical martyr's hagiography. In the midst of his praise for the serene Sudbury patiently awaiting his executioners, Walsingham writes, "Words could not
be heard among their horrible shrieks, but rather their throats sounded with the
bleating of sheep, or to be more accurate, with the devilish voice of peacocks."[32]
Insurgent humanity is effaced and replaced with an image of *rustici* becoming
the animals with which they associate as Walsingham ruralizes the movement.
No attempt is made by Walsingham to explain the rebels' accusations of treason.
What I am suggesting is that the natural bias arising from the denigration of
the Third Estate precluded any rational understanding of the rebels' complaints
or what Hilton, among others, has demonstrated to be fairly targeted violence.
Hilton explains that, though violence against lawyers was "indiscriminate," other
officials who were victims of attacks "were usually singled out as individuals."[33]
While violence is included in the letter with references to "Might," an emphasis
on that violence credits biased chroniclers perhaps too much. Their alarm over
the violence and the reasons behind it (that are only minimally addressed in their
histories) can cloud understanding of what happened and of what Ball advocates
in his letter. In short, "Grinding small"—or, roughly in modern parlance, "beat-
ing to a pulp"—need not be taken as a reference to brutality against lords and
corroboration of the violence described by chroniclers.

Two other associations with the windmill and milling provide possible alternative readings of the references to grinding small and the redemption by Christ,
each moving away from what has been a focus of medieval and modern historians on the violence of the revolt. The first comes from the medieval German
poem,*Uhland*, used by George Fenwick Jones to create a context for Chaucer's
miller.[34] The second is the elaborate second illumination of the *Windmill Psalter*. Considering these possibilities has the benefit of recuperating a lost insurgent voice—a process never complete, even if we gain clear indications of it. The
problem, as I have said, is that the violence of the revolt receives great attention,
at times (particularly in the medieval chronicles) being over-emphasized, displacing any clear sense of the rebels as rational beings who brought to London

clear complaints and suggestions for how to address them, at times including violence. The violence perceived by Astell and Justice in "The Letter of Jakke Mylner," while present, is tempered by Ball's ideological framing of the rising.

The lines from *Uhland* can clarify the enigmatic sentence "He hath grounden smal smal; the kings sone of heven he schal pay for alle," and has the added benefit of reconciling problematic associations of the miller with the letter and its call for participants to rise and help a miller. In "Chaucer and the Medieval Miller," Jones positions Chaucer's miller in relation to the tradition of millers as untrustworthy social figures in the middle ages. Noting that Chaucer's miller was "a thief, lecher, bully, and mischief maker," Jones locates a long tradition of millers being connected with dishonesty and observes that "because of his strategic position, the miller was often accused of theft."[35] From out of that tradition grow the English nursery rhyme "Millery, millery, dusty soul, how many sacks have you stole?" and the proverbs "You can never tell upon whose grain the miller's pig was fattened," and "The miller's horse is fed upon the grain of others." In the literary canon, those examples include John Lydgate's assertion that were the bakers and millers to form a guild, their chapel should be built "undir the pillory."[36]

Moreover, says Jones, in his research only two references in defense of millers turn up, one of those being *Uhland*. In *Uhland* the poet writes "Why is it that so many millers now steal and say they have ground so small? I shall tell you that well: the rents are set too high for them, they get nothing out of it themselves."[37] The reference to grinding small in connection to theft suggests that millers—whose job it was to grind down grain, thereby reducing the volume of the material processed—were suspected of hiding theft by claiming that the corn was ground particularly fine to explain away a loss of volume caused by theft. This association between grinding small and theft by the miller creates a difficulty in the letter of John Ball: that connection would position a thief as the rallying point for the victims of his crimes. As a stratagem for calling out potential insurgents, Ball's letter would seem destined to fail.

That problem points to the inclusion of reference to Christ's redemptive grace in a juxtaposition that we might understand as calling on unity among the rebels. Recalling the emphasis on communal labor, we can see how highlighting wrongdoing among members of the third estate might be intentionally raised in order to banish the divisions that those private suspicions could create. We might read the first line, Jakke Mylner's call for help, as uttered in awareness of the problematic image of millers in general. Confirmation of the miller's unjust activities is confessed in the second sentence's reference to the excuse of grinding small—which may well be invoked to refer consciously to associations of theft. But the lines quoted from *Uhland* suggest that there may have been an awareness of why millers' theft was so common: the millers' oppressive obligations to the lord owning the mill necessitated illicit measures to secure a livelihood. Ball, then, may be invoking more than the typical image of the conniving miller to make a point about the shared depredations of the subservient class.

What unites the insurgents is their place in a hierarchical system that limited the benefits of resource and commodity production to the lords and landlords (such as abbeys) that had control over them. The effect of Ball's invocation is to displace blame for the millers' theft onto the lords who hold rights or toll privileges to the mills. Ball taps that location of blame in the next sentence. Ball claims that all are saved by the sacrifice of Christ: "the kings sone of heuen he schal pay for alle." By writing that "alle" will be redeemed, Ball perhaps implies that millers are not the only ones guilty of compensating for lords' oppressive demands by displacing the sacrifice onto fellows in the third estate. Recall that Justice points to disputes over milling rights as a context. With the windmill standing as an image of rural tenants' production controlled by lords, Ball suggests that discord among laborers and craftsmen emerges from harsh economic structures that maintain privileged classes on the backs of the subservient. The remainder of the letter follows logically from that. The cause of the problem given by Ball is the rendering of the windmill's sails as Right, Might, Will, and Skill, as Astell has explicated, and he claims that they spin in the wrong direction. In concrete terms, lordly might has been used to justify the oppression of the third estate, and the force of will ignores what is right thinking. Members of the third estate, says Ball, require unity to effect change.

A call for unity among insurgents who may see the rising as a chance to settle personal vendettas results from Ball's rhetorical strategy. The idea is not as farfetched as it may seem. Sylvia Frederico has demonstrated, within her argument that women figured significantly in the Peasants' Revolt of 1381, that just these sorts of personal conflicts were "settled" amid the upheaval of that summer's rising.[38] Many of these seem to be largely petty rivalries and disputes over property, suggesting that there may have been some need to call for concord among the rebels. With that information in mind, then, Ball makes of his pseudonymous miller a synecdoche. Jakke Mylner, admitting to grinding small, stands in for all those with personal or property disputes with their neighbors, disputes that create local conflict and may jeopardize a mass rising.[39] What Ball highlights in his four-sail explication of their local conflicts is their shared experience of an oppressive socio-economic system, and in so doing he gives motivation not only for letting go of disputes, but for rising with local disputants against the larger foe. Reading the letter this way lends support to Justice's argument that Ball makes a call for "corporate discipline." Moreover, while force remains an implicit part of the agenda in the formulation that Might will support Right, this reading liberates the letter from the vengeful, retributive violence that Justice locates in the grinding down of lords to smaller size and replaces it with an emphasis on unity in the face of shared oppression.

Alternatively, we can add to Ball's "elliptical" style of the first few sentences a possible allegorical tradition of windmills as symbols of righteousness and wisdom by looking at the *Windmill Psalter*. Pierpont Morgan Library MS M.102 features a peculiar illumination from which the manuscript takes its name. Four images are drawn in the second letter, 'e', of the "beatus" that begins Psalm 1. Within the top half of the 'e' sits Solomon, "seated with his legs crossed on a faldstool and holding an upright sword in an attitude typical of the ruler as judge,"[40] pointing to the second element, a vignette of a soldier ready to halve an infant held by each of two claimant mothers. Above Solomon in the image is the windmill that lends the psalter its name, and below him is an angel, appearing to have swooped past the windmill and through the judgment. Adelaide Bennett has analyzed the illumination to draw these components in relation to one another in an interesting combination that suggests the windmill to be the working of Solomon's justice made to turn by the angel. Bennett explains that the angel signifies not just the wisdom of Solomon, a gift from God above, but also the wind, associated with the Holy Spirit by Ambrose and other medieval theologians, which turns the sails of the mill.[41] She writes, "The angel powering the windmill thus becomes the visual manifestation of the Holy Spirit of Wisdom, inspiring the wisdom for which Solomon became legendary."[42] The angel also produces the wind that blows the dust of milling away, leaving only the wheat. The windmill signifies Solomon's God-given wisdom, which, as Bennett points out, allows him to tell false from true.

As the pseudonymous miller, then, Ball identifies himself as one adept at discerning true from false, and in his grinding small he indicates that he has done so. Grinding small, making that discernment, may have two resonances. First, Ball may claim insight into the particular ills of England. This option has logic to it, since the repeated permutations of the order of the four named sails seem to assess the country's problem. Ball, if we take this option, claims to have special insight into England's current situation. Importantly, that insight is divinely given. To declare Godly inspiration in locating not just the problems that cause England to decline but also their solutions, Ball gives the insurgents a divine mandate to rise. In rising against the first and second estates, they do not defy some religiously defined social order: they repair that order for He who established it. God becomes the agent behind the rising, and thus any "wrongs' committed to effect change are atoned for under Christ's sacrifice. This reading reinforces Astell's assignation of the windmill as representing England and Ball's ideal ordering of the sails as the cure for what ails it, but the reading sees him locate himself as a prophet sharing out God's wisdom.

Alternatively, given that Bennett makes specific association between discerning truth/falsehood and Ambrose's interpretation of Psalm 1:4-5, in which he claims that, like wind carrying away the dust, the wicked will be swept away, Ball's grinding small may refer to the identification of individuals who are false—those lords who abuse their authority over the third estate—and an exercise in justice to reform England by turning the mill around.[43] Recall the proverb "the wheels of justice grind slow but small," which claims that justice works slowly, but extracts the truth in the end. In the Solomon story depicted in the *Windmill Psalter*, Solomon discovers the lying claimant by ordering that the baby be cut in half. When one mother gives up her claim, Solomon knows her to be the true mother, and the other to be false. As Bennett explains, the situating of Solomon, the windmill, and the angel together with the scene of the rival mothers promotes the idea that Solomon determines who the wicked mother is; through his wisdom he is able to identify wrongdoers. Ball, then, if we choose to see him as invoking these associations, again casts himself as prophet or Solomon-like judge, given the ability identify those who are false.

Reading the letter this way reinforces Justice's argument that "the grinding of the corn passing through the mill figures the discrimination and judgment that separate 'frend' from 'foo,'" but whereas he claims that the reference to Christ's atonement indicates "that lords will be punished (and their victims rewarded) for the lordly oppressions represented metonymically by the restriction of milling rights," we need not assume that to be so.[44] Rather, if Ball has just established that he knows, by divine grace, friend and foe, then he gives a sense of a clear identification of wrongdoers. The foes are not a nameless class, but, as discernment would suggest, specific individuals. The chronicle record indicates that this was much more the practice, as revealed by the demands that named individuals be turned over. For example, all the chroniclers agree that when the rebels stormed the Tower in London, they demanded Archbishop Sudbury by name; and in his account of the rising in Norfolk, Walsingham claims that the rebels specifically pursued the prior of Bury St. Edmunds, John de Cambridge, who fled to Mildenhall.[45] Furthermore, rather than categorically referring the wrongdoers to Christ's atonement, the reference to "the kings sone of heuen" paying for all more likely offers absolution to those insurgents who will be executioners within the divinely revealed plan that Ball claims to carry. The net result is the creation of a figurehead. Ball locates authority in himself as God's messenger and positions himself as a rallying point. This strategy, like the references to theft, promotes order and unity among the rebels.

Connecting the Mylner letter to these other references suggests that violence need not be the organizing concept or the primary mode of understanding how Ball or the insurgents who followed perceived their activities. These readings of the first three sentences indicate that the violence we see exaggerated in the chronicles may have been seen as a more limited tool of insurrection than the chroniclers tell us—after all, history is written by the victors. These readings share a location of ideological causes motivating Ball to call for help. Not merely a band of rural laborers with an axe to grind, the rabble depicted in the chronicles are elevated to rational people with plans for effecting changes in areas that we can begin to discern from Ball's choice of allegorical signifier. The windmill, a mundane image of agricultural production, emerges as an embodiment of social concerns and the ability to address them wisely. Ball and his followers assert by their manumitting the letter that this windmill, a technology for production, is not productive and that the rising is an act of correcting the dysfunctions in mundane practices. Reading the letter this way positions Ball as preaching in the first sentences what he describes in the last: Right must precede Might. Turning the windmill presumes knowledge of the right position for the buck and its sails.

The Insurgent Sense of Oppression

We have seen that the windmill was a powerful choice for Ball for several reasons: First, it allowed him to invoke ideas of unifying, sacrificial labor implicit in the doctrine of mutuality; second, the windmill could evoke potential local rivalries that can be erased to further promote unity, while at the same time justifying the rising within the rhetoric of a divine mandate; third, it likely promoted belief in the vision of the rebel leaders and provided a means of ordering the insurgent masses. A final reason for the windmill's effectiveness as a signifier flows from its linking the mill as a site of production with the perception of it as a place of oppression. The power of Ball's metaphor here lies in its invocation of the mill's mechanics, which cannot be raised without some implicit connection to the audience, who would understand the mill to be a site of agricultural production, perhaps even commodity production.

While the mill would have been a common sight and important element of medieval culture, both rural and urban, its purpose in producing sustenance would resonate for a people who depended on that production for survival. After all, it is to the mill that agrarian laborers would carry their harvest to convert it from raw materials into processed goods—flour—that could be used for bread. The Mylner letter thus taps the desire of the rebels to have an increased stake in that production, as Justice explains.[46] Moreover, the chroniclers agree that one of the demands made by Wat Tyler on behalf of the insurgents was the abolition of serfdom. Within the Marxist perspective used so productively by Hilton and Justice to expand understanding of the 1381 rising, we can see that this demand to eliminate bondage would have the result of creating an increased class of third estate members who have an interest in production and the benefits of being a part of that process or benefitting from it to a greater extent.

Most often rising from a mound, the windmill would have been an integral part of the landscape, associated with the rural labor undertaken by England's largest group, the third estate. However, the windmill was also a point of contact between landlord (lord or abbey) and the laborers as tenants or servants. Milling rights were typically owned by the landlord, and as noted above, Justice observes that they were a long-running source of conflict. The miller was obliged to deliver tolls to the landlord, often rendered as a portion of the grain produced by the mill, a practice to which the poet of *Uhland* attributes the miller's bad reputation. This rural landmark, then, becomes an easily imagined point of conflict: the socio-economic system by which the lords bilk tenants of quantities of their sustenance through a middleman. The windmill becomes an image of the lord's motte in miniature, to which the tenants are beholden. According to Ball, the system is flawed. Ball, like a miller, converts the raw materials of manpower into insurgents ready to challenge the authority of the empowered landholders, be they lords or abbots.

Returning to the mechanics of Ball's allegorical windmill illustrates this point. The Mylner letter suggests that the sails are turning in the wrong direction, not an impossibility on the medieval post mill. If the wind were to come from abaft of the windmill, then the sails would turn less efficiently, considering that the millhouse would obstruct wind flow into the sails as they dipped behind it. Concomitantly, the mill's gears would reverse, turning the millstones opposite to their intended direction. While reversing the gears might have resulted in breaking or binding within the mill, turning the sails "backwards" would at least have caused potential problems for the production of flour. First, wind power decreased by the buck's obstruction would likely slow the stones and, as a result, the rate at which corn could be ground. Second, should the stones turn "backwards," a chance exists that the center hole could clog as grain would back up into it, further hampering production. The improper turning of the sails very likely leads to a pointless or even endangered mill, as Ball—and most anyone who might have an opportunity to observe a windmill—would be aware. One need see only that the entire mill is turned to become aware that the turning promotes better operation.

When we consider that the labor statutes were still a contentious issue in their limiting of the third estate's ability to demand a price for services or goods (in the case of artisans), we can identify why Ball may see the social system turning backward, as decried by the Mylner letter. In the statute of 1351, carters and plowmen are limited to wages customary four to five years prior. Agrarian laborers are prevented from earning more than 1d a day for weeding and haymaking, 5d a day for mowing, and 2½d a day for threshing. Artisans are restricted to selling only those goods that had been customary in 1346-7 and at rates that were standard for that time.[47] While these statutes may not have been a trigger to the revolt, their existence was considered both onerous and regressive; these, then, were certainly one reason the wind strikes the letter's windmill abaft, turning the sails backwards.[48] Furthermore, the demands made by Wat Tyler, according to the chronicles—which largely agree on the point—indicate that what was desired was freedom from villeinage and bond service. While we might think of this as simply serfdom, as Hilton has suggested, the lives of those free peasants were not much better than those of the bonded. Even free laborers owed landholders a minimum of one year's service when a labor agreement was made.[49] In short, the labor laws prevented access to the economic benefits of market economics, and Ball calls on his followers to turn the windmill into the wind to correct that problem.

Read in this context, the signifying mill, grinding small as it may, becomes a metonym in which production is reduced as the sails turn backward, blocked from the full effects of the wind by the buck or with the center hole on the millstones clogged, providing flour slowly or not at all, depriving flour from those laborers who depend on it. As Ball calls on comrades to aid him in heaving against the tail-pole, he advocates the position that the landlords hold to a dysfunctional system and systematically deprive tenants of the full benefits of production. Turning the windmill not only makes it fully productive, but also gives tenants control over their landscape and its products. The letter, then, may imply the desired outcome of the rising: equal access to the financial possibilities available in the emerging market economy of later medieval England.

We might also hypothesize that this theme of production bespeaks a concern over the misappropriattion of tax revenues for England's war efforts against France, efforts bearing little fruit for all the expense. As the initial episode of violence at Fobbing indicates, the government's tax policies were part of the reason for Ball's windmill needing to be turned. The poll tax levied at the end of 1380 to subsidize a revival of the campaigns in France was met with widespread evasion, which necessitated the commissioning of men like Thomas de Bamptoun who were charged with tracking down those who still owed payment. Interestingly, Hilton argues that it was not the payment of taxes, per se, that weighed on the rebels, but the corrupt executors of tax policies. Claiming that ordinary people "perceived the state as the king," Hilton states that the commons saw corrupt officials as the problem. He goes on to assert, "the tax-payers realised—quite correctly—that the purpose of most taxation was the waging of war against the king's enemies....The king's enemies would become their enemies, and payment of tax for what they would be taught to regard as just wars would seem to be a necessary burden."[50]

While the war effort against France may have been acceptable, popular frustration with such little progress in it may have been prevalent. W.M. Ormrod claims that "the assumption that lack of success in war could be explained by the misappropriation of supplies had clearly permeated all the taxpaying classes and probably did much to create a sense of solidarity among the various rebel groups that descended on London in June 1381."[51] John Ball's windmill, then, may also address a specific national interest in the conflict with France. The implication that the millstones are producing less flour than the people needed may point to popular concerns about the misappropriation of tax funds in wartime expenditures that fail to deliver on the investment. Similar to the concerns about domestic production, we see Ball potentially using his windmill to voice concerns about the alienation of the masses from social, governmental, and economic systems that depend on them.

What becomes clear in all of this is that John Ball saw in the windmill the symbolic power of a familiar image to embody the concerns of his audience. The effectiveness of the image grows largely from its position as a form of domestic technology. This technology implies process—the turning of sails, the turning of gears, the turning of stones—to produce a desired end. "The Letter of Jakke Mylner" takes full advantage of the implicit processes of this technology to communicate directives to potential rebels, drawing them around a single vision, just as a community would be drawn around the mill that serves them. But technology also implies utility, a fact that cannot be overemphasized. The windmill is a tool used to facillitate certain ends, the production of flour. The windmill in "The Letter of Jakke Mylner," then, is not merely a plea for participants in a violent uprising. It voices practical concerns that Ball claims must be addressed. This rising is merely the tool to achieve those ends and is not an end in itself. While I have not offered a single reading of the letter, the range of possible resonances suggests that Ball's technological signifier held enormous potential to address the full scope of rebel complaints. This allegorical and elliptical windmill turns the soft creak of sail stocks, the muffled click of gears, and the soft grinding of stones into a potent voice. The ability of Ball's quiet windmill to speak so fully to the people dependent on it makes it perhaps the strangest of all the medieval English windmills.

Notes

[1] I would like to thank Patricia Ingham for reading this essay in draft and offering her very helpful comments and suggestions.

[2] Terrence Paul Smith, "The English Medieval Windmill," *History Today* 28.4 (1978): 256-63, at p. 256.

[3] "In illa misera multitudine recensebantur xx. mille. Isti fuerunt ductores eorum, Thomas Baker primus motot sed postea principalis doctor, Jakke Strawe, Jakke Mylner, Jakke Carter, Jakke Trewman": Joseph Rawson (ed.), *Chronicon Henrici Knighton*, Rolls Series 92 (London: HMSO, 1895), II:138 [hereafter, Knighton, *Chronicon*]; translated in R.B. Dobson, *The Peasants' Revolt of 1381* (1970; rpt. London: The MacMillan Press, 1983), p. 381.

[4] Knighton, *Chronicon*, XCII: 2: "Jack Miller asks for help to turn his mill aright. He has ground small, small; the king's son of heaven, he shall pay for all. Look that your mill goes aright, with the four sails and the post in steadfastness. With right and with might, will skill and with will, let might help right, and skill go before will, and right before might; then our mill will go aright. And if might goes before right, and will before skill, then our mill is situated poorly" (pp. 138-39, translation mine).

[5] See Steven Justice, *Writing and Rebellion* (Berkeley: University of California Press, 1994), pp. 136-37, and Ann Astell, *Political Allegory in Late Medieval England* (Ithaca, NY: Cornell University Press, 1999), pp. 54-55. Both are treated at length below. Additionally, see Richard Firth Green, "John Ball's Letters: Literary History and Historical Literature," in Barbara Hanawalt (ed.), *Chaucer's England: Literature in Historical Context* (Minneapolis: University of Minnesota Press, 1992), pp. 185-86. Also see more general treatments of the letters in Konrad Burdach, *Der Dichter des Ackermann aus Boehmen und seine Zeit*, in *Vom Mittelalter zur Reformation: Furschungen zur Geschichte der deutschen Bildung* (Berlin: Weidmannsche Buchhandlung, 1926), 3:171-96; Susan Crane, "The Writing Lesson of 1381," in Hanawalt (ed.), *Chaucer's England*, pp. 201-21; Rodney Hilton, *Bond Men Made Free: Medieval Peasant Movements and the English Rising of 1381* (London: Methuen, 1973), pp. 214-15, 221-23.

[6] The two fullest treatments of the Mylner letter are those by Justice, *Writing and Rebellion* (pp. 136-37) and Astell, *Political Allegory* (pp. 51-56).

[7] Thomas Walsingham, in his account of the rising, identified Ball as the source of a letter found in the pocket of an executed rebel. Walsingham states that Ball admitted authorship prior to his execution, then transcribes the letter in the chronicle, offering us a comparison to the Knighton letters. The similarities are many, with whole sentences appearing verbatim in the Walsingham letter and the Knighton letters. This fact leads many scholars to link the two letters and follow Walsingham in attributing them to Ball, who features greatly as the ideological leader of the rising in many of the chronicle sources, particularly Froissart. See Edward Maunde Thompson (ed.), *Chronicon Angliae*, Rolls Series 28 (London: HMSO, 1874), 2:33-34; Dobson, *The Peasants' Revolt*, pp. 380-81.

[8] This statement deserves some qualification. The letters have been traditionally regarded as puzzling texts that obscure their intent. Ronan describes the use of allegory, clearly in the *Piers Plowman* tradition, as being an anti-allegory, used not "to expound complex spiritual truth, but to exclude the unwanted reader and evade censorship": Nick Ronan, "1381, Writing in Revolt: Signs of Confederacy in the Chronicle Accounts of the English Rising," *Forum for Modern Language Studies* 25.4 (1989): 304-14 at p. 306.

[9] Walsingham, *Chronicon Angliae*, 2:33. This letter is the sixth and last of the letters suspected to be written by John Ball. As to the reliability of this attribution, most scholars accept Walsingham and Knighton's assignation to Ball based on the similarity of the texts and the shared attribution to him.

[10] The Ball letters offer perhaps the earliest example of reception of Langland's *Piers Plowman*. Langland revised his poem multiple times, producing a complex textual tradition for the work. Notably, one revision may have been made as a response to the use of the work in the Ball letters, which took the abstract allegory and read it as direct social complaint. As Astell puts it, "When estates satire and complaint take place within a dream vision, that contextualization can turn proverbial wisdom into something more. Indeed, it can transform a seemingly timeless moral observation about human folly and vice into a veiled reference to living persons and topical events": *Political Allegory*, p. 51.

[11] Burdach offers arguments for the presence of no fewer than five evocations of Langland's *Piers Plowman*, claiming that in addition to the above listed items, the letters' emphasis on righteous labor is an appropriation of one of Langland's central ideas: "Der Dichter" (note 5), pp. 171-202. Astell has also productively treated the echoes and Ball's appropriation of Langland; see *Political Allegory*, pp. 57-59.

[12] Green, "John Ball's Letters" (note 5), p. 191. Grimestone's notebook is British Library MS Harley 2316.

[13] Gustaf Holmstedt (ed.), *Speculum Christiani: a Middle English Religious Treatise of the fourteenth century*, EETS o.s. 182 (London: Oxford University Press, 1933), p. 124.

[14] *Ibid.*, p. 130; Astell makes an incontestable argument for the connections between Ball's Mylner letter and the *Sayings*. For a full explanation, see *Political Allegory*, pp. 51-56.

[15] Astell, *Political Allegory*, p. 55.

[16] Justice, *Writing and Rebellion* (note 5), p. 130.

[17] *Ibid.*, p. 137. Justice's reference to handmills invokes an earlier discussion of the conflict at St. Albans between the monastery, which held milling rights, and the insurgents, who broke into the monastery and reclaimed the stones of handmills that had been seized by an ab-

bot and used to pave an area of the grounds. The rebels broke the millstones into small pieces, sharing them out to be worn around the neck.

[18] Astell accepts this position but suggests that the letters' being elliptical "does not preclude their being full of riddles; rather it defines the very nature of their allegory as a concealment to some and a communication to others." See Justice, *Writing and Rebellion*, p. 130; Astell, p. 47.

[19] Walsingham, *Chronicon Angliae* (note 7), 2:34.

[20] Justice, *Writing and Rebellion* , p. 137.

[21] Astell, *Political Allegory*, p. 48.

[22] Justice, *Writing and Rebellion*, p. 136.

[23] "The English Medieval Windmill" (note 1), p. 262.

[24] For a full explanation of the doctrine, see Paul Freedman, *Images of the Medieval Peasant* (Stanford: Stanford University Press, 1999), pp. 20-24.

[25] Astell, *Political Allegory*, p. 55.

[26] Hilton refers to this portion of the letter, which also appears in the "Letter to the Essex Commons," as a "menacing phrase": *Bond Men Made Free* (note 5), p. 223.

[27] According to the *Chronicle Anonimalle*, when Thomas de Bamptoun came to Fobbing to collect the evaded Poll Tax, the locals refused to pay and threatened to kill de Bamptoun and his assistants. See Charles Oman, *The Great Revolt of 1381* (Oxford: Clarendon Press, 1906), p. 187; or Dobson, *The Peasants' Revolt* (note 3), p. 124. Oman was the first to translate the Old French text, and his translation serves as an appendix to his study of the 1381 rising.

[28] See in particular Walsingham's account in Walsingham, *Chronicon Angliae* (note 7), I: 459-62. Walsingham creates a traditional martyr's hagiography by casting Archbishop Sudbury as the patient victim awaiting his death at the hands of the devil's minions.

[29] Walsingham gives a short account. See Walsingham, *Chronicon Angliae*, 2:2.

[30] Justice argues that the rebels burned records related to a broad range of feudal administrative areas in order to create a void in which they could rewrite the documentary system that organized English society: *Writing and Rebellion* (note 5) pp. 38-51.

[31] The identification of the revolt only with "peasants" is mistaken given the more widespread participation of some nobles and a large number of artisans and textile workers. See Rodney Hilton's authoritative discussion of the social composition of the rising in *Bond Men Made Free*, chapter 7.

[32] Translated in Dobson, *The Peasants' Revolt*, p. 173. "Non tamen resonabant verba inter horrificos strepitus, sed replebantur guttura multisonis mugitibus, vel quod est verius, vocibus pavonum diabolicis": Walsingham, *Chronicon Angliae*, 2:460.

[33] *Bond Men Made Free*, p227. See also his "Resistance to Taxation and to Other State Impositions in Medieval England," in which he argues that "it would seem that, although at the beginning of the revolt, there were some attacks on tax collectors, more important targets at the local level were rather the justices who had been sent to punish their resistance to the tax payment": in J.-Ph. Genet and M. Le Mené (eds.), *Genèse de l'état moderne: prelèvement et Redistribution* (Paris: Editions du CNRS, 1987), p. 167. Additionally, see Nicholas Brooks, "The Organization and Achievements of the Peasants of Kent and Essex in 1381," in H. Mayr-Harting and R.I. Moore (eds.), *Studies in Medieval History Presented to R.H.C. Davis* (London: Hambledon Press, 1985), pp. 264-66.

[34] George F. Jones, "Chaucer and the Medieval Miller," *Modern Language Quarterly* 16 (1955): 3-15. Jill Mann has also usefully addressed the Miller as figure of deceit in *Chaucer and Medieval Estates Satire* (Cambridge: Cambridge University Press, 1973), pp. 160-62, 282-83.

[35] Jones, "Chaucer and the Medieval Miller," pp. 5, 10. Jones relies heavily on German sources to make his argument, but the similarities that occur between the sources he quotes and the Mylner letter suggest, as Jones argues of the connections in general between English and German traditions, that English writers/people had the same semantic field for representing the miller as a type; see pp. 3-4.

[36] "Against Millers and Bakers," *The Minor Poems of John Lydgate*, EETS o.s. 192 (London: Oxford University Press, 1961), 2:448-49.

[37] Translated by Jones, "Chaucer and the Medieval Miller," p. 10.

[38] Sylvia Frederico, "The Imaginary Society: Women in 1381," *Journal of British Studies* 40 (2001): 159-83; Frederico catalogues a series of conflicts involving women that seem to be unconnected to the agenda of the insurgency, although justices hearing the cases after the fact considered them to be part of the rising.

[39] As Franz Fanon explains in his examination of anti-colonial resistance, the native masses will war with themselves before recognizing their solidarity in the face of oppression from above. See his *Wretched of the Earth* (New York: Grove Press, 1963), p. 52.

[40] Adelaide Bennett, "The Windmill Psalter: The Historiated Letter E of Pslam One," *Journal of the Warburg and Courtauld Institutes* 43 (1980): 62.

[41] *Ibid.*, pp. 59-63.

[42] *Ibid.*, p. 62.

[43] *Ibid.*, p. 63.

[44] Justice, *Writing and Rebellion* (note 5), p. 137.

[45] Walsingham, *Chronicon Angliae* (note 7), 2:2.

[46] Justice, *Writing and Rebellion*, p. 136.

[47] *The Statute of Laborers, 1351*, translated by Dobson in *The Peasants' Revolt* (note 3), pp. 63-68.

[48] E.B. Fryde writes that the statutes of 1349-51 "continued to be enthusiastically applied" despite the lack of "machinery for effective enforcement": *Peasants and Landlords in Later Medieval England* (New York: St. Martin's Press, 1996), p. 35.

[49] Hilton, *Bond Men Made Free* (note 5), pp. 58-62.

[50] Rodney Hilton, "Resistance to Taxation" in Genet and le Mené (eds.), *Genèse de l'état Moderne: prélèvement et redistribution* (Paris: Édition du Centre Nationale de la Recherche Scientifique [CNRS], 1984), pp. 174-75.

[51] W.M. Ormrod, "The Peasants' Revolt and the Government of England," *Journal of British Studies* 29.1 (1990): 17.

The 'Mystic Mill' Capital at Vézelay

Kirk Ambrose (University of Colorado, Boulder)

The inclination to interpret historical events and natural phenomena in symbolic terms, as signifiers of transcendent truths, has long been recognized to be a hallmark of twelfth-century monastic thought.[1] Monks commonly extracted moral and theological insights from, among other things, the bark of a dog, the sparkle of a gemstone, or the gesture of a king. The guidelines governing interpretations, if any, are obscure, but there existed widespread optimism in the clarity of God's communication and in the human ability to decipher His messages, no matter how deeply encoded within the physical realm. The visible world was commonly likened to a book, the constituent parts of which, as with so many instances of writing, could reveal insights into their Author.

In view of this intellectual climate, the field of Romanesque sculpture studies has focused largely on elucidating the symbolic content of carvings that adorn monastic buildings. A representative example is a nave capital of the Sacrifice of Isaac from the abbey church at Vézelay, constructed in northern Burgundy c.1120 (Fig. 1). Art historians have typically construed this and similar carvings as more than illustrations of an Old Testament episode, as signifying something beyond their manifest content. In the case of the Vézelay capital, potential associations include the prefiguration of other Biblical events, especially the Crucifixion, or the allusion to any number of Christian rituals, including the Eucharist and the monastic tonsure ceremony. A cynic might ask what pictorial elements specifically enjoin a symbolic interpretation here. Does the oversize knife held by Abraham draw attention to themes of sacrifice often highlighted in medieval commentaries on this episode? Alternatively, might the scene allude to contemporary polemics which cast violent Jews in contrast to pacific Christians? Or, does the large, carved weapon function in part as the dramatic flourish of an artist who delights in the construction of vivid narratives, so characteristic of contemporary sculpture? Answers to these and other questions need not be exclusive, but it bears stating that Romanesque art objects rarely offer unambiguous clues as to how to read them.

Figure 1: **Sacrifice of Isaac, Vézelay.** Photo by Nick Havholm.

The problem of interpretation appears to be the core concern of another capital located halfway down the south aisle of the church at Vézelay, the so-called "Mystic Mill" (Fig. 2). That this sculpture seems to condone a specific mode of reading has undoubtedly contributed to its fame. Of the 135 nave capitals, none has been reproduced or discussed as frequently in print as this image of two men grinding grain into flour. Increasingly, the trend has been to interpret this scene as an allegory of Christian reading: the mill pulverizes the bran of the wheat to extract the core fruit as a reader should peel away the husks of transitory physical appearances to glean transcendent spiritual insights. This allegorical interpretation has become so current, reiterated countless times by tour guides and guide books, that it is easy to overlook the fact that there is little in the carving to support it. Indeed, within the course of nearly two centuries of scholarship on Vézelay, this interpretation is a relative newcomer, first articulated in 1961 by

Figure 2: **The 'Mystic Mill,' Vézelay.** Photo by Nick Havholm.

Louis Grodecki.[2] For most of the nineteenth and twentieth centuries, art historians interpreted the capital as a charming genre scene[3] or as signaling the mystical unity of the Old and New Testaments.[4] These discrepancies signal, at the very least, that the meaning of this milling scene is not transparent and deserves reevaluation. Rather than focus exclusively on semantics, considering the capital as an instance of symbolic writing, I will suggest here that it offers insight into the active viewing expected of its audience.

As the earliest surviving image of two men working a mill, the viewer cannot rely on pictorial conventions to help specify its meaning. Despite the unusual subject, the artist employed a generic mode of representation in which vagaries and ambiguities abound. To begin with the figure on the left, nothing secures his identity. The sack of grain slung over his shoulder seems more in keeping with the visual economy of the scene than an attempt to provide a distinctive attribute. The uncertain identity facing the modern viewer might have been absent for the medieval viewer, who may have been aided by painted inscriptions (*tituli*) that named one or both figures. As recently as the 1960s, silhouettes of painted inscriptions could still be seen on the borders between compartments in the celebrated Pentecost tympanum, above the central western portal of the same church.[5] While their content is now illegible, presumably they would have identified the adjacent marvels of the East, including dog-headed men and pig-nosed Ethiopians. Traces of polychromy found on capitals throughout the nave make it conceivable that *tituli* could have originally accompanied some capitals. Indirect evidence further lies in a number of capitals that include carved names, typically positioned on the abacus as in a scene of Saints Anthony and Paul sharing a meal of bread. It was common for painted and carved inscriptions to coexist within the same sculptural ensembles. If *tituli* originally identified the dramatis personae of the 'Mystic Mill', the sculptor might not have felt compelled to elucidate his theme through pictorial means.[6] Rather, he could focus his efforts on rendering the content of these works in a visually compelling manner. This might help to account for why over twenty percent of the historiated subjects at Vézelay today remain insecurely identified.

The Moses identification, typically assigned the figure to the left of the mill, rests largely on a later inscription from a stained glass window from the Royal Abbey Church of Saint-Denis. In his description of its choir, completed in the 1140s, Abbot Suger described a window that urges "us onward from the material to the immaterial, [that] represents the Apostle Paul turning a mill, and the Prophets carrying sacks to the mill."[7] The celebrated patron then transcribed the verses that accompanied the various roundels that originally comprised this window, most of which offered allegorical interpretations of pictorially rendered events from Moses' life. The pertinent one reads:

> By working the mill, thou, Paul, takest the flour out of the bran.
>   Thou makest known the inmost meaning of the Law of Moses.
>   From so many grains is made the true bread without bran,
> Our and the angels' perpetual food.[8]

The reference to the Law of Moses, a common epithet for the first five books of the Old Testament, does not make it clear whether the figure of Moses originally featured in this stained-glass panel. The only version of the window which survives is an unreliable nineteenth-century restoration that shows two prophets transporting grain to Paul, who bears down on a lever of the mill. A late eighteenth-century drawing of Charles Percier probably records its original composi-

Figure 3: **Moses and the Golden Calf, Vézelay.** Photo by Nick Havholm.

tion.[9] It features sketchily-rendered figures, perhaps transporting sacks of grain, that occupy two registers, divided by a horizontal band. This accords with Suger's introductory description, which mentions multiple Prophets. Moses probably ranked among their numbers, but this must remain speculative.

Returning to the earlier sculpture at Vézelay, a carving of the Golden Calf (Fig. 3) provides indirect confirmation of the Moses identification on the 'Mystic Mill'. On this example the patriarch stands before the idol, ready to smash the tablets of God's commandments. The figure of Moses resembles the figure pouring grain into the mill in physiognomy, hairstyle, and dress. In addition to signaling the work of the same artist,[10] these similarities suggest that the works were conceived in tandem. The theme of Jewish law fosters a typological anti-type to the spiritual reading commonly assigned to the Mystic Mill. Nevertheless, the absence of any specific attributes for the left-hand figure of the Mill means that this identification, although plausible, remains hypothetical.

The figure to the right of the mill can be securely identified as Paul by his receding hairline, an attribute that distinguishes him in countless medieval images. This convention features at Vézelay, among others, on a capital that represents the Fall of Simon Magus.[11] Along with Peter, Saint Paul features five times within the sculpture of the nave, more than any other figure. The visual stress on Peter and Paul complements their role as original patrons of the monastery, founded in 853. Much has been made of the discovery of the relics of Mary Magdalen at Vézelay in the mid-eleventh century. At this time she was added to the list of patrons of the monastery and pilgrims flocked to venerate her relics at the site. Today, scholars commonly refer to the church by her epithet, *La Madeleine*. Nevertheless, there is considerable evidence that monks continued to regard their founding patrons as equally, if not more, significant than the Magdalen in the early twelfth century.[12] Salutations in charters asserting the rights and privileges of the monastery often mention the princes of the apostles, while excluding any mention of the celebrated patroness.[13] Other monastic sources, including a collection of sermons[14] and a chronicle, are similarly silent about the saint's cult, but detail rituals associated with Saints Peter and Paul. On the several occasions that local ecclesiastical officials attempted to assert their executive authority over the community, the monks successfully prayed to these two apostles to guarantee their exemption from all governance save that of the pope in Rome.

The identification of Paul in the Mystic Mill capital accords with wider artistic and devotional trends at Vézelay, but the rendering of his figure is idiosyncratic in that he wears only a cloak that fails to cover his exposed torso and right leg. This semi-nudity has received surprisingly little commentary. Robert Pirault interpreted the cloak as an allusion to the metaphors of veiling and unveiling that permeate Paul's epistles.[15] However redolent these associations, they find little support in medieval artistic or exegetical traditions. Among the images of veiling and unveiling in Paul's writing, 2 Corinthians 3 received the most commentary during the Middle Ages.[16] This passage develops and elaborates a metaphor of Christ lifting from the face of Moses the veil that conceals the Spirit. Indeed, the book of Exodus repeatedly describes the veil that the patriarch often wore over his face. Paul seized upon this image to differentiate the quality of the relationship between God and humanity after the advent of Christ. Only a handful of medieval images incorporated the metaphor, including a frontispiece to the book of Revelation of the first Bible of Charles the Bald (Paris, B.N., MS Lat. 1, fol. 415ᵛ). In his scrupulous study of this painting, Herbert Kessler inter-

Figure 4: **Detail of the south portal in the narthex, Vézelay.** Photo by Nick Havholm.

preted the seated figure holding a veil as a composite of John, Paul, and Moses, among others, because of similarities among the facial features of these figures throughout various miniatures of the manuscript.[17] Instead of a portrait in the conventional sense, Kessler argued that the image represents the revealed face of the Bible, a notion that finds support in contemporary exegesis like the *Adversus Elipandum* of Heterus and Beatus of Liebana.[18]

Inscriptions accompanying twelfth-century works of art occasionally used veil imagery. The allegorical window of St.-Denis, already mentioned, included a panel of Christ removing a veil from the face of Moses. The accompanying verses that glossed the image read: "What Moses veils the doctrine of Christ unveils. They who despoil Moses bare the Law."[19] In at least one instance, Moses and Paul were correlated in terms of an unveiling. Among the jamb figures on the west façade of St.-Trophîme, Arles, which dates to the middle of the twelfth century, a figure of Paul holds a scroll that reads:

> The law of Moses hides what the word of Paul reveals. The grain
> given by him at Sinai has been made into flour.[20]

However, the apostle wears a full set of garments and there is no mill at Arles. While the gaping cloak of Paul at Vézelay might be interpreted in terms of a spiritual revelation, the short tunic and uncovered head of the opposing figure fail to complete the logic of this metaphor.

Further insight into the significance of Paul's nudity might be gleaned from the tympanum above the portal that gives access to the south aisle of Vézelay (Fig. 4). In the upper register of this Infancy cycle, the enthroned Madonna and Child receive the adoring Magi,[21] but the two figures on the left are unusual. It seems highly unlikely that these are additional magi, for although the Bible fails to specify their number, by the twelfth century artists and writers had long concurred that three men from the East bowed before Christ and offered him gifts. Names were invented for all three, probably first in the West in Pseudo-Bede's *Collectanea*, and their remains were translated from Milan to Cologne in 1164. In the Vézelay tympanum, the carved figure closest to Mary may be Joseph, who sometimes features in scenes of the Adoration; however, it is not clear why he bears what appears to be a gift, a detail, to my knowledge, without parallel in medieval art.[22] This figure is insignificant for the present study, but the man next to him wears only a cloak, draped about him in a fashion similar to Paul's. Nudity and semi-nudity generally signal moral laxness in medieval art, such as one of the Vézelay capitals representing personifications of the vices lust and anger. The reverse is sometimes true. Another nave capital shows the "cross-dressing" Saint Eugenia baring her torso at a trial to demonstrate her innocence from a false accusation of rape. In an inversion of traditional expectations, the saint's exposed breasts signal chastity.

Male bodies can likewise signal virtues in medieval art. Two examples suffice, both of which feature figures clad only in cloaks. In Psalter illustrations David is sometimes shown naked, an allusion to his dance before the Ark of the Covenant, performed to demonstrate his humility.[23] In several Romanesque miniatures, Job sits on a dunghill, wearing only a cloak as with a potsherd he scrapes the boils ravaging his flesh.[24] Having lost all his worldly possessions, he sits naked before God.

Medieval culture produced manifold interpretations of the human body, the meaning or significance of which was inflected in radically different ways.[25] The connotations of poverty and humility observable in images of nudes have textual parallels. Perhaps most striking is Jerome's claim that "nude, I follow a nude Christ" (*nudus nudum Christum sequi*).[26] In succinct fashion, the phrase likens the physical aspect of Christ with that of the devotee in order to bridge the gap between the human and the divine. Reiterated through the Middle Ages, the

formula became particularly popular among twelfth-century monks, part of a
wider trend toward increasing interest in the *imitatio Christi*, including aspects
of the savior's body. Peter the Venerable, who served as prior of Vézelay before
his election to abbot of Cluny, used a number of variations on the formula.[27] As
Giles Constable has argued, the substitution of terms like "pauper" and "humilis"
more or less interchangeably with "nudus" by Peter and other twelfth-century authors marks an effort connote virtues like humility and poverty.[28] Similar ideals
inspired monastic reformers during the twelfth century.

The stress on the poverty of the Holy Family at the moment of the Adoration
stands as the central theme of a sermon written at Vézelay in the 1160s by a monk
named Julian. The author imagines the scene in the manger as follows:

> *And opening their treasures, they offered him gifts* [Matthew 2:11]. See
> the great faith of the Magi: they saw in a poor and humble manger
> an infant dressed in rags, a mother poorly and humbly dressed in
> clothing that was sullied by the carpentry work of her spouse; and
> lastly they saw the father of so great a king looking filthy and re-
> pulsive because he works with his hands at dirty work. The Magi,
> I say, seeing all these things were not deceived, nor did they believe
> themselves to have been duped or misled, nor did they say silently to
> themselves, "What! This poor, common boy will become King of
> the Jews? Because of him we have endured a long voyage? How does
> someone so poor, so humble, and so vile dare to assume the honors
> reserved for kings? We regret our great travail, we are disgusted with
> the journey; at least return the gifts we have offered you." The Magi
> thought nothing of the kind, but, assured by the Spirit that gave them
> grace, they knew that this boy was royal and divine: they prostrated
> themselves, worshipped him, and opening their treasure they joyfully
> offered him gold, frankincense, and myrrh.[29]

At the beginning of this passage, the imperative "see" (*vide*) directed toward
the reader or listener conflates the vision of the audience with the seeing of the
Magi (*videbant*) that initiates the next phrase. Recurrent use of the imperfect
tense lends a sense of historical authenticity to the scene, as does the occasional
inclusion of paraphrased Biblical passages. Only the insertion of the first-person
inquam signals that many of the unfolding events arise from the author's imagination. Qualitatively there is a theatricality verging on the histrionic in this vision, as the potential for intense anger among the magi yields to heartfelt joy.
This does more than establish an empathic connection between the reader and
the characters of a story, for in this passage an imagined emotive response, rather

than a passage from the Bible, serves as the foundation for theological specu-
lation. The ability of the Magi to overlook the humble surroundings provides
crucial evidence that their recognition of Christ's divine nature must have been
fortified with a spiritual seeing, bestowed by the Holy Spirit. Ruminations on
the physical world offer insights into the divine.

The "realistic" treatment of Christ's life is a defining characteristic of Julian's sermons.[30] His reliance on vivid images, from the squalor of the manger
to the rivulets of blood that flowed at the Passion, is far from gratuitous, for the
imaginative reconstruction of the minutiae of physical aspects of Christ's life in
the author's mind lead him to religious insights. This modus operandi was far
from idiosyncratic and has been characterized as conforming to wider currents
of spirituality.[31] Reliance on vivid, often emotive, mental images characterizes
monastic thought and memory processes in a variety of cultural arenas.[32] Histories written in the cloister, for example, have been seen to mark a common desire
to make past events seem present.[33] Rather than aim to offer a rationalistic or
objective account, these texts generally describe the passage of time in distinctly
experiential terms.

It is in relation to this representational strategy that we can better understand the emphasis on corporeality on the Mystic Mill capital, from the exposed
body of Paul to the carefully-rendered bulging sacks. The attention lavished on
palpable details conforms to wider artistic trends. In her magisterial analysis of
portable wood sculptures of the Virgin and Child, Ilene Forsyth linked the increasing plasticity in the visual arts during the eleventh and twelfth centuries
with an emerging desire to experience the sacred in a decidedly tangible format.[34]
Analogous to the logic of the Incarnation, the physical presence of wooden Ma-
donnas, sculpted fully in the round, made them particularly suited to act as inter-
mediaries between the human and divine worlds. The earthy rendering of forms
in so much Romanesque sculpture need not have precluded spiritual interpretations by monks, and may, somewhat paradoxically, have encouraged them.

The piquancy of the 'Mystic Mill' imagery further lies in the central position
given to a quotidian object. The monks of Vézelay owned and operated a number
of water mills.[35] The rates charged for grinding grain were apparently considered high, as an 1137 agreement negotiates lower prices as part of a wider effort
to alleviate tensions between town and gown.[36] Given the incomplete nature of
the records, most of which were destroyed during the sixteenth-century struggles
between Catholics and Huguenots, the rates charged and the percentage of the
community's income derived from milling are unknowable. However, it seems
reasonable to infer that their desire for healthy profits was keen.

Despite the communal familiarity with mills, the sculptured representation in the abbey church does not resemble any known medieval designs of this machine. It has been suggested that a quern features here,[37] but these simple tools generally consist of two superposed millstones and lack hoppers and cogwheels, among other features. The artist has apparently reduced salient features of larger machines to produce something akin to a pictorial shorthand for a mill. Whether wind, water, or something else drives the mill is not indicated. It cannot be hand-powered, for both figures hold sacks with two hands. Nevertheless, the emphasis on machinery through distortions in scale, especially the prominent gear at left, effectively conveys the action of the mill. The grinding and pulverizing suggested here, which transforms inedible grain into nourishing flour, palpably evokes the interpretive move "from the material to the immaterial."

Before addressing medieval exegetical traditions undergirding this notion, it should be noted that some have interpreted the mill as an embodiment of the inverse of this process, the Word made flesh. Jacqueline Gréal first identified in the crossed struts of the machine's prominent beveled wheel a reference to the crucifix, and, by extension, to Christ.[38] Yet these struts tilt slightly off the vertical and horizontal axis, uncharacteristic among images of the cross. Therefore, this detail might be better understood as an attempt to convey the motion of the gear, as is the case with the closest parallel to the Vézelay capital, a miniature from Herrad of Landsberg's *Hortus Deliciarum* that dates to the final decades of the twelfth century.[39] A reconstruction of the original painting illustrates an eschatological parable that tells of two women at a mill, of whom only one is taken to heaven. Despite illustrating a metaphor articulated by Christ himself, the diagonal disposition of the four struts in this image makes no ostensible reference to the instrument of His Passion.

Supporters of a Christological interpretation often point to later images of eucharistic mills and presses. Beginning in the fifteenth century, images of agricultural machines that pulverize and transform the body of Christ into the two elements of the Eucharist became somewhat common. No comparable images survive from the thirteenth or fourteenth centuries, nor is there any clear connection between early modern and Romanesque images of mills.[40] Despite the lack of evidence for a continuous pictorial tradition, many have linked early and late examples, seeing in both a reference to the doctrine of transubstantiation.[41] While it is possible that this is so, it must be stressed that such a reading, which projects meanings backward in time, runs the risk of producing anachronisms. Consequently, more compelling for twelfth-century examples of the mill are contemporary sources, such as sermons in which the body of Christ was likened to a sack of grain, ripped apart by the action of a mill, an allegory of the crucifixion.[42]

Still, too much could be made of these texts. Metaphors of grinding grain were relatively common within medieval exegesis, often without Christological references. Indeed, it was typically the pulverizing *action* of the mill, rather than what the mill as *object* might symbolize, that drew the bulk of commentary. Many moralized the act, comparing flour or dough to the bodies of the faithful, from which the impurities of sin must be expunged. Building on an image from the writings of the Apostle Paul, Paul of Verona compared the transformation of the baptism to various stages in the production of bread, including the milling of flour from bran, *furfure*, the term used in the St.-Denis inscription.[43] The same word appears in a twelfth-century commentary, sometimes attributed to Hugh of St. Victor, that compares the casting away of sin to the extraction of flour from bran.[44]

Ambrose did much to popularize the allegory that likened the extraction of spiritual meanings from the letter of God to the milling of flour from husks of grain. In his *De poenitentia*, the mill stood for the church, which through its machinations softens the letter of the Old Testament Law in favor of a spiritual reading under the reign of Christ.[45] The contrast between Jewish and Christian modes of interpretation is developed further by the bishop of Milan in his influential commentaries on the gospel of Luke: the two women grinding flour together represent *synagoga* and *ecclesia* (Luke 17: 35).[46] Only the latter can adequately grind the grain to retrieve spiritually sustaining flour. Maximus of Turin stressed the necessity of two millstones, which he interpreted as the two Covenants, for the production of flour.[47] By itself the law of Moses grinds in vain; the spiritual food described by Paul can only be produced with the second stone of the Holy Church.

A number of twelfth-century authors articulated similar constellations of ideas. Peter Damian, Pascahsius Radbertus, Bruno of Segni, and Baldwin of Canterbury, among others, used mill imagery to contrast literal and spiritual readings.[48] Typically these authors made the distinction in terms of the Old and New Dispensations, but their principal interest lay in articulating a spiritual mode of interpretation. Some authors did not refer explicitly to a mill. In his commentary on Psalm 147, Bruno the Carthusian glossed the paean that God "filleth thee with the fat of corn" in a spiritual sense, pointing out that in this instance corn refers not the entire grain (*furfure*), but exclusively to the fruit: that is, the mystical understanding of God's word, not the literal.[49]

In addition to scriptural interpretation, the act of thinking was sometimes imagined in terms of the workings of a mill. In his influential *Conferences*, John Cassian maintains that as grindstones can grind only what they are fed,[50] so too are thoughts the product of the sensory experiences of the individual—the mental equivalent of the cliché "you are what you eat." Mary Carruthers relates this cognitive model to the Vézelay capital and imagines that as a visitor to the church walked up the south aisle, he would encounter a number of images of sin and temptation, including a personification of lust.[51] Accordingly, when the medieval viewer reached the Mystic Mill capital, he felt compelled to reform his sinful ways, to turn his thoughts away from worldly things to the Word. However, there is no evidence that visitors ever followed prescribed paths within the church, nor are there indications that an underlying theme guided the choice and placement of carved themes. Archaeological evidence points to masons working in additive fashion, incorporating whatever sculptures were readily available as they proceeded eastward in the construction of the nave. Walking down the south aisle of the church, the viewer further encounters foliate carvings, a scene tentatively identified as the education of Achilles, and one of two warriors battling, among others. As a group, these capitals do not obviously conform to any moralizing schema or to a linear notion of program. The modern expectation that artistic ensembles have a higher, consistent meaning than what is readily visible appears to have its roots in late medieval discussions of allegory.[52] Little surprise, then, that Romanesque sculptural groups have resisted scholarly attempts to discern overarching schemes.[53]

The value of Carruthers' discussion rests in its emphasis on the act of thinking, regulated and affected by the behavior of the individual. Other medieval authors, in addition to those she cites, developed similar cognitive models using the image of grinding millstones.[54] The yoking of vigorous activity with the reformation of one's behavior would have been familiar to monks, for it defined the central activity of the *lectio divina*. Monks approached their texts with gusto, uttering each word over and over in an effort to make phonic and semantic associations.[55] This was not a hollow exercise, for through an energetic engagement with the divine page a monk sought to transform himself more fully into the likeness of God's image.

Many of the capitals at Vézelay encourage a robust physical interaction with the sculpture in ways that are highly inventive in comparison to contemporary art. On a capital representing an episode from the life of Eustace (Figs. 5, 6), a galloping horse and a leash tethering a dog articulate a horizontal line that continues across the surface of the carving. At its terminus awaits the stag that

Figure 5: **Saint Eustace, Vézelay.** Photo by Nick Havholm.

will convert the Roman general to the Christian faith. The disposition of hunter and prey on opposite sides of the basket of this capital precludes the possibility of viewing the various figures simultaneously. Rather, one must move around the corners of the capital to link the various elements of the story and thereby become physically absorbed within the temporal structure of this narrative of conversion, moving from the various mundane trappings of the hunt to be arrested by the heavenly vision of the cross lodged among the antlers of the stag.

   With figures confined to its central face, the composition of the "Mystic Mill" does not encourage the viewer to interact with it in so physical a fashion. But like a number of other nave capitals, the representation of an action garnered the artist's attention. This becomes particularly evident when one analyzes examples that stand within a long pictorial tradition, such as a scene of Noah's Ark (Fig. 7). This is the sole sculpture from Burgundy to concentrate on the con-

Figure 6: **Stag pursued by Saint Eustace, Vézelay.** Photo by Nick Havholm.

struction of the ship.[56] With an ax, the patriarch chops at the sprawling limbs of a tree that threatens to overrun the composition. His son carefully weaves a wattle-and-daub wall. The vegetation, which encroaches on the figures from all sides further announces the materiality of the ark. Scores of medieval commentaries on the ark identified it as a symbol of the church or the cosmos,[57] but the focus on building finds a parallel in the writings of Gregory the Great, who often likened the process of exegesis to the act of construction.[58] In the epistle prefacing his widely read *Moralia in Job*, Gregory described a tripartite model of Scriptural interpretation:

> First, we lay the foundation of history; next, by pursuing the 'typical' meaning, we build up a structure in our mind to be a fortress (*arcem*) of faith. Lastly, by the grace of morality, we paint the structure over as with the most beautiful of colors.[59]

Figure 7: **Noah constructing the ark, Vézelay.** Photo by Nick Havholm.

Medieval authors, including Rabanus Maurus,[60] Alcuin,[61] and Bernard of Clairvaux,[62] frequently described the interpretation of Scripture through analogues
with building processes. Hugh of St. Victor encouraged his readers to internal-
ize the act of construction, to build arks in their hearts in which God could
dwell.[63]

The kinetic metaphors favored by medieval exegetes to describe the act of
interpretation might well have a bearing on our understanding of Romanesque
sculpture. In the case of the 'Mystic Mill', we have seen that there was an established tradition of defining spiritual reading in contrast to Judaic law by means
of an image of the mill. This choice of theme might seem particularly apt in
a building predominated by scenes from the Old Testament, which comprise
roughly half of the historiated capitals. Yet I argue that the capital offers something very different than a key to unlock an underlying program. As noted ear-

lier, capitals featuring subjects from the Old Testament, classical poetry, saints' lives, and other sources stand in any number of inscrutable juxtapositions: Saint Eugenia removes her tunic across the aisle from a basilisk, David combats a lion adjacent to four personifications of the winds, and so on. Regardless of the path followed through the church, the viewer encounters a disjunctive series of images that resists any attempt to adumbrate a unifying theme.

In the early decades of the twelfth century, traditional monastic scholarship failed to produce anything that resembles the sustained and unified structure of the scholastic *Summa*. It is misguided then to search for the equivalent in contemporary sculptural ensembles produced for monasteries across Western Europe. In its focus on active reading the 'Mystic Mill' suggests a more fruitful avenue of analysis. The capital enjoins the viewer to engage the carved stories as so many grains to feed the mill of contemplation. If such an active engagement was widely anticipated by medieval artists,[64] the significance of Romanesque sculptural ensembles might lie less in the discovery of an underlying thematic among constituent parts than in the recognition of the active role expected of the viewer. Not merely a passive recipient of information or preconceived messages, the interpreter participated in the construction of meaning. To pursue this, the art object, the grain fed into the mill of cognition, likewise has a determinative role. This capital thus does not seem to be an early emblem of the freedom or *jouissance* championed in a number of reader-response theories sometimes applied to medieval art.

The question then arises as to what it means to regard Romansesque sculptures as vehicles of contemplation, instead of illustrations of Bible stories or as utterances within a pictorial language. Manifold types of relations between viewers and images existed during the Middle Ages, from the veneration of icons to the didactic uses of diagrams. A chapter of that history is the use of Romanesque sculpture as a platform for ruminations, a notion that has only begun to be explored recently in sustained fashion.[65] The contours and character of medieval viewership, however faint, can be seen through careful study of the 'Mystic Mill' capital at Vézelay.

Notes

[1] See the classic study of Marie-Dominique Chenu, "The Symbolist Mentality," in Jerome Taylor and Lester K. Little (eds. and trans.), *Nature, Man and Society in the Twelfth Century: Essays on New Theological Perspectives in the Latin West* (Chicago: University of Chicago Press, 1968), pp. 99-145.

[2] Louis Grodecki, "Les vitraux allégoriques de Saint-Denis," *Art de France* 1 (1961): 24. Other articulations of this thesis include Marcello Angheben, *et al.*, *Le patrimoine de la basilique de Vézelay* (Paris: FLOHIC, 1999), 94; M. B. Pranger, *The Artificiality of Christianity: Essays on the Poetics of Monasticism* (Stanford: Stanford University Press, 2003), pp. 70-71; Donald W. Robertson, *A Preface to Chaucer: Studies in Medieval Perspectives* (Princeton: Princeton University Press, 1962), p. 290. A helpful historiographical overview is found in Peter Diemer, "Stil und Ikonographie der Kapitelle von Ste.-Madeleine, Vézelay," Ph.D. diss., Ruprecht-Karl-Üniversität (Heidelberg), 1975, pp. 296-99.

[3] Charles Bausson, *La Basilique de Vézelay* (Paris: Plon, 1947), p. 50; Charles Porée, *L'abbaye de Vézelay* (Paris: Henri Laurens, 1909), p. 66. Cf. Marcel Aubert, *La Bourgogne, la sculpture*, (Paris: G. van Oest, 1930), 3:17, pl. 40; Charles Cahier and Arthur Martin, *Mélanges d'archéologie, d'histoire et de littérature sur le moyen âge* (Paris: Poussielgue-Rusand, 1847-49), 1:150-53; Joseph Calmette and Henri David, *Les grandes heures de Vézelay* (Paris: SFELT, 1951), pp. 249-50; Chanoine Despiney, *Guide-Album de Vézelay* (Vézelay: Magasin du pèlerin de Vézelay, 1930), p. 125; Victor Terret, *La sculpture bourguignonne aux XIIe et XIIIe siècles, ses origines et ses sources d'inspiration: Cluny* (Paris: Librairie d'art catholique, 1914), p. 85, pl. 22.

[4] Émile Mâle, *L'art religieux du XIIe siècle en France* (Paris: Librairie Armand Colin, 1922), pp. 167-68. This thesis was first articulated by Pierre Meunier, *Iconographie de l'église de Vézelay* (Avallon, 1859), p. 26. It has been rearticulated many times, including Jean Adhémar, *Influences antiques dans l'art du moyen âge français* (London: Warburg Institute, 1937), p. 244; Hans R. Hahnloser, *Chorfenster und Altäre des Berner Münsters* (Bern: Benteli, 1950), p. 30; Peter Heimann, "*Mola mystica*: Wandlungen eines Themas," *Zeitschrift für Schweizerische Archäologie und Kunstgeschichte* 39 (1982): 229, 231-32; Engelbert Kirschbaum, *et al.*, *Lexikon der christlichen Ikonographie* (Rome: Herder, 1971), 3:col. 297; Francis Salet, *Cluny et Vézelay: L'oeuvre des sculpteurs* (Paris: Société Française d'Archéologie, 1995), pp. 118-19, 122, 154; *idem* and Jean Adhémar, *La Madeleine de Vézelay* (Melun: Librairie d'Argences, 1948), pp. 114, 152-53, 184. Charles Cahier and Arthur Martin come to a similar conclusion in their discussion of an inscription of Suger: *Monographie de la cathédrale de Bourges. Première partie. Vitraux du XIIIe siècle* (Paris: Poussielgue-Rusand, 1841), p. 126. In a brief formal analysis, Arthur Kingsley Porter called the capital the "Mill of St. Paul": *Romanesque Sculpture of the Pilgrimage Roads* (Boston: Marshall Jones Co., 1923), 1:139.

[5] Neil Stratford, "Romanesque Sculpture in Burgundy: Reflections on its Geography, on Patronage, and the Status of Sculpture and on the Working Methods of Sculptors," in Xavier Barral i Altet (ed.), *Artistes, artisans et production artistique au moyen âge* (Paris: Picard, 1990), 3:246. See also Diemer, "Stil und Ikonographie" (note 2), p. 441; Salet, *Madeleine* (note 4), p. 135. Lydwine Saulnier and Neil Stratford, *La sculpture oubliée de Vézelay* (Geneva: Droz, 1984), p. 77. In the eighteenth century, the Comte de Chastellux visited Vézelay and recorded the names of Saint Benedict and the Devil in his drawing of this capital in the south aisle of the church in an account reprinted in "Une voyage de touristes dans l'Avallonais au XVIIIe siècle," *Bulletin de la Société d'études d'Avallon* 19 (1878): 143-47. No trace of these letters, which were presumably painted, can be observed today.

[6] It has been suggested that the mill metaphor was so arcane that an explanatory inscription would have been needed: Stratford, "Reflections" (note 5), p. 246. There is no evidence that the capitals of Vézelay were accompanied by such inscriptions, but the trumeau figure of John the Baptist, which supports the Pentecost tympanum, features the following explana-

tory text at its base: "AGNOSCANT OM[ne]S QVIA DICITVR ISTE IOH[anne]S+ C[um] RETINET POP[u]L[u]M DEMONSTRANS INDICE XP[istu]M". In addition, the hemicycle capitals of Cluny III, produced by the same workshop, feature allegorical inscriptions on banderoles surrounding the figures. However, the currency of mill metaphors in monastic thought might have obviated the need for an explanatory inscription.

[7] "Una quarum de materialibus ad immaterialia excitans, Paulum apostolum molam vertere, prophetas saccos ad molam apportare repraesentat," in Erwin Panofsky (ed. and trans.), *Abbot Suger on the Abbey Church of St.-Denis and its Art Treasures*, 2d ed. by Gerda Panofsky-Soergel (Princeton: Princeton University Press, 1979), pp. 74-75.

[8] "Tollis agendo molam de furfure, Paule, farinam. / Mosaicae legis intima nota facis. / Fit de tot granis verus sine furfure panis, / Perpetuusque cibus noster et angelicus," *ibid.* Important discussions of this passage include Grodecki, "Vitraux allégoriques" (note 2), pp. 21-22; *idem*, *Les Vitraux de Saint-Denis, Étude sur le vitrail au XIIe siècle* (Paris: CNRS, 1976) 1:98-102; Konrad Hoffmann, "Sugers 'Anagogisches Fenster' in St. Denis," *Wallraf-Richartz-Jahrbuch* 30 (1968): 71ff; Herbert Kessler, "The Function of *Vitrum vestitum* and the Use of *Materia saphirorum* in Suger's St.-Denis," in *idem*, *Spiritual Seeing: Picturing God's Invisibility in Medieval Art* (Philadephia: University of Pennsylvania Press, 2000), p. 199.

[9] Illustrated in Grodecki, "Vitraux allégoriques" (note 2), p. 22.

[10] The problem of the number of hands active at Vézelay has never been resolved. For example, Salet believed the sculptor of the Pentecost tympanum carved these two capitals: Salet and Adhémar, *Madeleine* (note 4), pp. 152-53. In contrast, Diemer believed they were carved by different artists: "Stil und Ikonographie" (note 4), pp. 85, 102.

[11] Kirk Ambrose, "The Fall of Simon Magus on a Capital at Vézelay," *Gazette des Beaux Arts*, ser. 6, 137 (2001): 152-53.

[12] This issue is discussed at length in Kirk Ambrose, *The Nave Sculpture at Vézelay: The Art of Monastic Viewing* (Toronto: Pontifical Institute of Mediaeval Studies, 2006).

[13] Charters and a chronicle of the monastery, among others, are found in R.B.C. Huygens (ed.), *Monumenta Vizeliacensia: Textes relatifs à l'histoire de l'abbaye de Vézelay*, Corpus Chistianorum Continuatio Mediaevalis 42 (Turnhout: Brepols, 1976). Many of these documents have been translated into English in John Scott and John O. Ward, *Hugh of Poitiers: The Vézelay Chronicle* (Binghamton: Pegasus, 1992).

[14] Damien Vorreux (ed.), *Julian of Vézelay, Sermons*, Sources Chrétiennes 193 (Paris: Éditions du Cerf, 1972).

[15] Robert Pirault, *L'école du moulin: Essai sur le message d'un chapiteau de Vézelay* (Paris: Éditions Franciscaines, 1986), pp. 103-14. Citing this detail, Grodecki questioned whether Paul was in fact represented here: "Vitraux allégoriques" (note 2), n. 53. These doubts can be allayed by the figure's pronounced receding hairline. Grodecki further doubts that Moses is represented here because the figure's head is uncovered in a manner unbecoming an Old Testament figure. Yet Moses is clearly represented with an uncovered head at Vezelay on a capital representing the Golden Calf.

[16] On this issue, see the recent discussion of Brian Britt, "Concealment, Revelation, and Gender: The Veil of Moses in the Bible and in Christian Art," *Religion and the Arts* 7 (2003): 227-73.

[17] Herbert Kessler, "'Facies bibliothecae revelata': Carolingian Art as Spiritual Seeing," in *Spiritual Seeing* (note 8), pp. 149-89.

[18] "Moses veiled his face and spoke to the people in this manner. The face of the Bible was veiled from Moses until Christ, and in the end of this Bible it is revealed. John reveals that the entire Bible is one book, veiled at the beginning and manifest at the end. Which book is called two testaments, Old and New, the law and the gospels, that is, the whole Bible," trans. *ibid.*, p. 178.

[19] "Quod Moyses velat, Christi doctrina revelat. / Denudant Legem qui spoliant Moysen," in Panofsky, *Suger* (note 7), pp. 74-75. Other examples of similar imagery include a miniature, probably eleventh-century German, that contrasts Peter and Moses as respectively veiled and unveiled (Städelsches Museum, Inv. 622): Georg Swarzenski, *Die Illuminierten Handschriften und Einzelminiaturen des Mittelalters und der Renaissance* (Frankfurt: Joseph Baer, 1929), 1:4-5. An incomplete inscription on a Mosan chasse of St. Domitian, now in Notre Dame de Huy reads, "Sed velata fuit Moysi frons verbaque Legis... At postquam Xristus venit velamina cessant": Anatole de Montaiglon, "De quelques inscriptions en vers," *Revue de l'art chrétien* 1 (1890): 6*ff.*

[20] "LEX MOISI / CELAT QVOD / PAV*LI* SERMO / REVELAT / NVNC DATA / GRANA SI / NA PER EVM / SVNT FACTA / FARINA": trans. in Calvin B. Kendall, *The Allegory of the Church: Romanesque Portals and their Verse Inscriptions* (Toronto: University of Toronto Press, 1998), p. 203. Ferdinand de Guilhermy first made the association between the inscriptions at Arles and St. Denis: *Revue des Sociétés Savantes des départements* 4 (1864): 367. Mâle subsequently related these to the Vézelay capital: *Art religieux* (note 4), pp. 167-68.

[21] Gilberte Vezin points to the unusual presence of a book among the presents, also observable at Autun, and interprets this in apocalyptic terms: *L'adoration et le cycle des mages dans l'art chrétien primitif* (Paris: Presses universitaires de France, 1950), p. 21.

[22] Hugo Kehrer suggested that this is a donor figure: *Die heiligen drei Könige in Literatur und Kunst* (Leipzig: Seemann, 1908), 2:123. However, medieval artists typically feature donors holding models of a building.

[23] Examples include an eleventh-century miniature in Munich, Bayerische Staatsbibliothek, Cod. clm. 13067, fol. 18. Herbert Kessler argues that David's semi-nakedness stems from a Touronian tradition manifest in the First Bible of Charles the Bald (Paris, Bibliothèque Nationale, MS lat. 1, fol. 215v): *The Illustrated Bibles from Tours* (Princeton: Princeton University Press, 1977), p. 97.

[24] Paris, Bibliothèque Nationale, MS lat. 15307, fol. 1v; ill. in Walter Cahn, *Romanesque Manuscripts: The Twelfth Century, A Survey of Illuminated Manuscripts in France* (London: Harvey Miller, 1996), 2:fig. 156. In numerous twelfth-century examples, Job features as completely unclothed.

[25] See, for example, Caroline Walker Bynum, "Why All the Fuss about the Body? A Medievalist's Perspective," *Critical Inquiry* 22 (1995): 1-33; Suzanne Lewis, "Medieval Bodies Then and Now: Negotiating Problems of Ambivalence and Paradox," in Benjamin C. Withers and Jonathan Wilcox (eds.), *Naked before God: Uncovering the Body in Anglo-Saxon England* (Morgantown: West Virginia University Press, 2003), pp. 15-28.

[26] Lists of medieval uses of this formula are found in Matthäus Bernards, *"Nudus nudum Christum sequi,"* *Wissenschaft und Weisheit* 14 (1951): 148-51; *idem, Speculum Virginum: Geistigkeit und Seelenleben der Frau im Hochmittelalter* (Cologne: Böhlau, 1955), p. 153, n. 169; Giles Constable, *"Nudus nudum Christum sequi* and Parallel Formulas in the Twelfth Century," in F. Forrester Church and Timothy George (eds.), *Continuity and Discontinuity in Church His-*

tory: Essays presented to George Huntston Williams on the Occasion of his 65ᵗʰ Birthday (Leiden: E.J. Brill, 1979), pp. 83-91; Réginald Grégoire, "L'adage ascétique 'Nudus nudum Christum sequi'," *Studi storici in onore di Ottorino Bertolini* (Pisa: Pacini, 1972), 1:395-409; Gregorio Penco, "L'imitazione di Cristo nell'agiografia monastica," *Collectanea Cisterciensia* 18 (1966): 29-32. For the application of this formula to the female body in the later middle ages see Caroline Walker Bynum, *Fragmentation and Redemption: Essays on Gender and the Human Body in Medieval Religion* (New York: Zone Books, 1991), pp. 181-238.

[27] Giles Constable (ed.), *The Letters of Peter the Venerable* (Cambridge: Harvard University Press,1967), I:35, 224. See the commentary in *ibid.*, 2: 108-109.

[28] Constable, "Parallel Formulas," 89-90. See also Giles Constable, *The Reformation of the Twelfth Century* (Cambridge: Cambridge University Press, 1996).

[29] "*Apertis thesauris suis, obtulerunt ei munera.* Vide mirabilem magorum fidem: uidebant in alieno diuersorio et paupere forte tugurio pannosum infantem, matrem uili et plebia ueste et forte propter fabrilia fabri coniugis opera denigrata uestitam; uidebant denique fabrum illum fabrili et manuali opere ac labore squalentem tanti regis nominatum patrem. Videbant, inquam, haec omnia magi nec tamen animo conciderunt, nec se uenisse insipienter et inaniter crediderunt, nec saltem tacita cogitatione dixerunt: Hiccine tam pauper, tam popularis puer rex futurus est Iudaeorum! Propter hunc tam longam perreximus uiam! Quomodo hic ad regii pertinget honoris insignia cuius tanta paupertas, humilitas, uilitas? Paenitet laboris, taedet itineris; saltem munera quae attulimus reportemus. Nihil tale magi cogitauerunt, sed certificati per aspiratam sibi gratiam de pueri huius regia et diuina maiestate supplices procidunt, adorant, et apertis thesauris hilariter offerunt aurum, thus et myrrham": in Vorreux (ed.), *Sermons* (note 14), 1: 82, 84.

[30] *Ibid.*, 1: 21-23.

[31] Manfred Bambeck, "Zu einer mißdeuteten Stelle bei Julian von Vézelay oder der Hahn als Symbol für den Prediger," *Frühmittelalterliche Studien* 18 (1984): 662-70; B.M. Kienzle, "The Twelfth-Century Monastic Sermon," in B.M. Kienzle (ed.), *The Sermon* (Turnhout: Brepols, 2000), pp. 271-323; Maria Magdalena Lebreton, "Les sermons de Julien moine de Vézelay," *Studia Anselmiana* 37 (1955): 118-32. See also the reviews of Vorreux's edition by Hubert Silvestre (*Revue d'histoire ecclésiastique* 69 [1974]: 625-29) and Pierre-Patrick Verbraken (*Revue Bénédictine* 83 [1973]: 456).

[32] The bibliography on this subject is large. See, for example, Marsha L. Dutton, "Intimacy and Imitation: The Humanity of Christ in Cistercian Spirituality," in John R. Sommerfeldt (ed.), *Erudition at God's Service* (Kalamazoo: Cistercian Publications, 1987), pp. 33-60; William Loerke, "'Real Presence' in Early Christian Art," in Timothy G. Verdon and John Dally (eds.), *Monasticism and the Arts* (Syracuse: Syracuse University Press, 1984), pp. 29-51; Karl Morrison, *History as a Visual Art in the Twelfth-Century Renaissance* (Princeton: Princeton University Press, 1990). For emotion in monastic literature as self-consciously artificial see Pranger, *Artificiality of Christianity* (note 2), pp. 1-12.

[33] Giles Constable, "Past and Present in the Eleventh and Twelfth Centuries: Perceptions of Time and Change," in *L'Europa dei secoli XI et XII fra novità e tradizione: Sviluppi di una cultura*, Atti del decima settimana internazionale di studio, Mendola, 25-29 agosto 1986 (Milan: Vita e pensiero, 1989), pp. 156-57; Richard Glasser, *Time in French Life and Thought*, trans. C.G. Pearson (Manchester: Manchester University Press, 1972), pp. 11-47; Aron I.

Gurevich, *Categories of Medieval Culture*, trans. G.L. Campell (Boston: Routledge & Kegan Paul, 1985), p. 112.

[34] Ilene H. Forsyth, *The Throne of Wisdom: Wood Sculptures of the Madonna in Romanesque France* (Princeton: Princeton University Press, 1972), pp. 154-55 and *passim*.

[35] Huygens (ed.), *Monumenta Vizeliacensia* (note 13), p. 439.

[36] Mathieu M. Quantin, *Cartulaire général de l'Yonne* (Auxerre: Perriquet, 1854), I:316-17; trans. in Scott and Ward, *Vézelay Chronicle* (note 13), pp. 321-22.

[37] Robert J. Forbes, "Food and Drink," in Charles Singer *et al.* (eds.), *A History of Technology* (Oxford: Oxford University Press, 1957), 2:127. On the technological inaccuracies of eucharistic mills in medieval art, see Niall Roberts, "Some Eucharistic Mills," *International Molinology* 70 (2005): 23-30.

[38] Jacqueline Gréal, *La basilique de Vézelay* (Paris: Éditions Franciscaines, 1950). This thesis has been rearticulated several times: Gottfried Richter, *Romanisches Burgund: zur Geschichte des christlichen Abendlandes* (Stuttgart: Verlag Urachhaus, 1962), p. 67; Michel Zink, "Moulin mystique. À propos d'un châpiteau de Vézelay. Figures allégoriques dans le prédication et dans l'iconographie romane," *Annales économies, sociétés, civilisations* 31 (1976): 481-89. Pirault extends the argument to argue that the circular form of the gear likewise alludes to Christ: *L'école du moulin* (note 15), pp. 117-26.

[39] Fol. 112r. See the comments of Rosalie Green *et al.* (eds.), *Hortus Deliciarum* (London: Warburg Insititute, 1979), 1:150; 2:183.

[40] Heimann construes later images as metamorphoses of the earlier images; "Mola mystica" (note 4), p. 229.

[41] Martin Schawe, "Zur 'Altagsseite" des göttinger Barfüsseraltares von 1424," *Niederdeutsche Beiträge zur Kunstgeschichte* 27 (1988): 64-68; Alois Thomas, "Die mystische Mühle," *Die Christliche Kunst: Monatsschrift für alle Gebiete der christlichen Kunst und Kunstwissenschaft* 31 (1935): 129-39. Others have cast the Vézelay capital as part of a continuous tradition of mill imagery, including Hans Hahnloser, "Pietro Calzettas Heiligblutaltar im Santo zu Padua," in *Scritti di storia dell'arte in onore di Mario Salmi* (Rome: De Luca, 1961-63), pp. 388-90.

[42] Zink, "Moulin mystique" (note 38). One can add to Zink's sources a text by Irimbert, *In Jud.*, 1.1; rpt. in Bernhard Pez *et al.*, *Thesaurus anecdotum novissimus* (Vienna: Veith, 1721-28), 4:310-11.

[43] Jacques P. Migne (ed.), *Patrologiae cursus completus. Series latina* (Paris: Garnier Frères, 1844-65), XI:col. 496. This builds on 1 Corinthians 5, which admonishes adulterers to purge out the old leaven so that they may be a new dough for Christ.

[44] Migne (ed.), *Patrologiae*, CLXXV: col. 909.

[45] *De poenitentia*, 1.15.82.

[46] *Expositio Evangelii secundum Lucam* 8.48, 52. Cf. *idem*, *De Cain et Abel* 1.8.30. Paulinus of Nola develops a similar interpretation of the two women (*Epistulae* 11.6). For this metaphor in medieval exegesis see Henri de Lubac, *The Sources of Revelation*, trans. Luke O'Neill (New York: Herder and Herder, 1968), p. 131; Boniface Ramsey (trans.), *The Sermons of St. Maximus of Turin*, The Works of the Fathers in Translation 50 (New York: Newman Press, 1989), p. 286.

[47] Ramsey (ed.), *Sermons*, pp. 20, 33, 48. For similar formulations see also Eucherius of Lyon, *Formulae spiritalis intellegentiae*; Eusebius 'Gallicanus', *Homilia* 17, 7; Hilary of Poitiers, *In Matthaeum*, 26, 5.

[48] Respectively, *Testimoniorum veteris ac novi testamenti* [Migne (ed.), *Patrologiae* (note 43), CXLV: cols. 1031, 1082]; *Expositio in Matthaeum (Ibid.*, CXX:col. 830); *In Deuteronomium (Ibid.*, CLXIV:col. 529); *Liber de sacramento altaris (Ibid.*, CCIV:cols. 761-62). See also Peter Riga, *Aurora* (Notre Dame: University of Notre Dame Press, 1965), ll. 1859-1896.

[49] Migne (ed.), *Patrologiae* (note 43), CLII:col. 1409.

[50] "Quod ingestum ab illo fuerit cui operis illius cura commissa est," *Conferences*, I,18 in Mary Carruthers, *The Craft of Thought: Meditation, Rhetoric, and the Making of Images, 400-1200* (Cambridge: Cambridge University Press, 1999), p. 91.

[51] *Ibid.*, pp. 92-94, 263.

[52] A classic articulation of this thesis is in Erwin Panofsky, *Renaissance and Renascences in Western Art* (Stockholm: Almqvist & Wiskells, 1969), pp. 188-200.

[53] See the helpful overview of scholarship in Ilene H. Forsyth, "The Monumental Arts of the Romanesque Period: Recent Research. The Romanesque Cloister," in Elizabeth C. Parker (ed.), *The Cloisters: Studies in Honor of the Fiftieth Anniversary* (New York: The Metropolitan Museum of Art, 1992), pp. 8-9.

[54] See, for example, Caesarius of Arles, *Sermon* 8, 4.

[55] Jean Leclercq, *The Love of Learning and the Desire for God*, trans. Catherine Misrahi (New York: Fordham University Press, 1961), pp. 72-75 and *passim*. See also Michael Camille, "Seeing and Reading: Some Visual Implications of Medieval Literacy and Illiteracy," *Art History* 8 (1985): 26-49; Ivan Illich, *In the Vineyard of the Text: A Commentary to Hugh's Didascalicon* (Chicago: University of Chicago Press, 1993), pp. 51-57.

[56] At Autun Noah loads the ship before the storm and at Beaune he receives the dove that carries an olive branch to signal the end of the deluge; ill. in Denis Grivot and George Zarnecki, *Gislebertus: Sculptor of Autun* (New York: Hacker Art Books, 1961), pls. 20a-c, D2.

[57] Ford L. Battles, "Hugo of Saint-Victor as a Moral Allegorist," *Church History* 18 (1949): 229; Joachim Ehlers, *"Arca significat ecclesiam*. Ein theologisches Weltmodell aus der ersten Hälften des 12. Jahrhunderts," *Frühmittelalterliche Studien* 6 (1972): 171-87; Edward K. Rand, *Founders of the Middle Ages* (New York: Dover, 1928), p. 90; Grover A. Zinn, "Hugh of St. Victor and the Ark of Noah: A New Look," *Church History* 40 (1971): 261-72; *idem*, "Mandala Symbolism and the Use of Mysticism of Hugh of St. Victor," *History of Religions* 12 (1973): 317-41.

[58] Gillian R. Evans, *The Thought of Gregory the Great* (Cambridge: Cambridge University Press, 1986), p. 88; Dietram Hofmann, *Die geistige Auslegung der Schrift bei Gregor* (Münsterschwarzach: Vier-Türme-Verlag, 1968), pp. 7*ff.* See also Carruthers, *Craft of Thought* (note 50), pp. 241-43. Cf. Edgar de Bruyne, *Études d'esthétique médiévale* (Brugge: De Tempel, 1946), 1:92.

[59] "Nam primum quidem fundamenta historie ponimus; deinde per significationem typicam in arcem fidei fabricam mentis erigimus; ad extremum quoque per moralitatis gratiam quasi superducto edificium colore uestimus," in Marcus Adriaen (ed.), *Moralia in Job*, Corpus Christianorum Series Latina 193 (Turnhout: Brepols, 1979), pp. 110-14.

[60] *De universo* [Migne (ed.), *Patrologiae* (note 43), CXI:cols. 400*ff*].

[61] *Interrogationes in responsiones in Genesim (Ibid.*, C: col. 559].

[62] Jean Leclercq (ed.), *Sermones super Cantica Canticorum* (Rome: Ed. Cistercienses, 1957).

[63] See, for example, Jerome Taylor (trans.), *The Didascalicon of Hugh of St. Victor: A Medieval Guide to the Arts* (New York: Columbia University Press, 1961), p. 138. See also the illuminating discussion of Patrice Sicard, *Diagrammes médiévaux et exégèse visuelle. Le Libellus de formatione arche de Hugues de Saint-Victor* (Paris: Brepols, 1993), pp. 210-20.

[64] Leah Rutchick argues that twelfth-century monasticism can be characterized as principally oral, instead of literary: "Sculpture Programs in the Moissac Cloister: Benedictine Culture, Memory Systems and Liturgical Performance," Ph.D. dissertation, University of Chicago, 1991. Building on anthropological research on oral cultures, especially that of Walter Ong, Rutchick suggests that the designers of Moissac's cloister anticipated active viewership.

[65] See, for example, Thomas E.A. Dale, "Monsters, Corporeal Deformities, and Phantasms in the Cloister of St.-Michel-de-Cuxa," *Art Bulletin* 83 (2001): 402-36; Ilene H. Forsyth, "Narrative at Moissac: Schapiro's Legacy," *Gesta 41* (2002): 71-94.

Of Mills and Meaning

Shana Worthen

(University of Toronto/Imperial College London)

Hugh of St. Victor wrote that there are two kinds of food: bread, and food which is served with bread.[1] Bread was a dietary staple in the Middle Ages. Its production occupied a large proportion of available labor, from plowing fields for planting to baking loaves. Mills played a crucial role in the process, grinding grain into meal from which bread could be made. No wonder, then, that images of mills acquired a variety of symbolic meanings for medieval people, meanings which began with the mill as a symbol of grain-grinding and nutrition and developed into sophisticated allegories for the Christian church, theology, and the world. Because so few medieval mills were used for non-agricultural purposes, their appearance was associated with food production first and foremost: they appear in the background of farm scenes, and workers lug bags of grain to them, as a common element of the landscape[2] (Fig. 1).

But mills were used in other ways in texts and artwork of the period. The way the upper millstone turned around a central axis became an analogy for the wheel of Fortune, and for the turning of the night sky around the North Star. The processing of grain into meal was used as an analogy for transformation, textual interpretation, spiritual nutrition, and gluttony. In an inversion of the driver and the driven, windmills could symbolize the wind, particularly in their earliest depictions. The distinctive shape of the horizontal-axis windmill, often found on hilltops for better access to wind, was also used to identify specific locations such as towns or hills, and to describe large and unusual sights, including exotic spinning buildings, giants, and Satan.[3] Yet, despite the rare association with gluttony or Satan, mills were not presented by their contemporaries as inherently evil. Indeed, most artists presented mills of all varieties as progenitors of virtue.

To generalize broadly, there are four different kinds of mills shown or mentioned by artists and poets: hand mills, or querns; animal mills, powered by human or animal labor; watermills; and windmills, including postmills and, later,

Figure 1: **Men carry grist to mill and carry Walsoken in litter over stream (1349)**; detail of funerary brass of Adam de Walsoken and wife Margaret, St. Margaret's church, King's Lynn; from John Sell Cotman, *Engravings of Sepulchral Brasses in Norfolk and Suffolk*, 2ᵈ ed. (London: H.G. Bohn, 1839), plate 2.

tower mills.[4] While most kinds of mills were used interchangeably for symbolic purposes, windmills acquired a range of distinct meanings which depended on their motive power, the air, and on their unusual shape. Windmills were shown in contemporary artwork more frequently than watermills despite the larger number of actual watermills, leading one scholar to observe that "the understanding of the place of windmills in the history and development of technology and the built environment is still haunted by their dynamism as symbols."[5] Windmills are simply the most strikingly shaped type of mill. Thus, the disproportionate attention to windmills in the following discussion is a product of the disproportionately numerous ways in which medieval and early modern artists and authors used them. Familiarity with mills' iconography is crucial for understanding what images of mills and allegorical texts mentioning them meant to the artists and authors whose work provides a foundation for many modern molinological studies. Additionally, understanding how mills actually worked in the Middle Ages can be crucial in understanding how mills worked metaphorically.

The Physical World

At their most all-encompassing, mills served as analogies for the turning of the night sky upon a central axis, even as celestial spheres turned around the Earth, or the millstone around its central axis. The analogy for the workings of the universe appears in diverse cultures, but seems to originate—for the western world, at least—in the work of al-Farghani, a ninth-century Arab astronomer and translator, who described the way the skies turned around the North Star, "like the turning of a mill."[6] Al-Farghani's words were incorporated by Dante in his *Convivio* and *Paradiso*, where he compares the turning of theologians in the circles of Paradise to the turning of millstones:

> Soon as the blessed flame had taken up
>   The final word to give it utterance,
>   Began the holy millstone to revolve,
> And in its gyre had not turned wholly round,
>   Before another in a ring enclosed it,
>   And motion joined to motion, song to song;[7]

The analogy between the movements of the skies and millstones was also read into the quern which appears in the Finnish epic *Kalevala*, as well as a similar mill which appears in Snorri's *Edda*.[8] These kinds of symbolic mills are referred to as "world" or "cosmic" mills.

Most mills did not purport to represent the entire world, nor was this the only way in which mills were used to describe the natural world. Windmills, particularly in their earliest depictions, were used to represent the wind, the air which propelled their sails. One of the earliest images of a post mill shows it being turned to face the wind. The image is from an illuminated initial in a manuscript of Aristotle's newly-translated *Meteorologica*. Edward Kealey, in *Harvesting the Air*, argues that one of the reasons for the design of this particular image was the newness of Aristotle's text to medieval iconographers: it did not already have a visual program, and so there was opportunity to fill the space with an innovative and appropriate image.[9] At least one other manuscript of the *Meteorologica*, possibly a copy, follows the symbolism of the first.[10] More literally, however, in the Greek sense, meteorology has to do with things in the air (Gk. *meteoros*, lofty things), making the windmill a natural symbol of the topic.

If the windmill in the *Meteorologica* was included for its ties to the variability of earthly winds, the very earliest known image of a windmill is shown for its ties to celestial winds. In the thirteenth-century Pierpont Morgan Library MS M.102, better known as the *Windmill Psalter*, the first psalm begins with an elaborately historiated letter E. Unusually, the illuminated letter is the second letter, not the first, of the initial word, *Beatus*, with which the psalm begins. The B is also illuminated, with a Tree of Jesse, while the E shows a Judgment of Solomon. The upper part of the E frames Solomon, while an angel flies across the space defined by the lower half. Above Solomon, at the top of the page, is a distinct post mill, resting on proportionally long legs (only three are visible, although four are assumed) and with four sails seen from behind and a ladder for climbing into the buck.

Adelaide Bennett, in her 1980 article on the illumination, analyzes its iconography and attempts to ascribe ownership of the psalter based on associations
with the windmill.[11] She writes that the angel, flying downwards, represents the
wind, his flight generating the breeze necessary to turn the windmill's sails. The
curls of leaves in the decorative borders reinforce the sense of movement in the
image. She sees the windmill as analogous to the Judgment of Solomon below
the illumination, both mechanisms which separate good from evil.

In the parable of the Judgment of Solomon, King Solomon offered to cut
the child claimed by two mothers in half, since neither would back down from
her claim, leading the true mother to renounce her claim so the child would
survive, thereby exposing the false one.[12] Various theologians, including Augustine, Isidore, and Rabanus Maurus, saw in the parable an allegory for the
church and the synagogue, the "true" and "false" faith (according to their religious prejudices).[13] Bennett suggests that the windmill is an analogy referring to
the separation of the good from the bad, "like the chaff which the wind driveth
away".[14] As evidence, she offers the story of the two women grinding from the
book of Luke, in which, on the Day of Judgment, "Two women shall be grinding
together; the one shall be taken, and the other left."[15] The scene was illustrated
in a variety of medieval manuscripts with handmills, an early phase of enduring
Christological association with milling. In one twelfth-century Homilies manuscript which Bennett cites, a pair of millstones appear in a Last Judgment scene
along with personifications of the church and synagogue. Bennett concludes
that "the sophisticated windmill of the Morgan Psalter may allegorize the separation of good from the bad. It may be taken as a visual metaphor of Solomon's
God-given wisdom which enabled him to discern between the true and the false
mothers."[16]

The windmill in the historiated E almost certainly does have a symbolic
meaning tied to the rest of the image, but Bennett's interpretation employs a
flawed analogy. Milling does not separate wheat from chaff; it processes threshed
grain from which the chaff has already been removed and grinds it into meal.
Threshing breaks down the grain from stalk and covering with repeated flailing
or crushing of the harvested wheat. It is winnowing that uses air—often simply
the wind—to blow away detritus from the grain, separating the wheat from the
chaff. The milling process itself is therefore transformative, not separative; grain
is not separated from chaff, but rather grain is transformed into the meal (which
is then sifted into various grades of flour). Based on other medieval mill analogies, the comparisons of mills to abstract concepts are closely based on the physical function of the mills. While many of them possess layers of meaning in ad-

Figure 2: **Hans Sebald Beham,** *Luna* **[detail] (1530-40);**
from Georg Hirth, *Kulturgeschichtliches Bilderbuch aus drei Jahrhunderten*
(Munich: Knorr and Hirth, 1882-1890; rpt. New York B. Blom, 1972), 1:290.

dition to the literal, the allegorical and the metaphysical are invariably grounded
in the actual. In the case of the historiated E, the mill has a meaning which fits
its accompanying imagery if it is read as transforming rather than separating.

In another case, an early sixteenth-century German allegorical woodcut series of the planets and their influences, Hans Sebald Beham offered a view of
the watermill as under the influence of the moon. The series of woodcuts depict
quotidian activities controlled by the planets—warfare by Mars, and courting by
Venus, for example. For Luna, Beham shows the "watery star" ruling activities
like fishing, boating, and here, milling (Fig. 2). Over Luna pulling her chariot
across the sky, Beham added a quatrain describing the scene:

Luna Kind man nich zemen kan
Ihre kind seind nyemandt unterthan.
In Acht und zwentzig tag und nacht
Wirt auch mein ganzer lauff verbracht

> [One cannot tame the children of Luna. Her children cannot be subjugated.
> In eight and twenty days and nights, my entire course is completed.]

The moon astrologically influences childhood, rules the waters and thus, by extension, watermills. That Beham, or the folk proverb, notes that mills themselves cannot be tamed suggests the recognition of the might of water, and by extension, the might of technology.

Transformation through Milling

If the mill does not separate wheat from chaff, it still processes a raw material into a refined one. By analogy, it represents any process which takes in a raw material and transforms it into one with more valuable properties, whether grain to meal or, in the case of the *Windmill Psalter*, the Psalms into an understanding of Christ. Thus the mill's transformative powers were incorporated into late medieval symbolic programs. One instance is on a twelfth-century mill capital in the cathedral at Vézelay: an Old Testament figure, probably Moses, pouring grain into a hopper attached to a pair of millstones. St. Paul stoops to gather up the meal coming out of the stones. Behind the mill is a gear or wheel, part of the mechanism. Symbolically, art historians agree that the raw grain which Moses pours into the mill represents the Old Testament, the antecedent of the meal of the New Testament; through rewriting and through textual transformation—both processing in their own right—the Old Testament becomes the New.[17] Returning to the historiated E from the *Windmill Psalter*, consider the windmill again. While it does not separate the wheat from the chaff, it still transforms from raw to processed, and at Vézelay is associated with textual transformation in particular. In the same way, Solomon processes the argument between the two mothers and produces the truth, and a bad situation becomes a good one.

European interpretations of mills as positively transformative are not specific to either windmills or Christianity. One of the most dramatic examples of mills' transformative powers comes from the Finnish epic, the *Kalevala*, first recounted in the twelfth century. In the story, the hero washes ashore at a place called Pohjola, where he agrees to "forge" a handmill, or *sampo*, in exchange for his freedom. The main character's companion and the man who actually makes the mill, Ilmarinen, is known primarily as a metalsmith and agrees to make the *sampo* from improbable materials: "I'll be able to forge the Sampo / beat out the bright-lid / from a swan's quill tip / a barren cow's milk / a small barley grain / a summer ewe's down / because I have forged the sky / beaten out the lid of heaven / with nothing to start off from / with not a shred ready made."[18] Mills at this point in history were obviously not made of metal, but functionally a *sampo*, although never defined, was clearly a mill of some sort. When the *sampo* is delivered, the inhabitants of Pohjola tell the mill to grind out gold, resulting in the town's prosperity. Jealous of the mill's success, the hero sails back to Pohjola and steals the *sampo*, breaking his agreement and earning the wrath of the Pohjolans in the process, who then pursue him and his companion out to sea. A vicious battle ensures, during which the mistress of Pohjola attempts to reclaim the *sampo*, but the mill is smashed. Even as all its pieces sink into the sea, it continues to churn out the last commodity it was ordered to produce, salt.[19] Bits of the mill later wash ashore, bringing fertility to the land. The tale accounts for the sea's saltiness and also incorporates fertility motifs, appropriate to a harvest-dependent tool, and for a poem that was used for ritual fertility purposes, sung before the spring sowing.[20] The changes which the mill creates are economic and mythic, but the heart of each interpretation relies on the mill's transformative abilities. The *Windmill Psalter*, the Vézelay capital, and the tale of the *sampo* each employ a mill as a symbol of transformation, an analogy which reflects the technology's primary role in the physical world, turning grain into meal. Not all metaphorical mills, however, are used to communicate a concept which mirrors function so closely. Sometimes their allegorical and physical purposes diverge so far as to confuse characters within stories, especially when they encounter a mill under entirely unexpected circumstances.

Misunderstood Mills

The meaning of a mill is not always clear. One of the most striking images in the *Divine Comedy* comes when Dante arrives at the lowest circle of hell. Looking out over the plains of ice, off in the distance, he sees a windmill: "Just as, when night falls on our hemisphere / or when a heavy fog is blowing thick, / a windmill seems to wheel when seen far off" [*Inferno*, Canto 34:4-7].[21]

The deceptiveness of fog and twilight represent a veiled meaning. Dante believes he has seen a windmill, but he is in a place of deception. The shape of a windmill is distinctive, the sails crossing the body of the tall structure, so it would be an unusual object to mistake for something else. But as it turns out, Dante is deceived and the windmill turns out to be a creature—a creature Virgil had already warned of, the creature in the previous terzina:

> [The banners of the king of hell come]
> "toward us; and therefore keep your eyes ahead,"
> my master said, "to see if you can spy him."   [*Inferno*, Canto 34:1-3]

Several verses later, Dante finally understands the confusing spectacle. He does not just see the banners of the king of hell, but the king himself. The banners are Lucifer's wings, confused for sails at a distance.

> Beneath each face of his, two wings spread out,
> As broad as suited so immense a bird:
> I've never seen a ship with sails so wide.
> They had no feathers, but were fashioned like
> A bat's; and he was agitating them,
> So that three winds made their way out from him   [*Inferno*, Canto 34:46-51]

Like a windmill's sails, Lucifer's wings are enormous and smooth. He has a pair of wings for each of his three heads; thus, his six wings form the shape of a typical six-sailed windmill most popular in the eastern Mediterranean. The physical analogy between Lucifer and a windmill goes further than the sails: the proportions of the scene makes sense once the king of hell is further described:

> The emperor of the despondent kingdom
> So towered—from midchest—above the ice,
> That I match better with a giant's height
> Than giants match the measure of his arms;
> Now you can gauge the size of all of him
> If it is in proportion to such limbs.   [*Inferno*, Canto 34:28-33]

Despite the prolonged allegory, it would be hasty to read in Dante's words a condemnation of windmills or a decisive association between industry and evil. To begin with, the analogy is one of many in the *Inferno* describing giants in terms of buildings. For example, in Canto 31, Dante "seemed to see high serried towers"; Virgil explains that he is mistaken, and, just as in Canto 34, twilight and fog are the veils which occlude Dante's sight:

> Just as, whenever mists begin to thin,
> When, gradually, vision finds the form
> That in the vapor-thickened air was hidden   [*Inferno*, Canto 31:34-36]

The towers prove to be rows of giants. Dante does not describe them as inherently evil, but instead builds an analogy between the size of giants and the size of buildings, for no other man-made structure in his world was as large. He compares the sight he sees through the "vapor-thickened air" to Montereggion Castle near Siena which originally had fourteen towers incorporated into its walls [*Inferno*, Canto 31:41-42]. Siena, like Pisa, Genoa, and Dante's own Florence, is condemned for its depravity by Dante, but nowhere does he indict the architecture. The same situation occurs yet again elsewhere in Canto 31 when Dante encounters the giant Antaeus:

> Just as the Garisenda* seems when seen   [*Bologna's leaning tower]
> Beneath the leaning side, when clouds run past
> And it hangs down as if about to crash,
> So did Antaeus seem to me as I
> Watched him bend over me.   [*Inferno*, Canto 31:136-140]

If analogies between giants and structures was a judgment upon the structures, then Dante was a bad judge of ships, for he compares part of a ship to the same giant: no sooner has Antaeus set Dante and his guide down in Cocytus, but he "rose up like the mainmast of a ship" [*Inferno*, Canto 31:145]. Yet ships are used metaphorically throughout the *Divine Comedy*, especially in the extended analogy in Canto 2 of the *Paradiso*. Comparing Antaeus to the mast of a ship is analogy, not judgment.[22] Thus, if the windmill misread as Satan is not metaphorically evil, its appearance must signal another idea.

Cervantes clearly believed Dante's windmills were benign when he switched the poet's metaphor to send Don Quixote tilting at windmills, mistaken for monsters, the reverse of Dante's confusion. Each author's scene is structured around an obscuring veil—fog, twilight, or madness—which hides the true reading of the landscape. Shapes are misinterpreted in the confusion, especially the landscape's most distinctive shapes, the tallest buildings, the buildings placed on hilltops, or the buildings with the most unusual forms. Landmarks such as windmills, normally the truest guide to location, become monsters for the delusional, and monsters become markers in the depths of hell. Further, their enormity may also symbolize the folly of building.

Another medieval literary use of deception—or deceptive perception—and mills is found in *The House of Fame*. Chaucer is best known for his thieving Miller, who works a watermill (although depictions of him sometimes depict a windmill instead).[23] While Chaucer's description of the Miller is a scathing description of corruption, it is a description which gives the reader warnings about millers, not mills.

At the somewhat literal level, the *House of Fame* describes the author's journey to and within the allegorical house of the personification Fame, but is more than that. The text is a commentary on the nature and use of poetry. The outside of Fame's castle is decorated with a series of four niches with sculptures in each, each representing a literary genre.[24] One of these scenes shows a group of jugglers and magicians, "jugelours, / Magiciens, and tregetours" surrounded by "quene Medea / And Circes eke [too], and Calipsa." Among them, the narrator sees

> Colle tregetour
> Upon a table of sycamour
> Pleye an uncouth thyng to telle—
> Y saugh him carien a wyndmelle
> Under a walsh-note shale.[25]

> Colle the illusionist, on a table of sycamore, played at a thing which is strange to describe—I saw him carrying a windmill under a walnut shell.

Colle, a scholar believed to be contemporary with Chaucer, plays a shell-game using walnut shells, although the miniature windmill is described no further. Put into the company of the three Greek goddesses—queen Medea was a devotee of Hecate, known for depriving men of their wits; Circe befuddled men's minds and could turn them into animals; and the goddess Calypso, daughter of Titan, offered Odysseus immortality—the mill in the shell suggests that this vignette speaks to supernatural transformation of things into other things they are not.

Robert Watson, in his dissertation on the *House of Fame*, argues that the windmill represents something larger than it seems. For Dante and Cervantes, the size of the windmill is used in analogy with another creature. In the case of Chaucer's Colle, Watson believes the mismatch between device and scale is a clue to its explanation. Indeed, at the time the *House of Fame* was being written mills themselves were increasing in size: tower mills, developed at the end of the thirteenth century and becoming widespread by the fifteenth, were considerably taller than post mills. By building to heights increasingly elevated over that of other buildings, mill owners exposed the mill sails to a more continuous flow of air; other than church spires, nothing stood higher in the medieval landscape. Consequently, by placing a windmill—and probably a new tower mill—under a tiny walnut shell, Chaucer depicts a vignette where size may not be what it seems in order to make a point: Watson argues that the deception represents a literary genre "involving journeys to a place whence the author gains something like a divine perspective."[26]

Watson arrives at this conclusion by interpreting the little windmill as a world mill. His analysis accounts for the diminutive appearance of the mill, but identifies no precedent for a windmill used as a cosmic mill. Although he describes it as a cosmic mill, his interpretation is ultimately meant to emphasize the power of interpretation and reinterpretation. He writes that Chaucer's windmill "symbolizes the earthly processes by which snippets of information become distorted in transmission, intertwined with other snippets, and inflated sometimes out of all proportion to their original import."[27] He uses the analogy of the grinding of grain to describe the transmission and development of literature from one source to another. The symbol is a conflation of transmission, rereading, deception, and misreading. Even without reading the mill as cosmic, there were enough alternative, established meanings for windmills in the fourteenth century which Chaucer could tap into. The mill was a symbol of transformation, textual reinterpretation, and beginning to be read as a symbol for Christ. The range of meanings offers enough support for Watson's interpretation without resorting to the rarer interpretation of a windmill as a cosmic mill.

Mystic Mills

In the early fifteenth century, a new iconographic type developed for mills. To the Christian West, grain was a source not just of bodily nutrition, but spiritual nutrition as well. The Eucharist is at the heart of Christian devotional services, written into scripture and enacted in every church and chapel. Bread is mentioned throughout the Bible, but particularly in Matthew 26:26: "And as they were eating, Jesus took bread, and blessed it, and brake it, and gave it to the disciples, and said, Take, eat; this is my body." Bread and wine became body and blood, a diet transformed into an epic of salvation.

The genre of mystic mill imagery was based on that correlation. Mystic mill images generally show a mill attached to a crank turned by the twelve apostles or to a waterwheel turned by the four rivers of Paradise (Fig. 3). The four evangelists, either represented or identified by their respective symbolic animals, drop quotation banderoles into the hopper while the Virgin Mary looks on. The words are crushed beneath the millstones, and in the process become the body of Christ, both literally and figuratively: at the bottom, a crowd of bishops, cardinals, and pope collect the infant Christ and a shower of Eucharistic wafers, the

Figure 3: **A Mystic Mill**; from L. Lindet. "Représentations allégoriques du moulin et du pressoir dans l'art chrétien," *Revue archéologique* 36 (1900): 403-13, Plate VII.

products of the mill. In the earliest known mystic mill image from the early fifteenth century, the four church fathers, Jerome, Augustine, Ambrose, and Gregory the Great, stand in for what later became the larger crowd of people waiting to receive the mill's products. They hold out a Eucharistic chalice to catch the body of Christ.[28]

The scene is a densely-constructed allegory for the function of the church and its relationship to Christ. The mill transforms evangelistic prophecy into Christ's physical body, crushing grain to create meal and wafers even as Christ was crushed by his suffering and delivered salvation. The imagery is based on Ambrose's interpretation of the Biblical reference to two women milling, one representing the church, the other the synagogue.[29] In Ambrose's exegesis, the church is not the mill, but rather the motive force which moves the mill, which grinds the "more pure bread" fit for consumption by priests.[30] The church, then, is the force that powers the mill, which brings together the laws of Old and New Testament and whose labor earns it the reward of the Eucharistic miracle. In the mystic mill symbolism, therefore, the apostles and the evangelical creatures stand in place of the church, providing the force which drives the millstones of the law, while the representatives of the church-on-earth, the church fathers, receive the benefits of their antecedents' labors in a large communal goblet.

None of the overt examples of mystic mills are windmills; some are water-mills and others turn through apostolic effort.[31] Yet there are other instances of artwork from the fifteenth century and earlier which demonstrate that the windmill had just as many Christological associations as other kinds of mills. Most western Europeans windmills are powered by four sails, their construction forming a cross-shape across the building, a visual parallel with that of the crucifixion. An image of the cross on which Christ was crucified, attached to a building whose primary function was the grinding of grain, was a natural symbol of Christ.

Modern analyses, particularly by James Smith Pierce and Ann Tzeutschler Lurie, have identified windmills which played just such a role.[32] In the instances examined by these scholars, the windmills are lone structures perched on the tops of hills in the background of a scene from the lifetime of Christ. The windmills are incorporated into the landscapes, but given particular prominence through height and silhouette which make it clear that the artist intended to emphasize their presence. Instances of these include the windmills frequently found in fourteenth- and fifteenth-century Passion scenes, crucifixions in particular.[33] They are also often found near St. Christopher in a number of fifteenth-century English stained-glass windows.[34] Alois Thomas in particular has argued that the Franco-Burgundian tradition of the mystic windmill first appeared in fifteenth-century manuscript illumination.[35] In each case, he argues this from the pairing of a prominently-placed windmill with a scene from the life of Christ, the argument made more likely by the existing tradition of association between other kinds of mills and Christ.

The argument for windmill as mystic mill is particularly compelling in the case of Pieter Bruegel the Elder's oil painting *The Procession to Calvary*.[36] In the landscape behind a crowded procession, a windmill clings to the top of an improbably precarious and vertical cliff. The verticality of the crag makes it unlikely that the windmill could be a real, buildable structure in such a location, both for the difficulty of raising the lumber for its construction, as well as for the extreme exposure to winds, not to mention the poor farmers having to bring their sacks of grain to the peak. Windmills may have been built in exposed, windy places, but not so exposed and windy as this. The painting is crowded with throngs of people in a typical Bruegelian manner, so many that major players in the scene

Figure 4: **The Windmill as a symbol of the Crucifixion (1495-98)**; from *The Complete Woodcuts of Albrecht Dürer* (New York: Dover Publications, 1963), p. 88.

are lost to the crowds. The striking windmill is centered above the small figure of Christ below on the road, helping the eye of the viewer to find the crux of the picture's plotline. The windmill works effectively as a symbol of Christ, through its framing by the living and the dead trees, its vertical visual correspondence with the figure of Christ himself, and through its improbable terrain which implies that it cannot literally work as a windmill within the painting. Similarly, when Albrecht Dürer engraved the Crucifixion in the late fifteenth century, he placed a small four-vaned windmill at the base of the cross (Fig. 4). Even if Bruegel's craggy windmill could be dismissed as atmospheric landscape details, the Christological associations with the windmill and the cross upon Cavalry are hard to miss.

In the middle of the fifteenth century, for over half a century, the mill also became a symbol of the virtue Temperance. The four Cardinal Virtues, Prudence, Justice, Fortitude, and Temperance, are frequently shown together in medieval and early modern imagery. The "new iconography" of the virtues, including Temperance's windmill, gave the personifications of the virtues a large number of attributes to hold.[37] To deal with the surfeit of objects, the images show the virtues balancing buildings on their head, holding items in both hands, and standing precariously on symbolically-meaningful pedestals or footrests. Temperance, for example, balances a clock on her head, holds a pair of eyeglasses and a bridle, wears spurs, and stands on top of a tower mill.[38] The mill's meaning becomes clear when given context, for Fortitude, often depicted next to Temperance, stands on a wine press. Even as there was a tradition of a mystic mill, so too was there a tradition of a mystic wine press—the pairing of the two surely indicates that the virtues were founded in Christ and the Christian Church, virtues rooted in faith.[39]

The mystic mill in all its forms improves the grain, literally creating a better substance in the form of meal and metaphorically creating the body of Christ. These mills, like the handmill in the *Kalevala* which creates gold, armies, and prosperity, are transformative. They improve whatever is given to them to grind, and, in the process, the mill creates a better, a more virtuous substance.[40]

Journeys with Windmills

In addition to the symbolic roles which the windmill shared with other kinds of mills, it acquired a number of other functions which were uniquely tied to its shape and *modus operandi*. These included the way the post mill turned on a central axis and its distinctive shape and positioning which led to its use in defining landscapes. The structure of the windmill caught the imaginations of medieval authors, particularly the way the entire building was turned to face the winds. There are several instances of romances in which a building is described as being like a windmill, pivoting around a central axis.[41] In the later twelfth-century *Pilgrimage of Charlemagne*, the title character journeys to the Middle East with a coterie of knights. En route to Jerusalem, the party stops in Constantinople, where they are invited to be the guests of the emperor. The party is housed in a special palace, a circular structure decorated with sculptures of two youths holding ivory horns. When the wind blows, the figures sound their horns, and the palace begins to rotate. No matter how fast the structure turns, the lavishly-decorated palace is serene and steady inside. While most literary scholars have analyzed the palace's turnings as an analogy with medieval discussions of the sun's cycle, a few historians of technology have seen in the rotating palace the functional infrastructure necessary for windmills.[42] Indeed, the text itself describes the palace as "made to turn with the axle of a mill."[43] No other kind of large structure regularly found in the Mediterranean world was constructed to pivot around a central axis the way the post mill was.

Another instance of a pivoting building in a medieval romance constitutes part of the slender evidence for the possible Middle Eastern origins of the horizontal-axis windmill. The twelfth-century Greek romance *Sophrosyne* describes the narrator's journey through the gardens and palace of Sophrosyne, the Greek term sometimes translated as Temperance.[44] The dome of the palace turns on a central axis in the same way as the one in which Charlemagne and his company stay. Margaret Schlauch observed in her article on the palace in Constantinople that the earliest instances of these describe a mechanically-turning building, while subsequent examples ascribe the rotations to magic.[45] Later instances of turning castles use rotation as a form of self-defense, but the early versions, in *The Pilgrimage of Charlemagne* and *Sophrosyne*, use it primarily to impress an audience, to intimidate with sophistication. In the former story, rotation is the major identifying trait possessed by the building. But when Dante confused Satan a windmill in the *Inferno*, it was because the silhouette he formed was so distinctive. From a distance, the purpose of a windmill is clear, even when it appears on a distant hilltop. And, being taller than all round them, windmills existed as landmarks throughout the Middle Ages and indeed into the nineteenth century.

Windmills were frequently used as definers of landscape from the fifteenth century onwards. Sometimes they are used to mark locations as distinctive, the way they are in the *Nuremberg Chronicle*, or in navigation maps. One fifteenth-century English navigation map uses a windmill as a guide for sailors searching for a "Golde-Stones" harbor near Berwick-upon-Tweed.[46] The landscape is defined by its buildings and by the contours of the shoreline: a town along the water's edge is framed by two dominant, raised landmarks: a flaming lighthouse is clearly visible the left side, while a post mill crowns the hill on the right. The windmill is used to orient the sailor, to define a destination.

In other instances, windmills are used to help define the shape of a landscape, and, more specifically, hills. Windmills were built in exposed locations for a very practical reason: they require free access to the wind in order to function. In fifteenth- and sixteenth-century Northern European artwork, they are frequently depicted on hilltops and seashores, on maps and in landscapes, simply because many of them were built in those places. The need to catch the wind is also why windmills were tall, raised buildings. Their height and their distinctive form made them noticeable from a distance, particularly when they were placed in exposed locations. Exposed locations also gave windmills striking silhouettes, even from a distance, and more so when abstracted by the backlighting of dawn or dusk. Consequently, the unusual shape and operation of windmills also led to their use as identifying features for navigation.

The city of Rhodes is defined largely through its windmills in legend, lore, and reality. In the entry for Rhodes in the *Nuremberg Chronicle*, for example, windmills throng the harbor walls, a dense line of industry, nothing between them and the sea winds. From afar, the island city's form is distinctive, the mass of six-vaned windmills creating diagonals between its fortified spires. Windmills in the image for Constantinople are contained within the city walls, implausible structures which visually offer no method of pivoting to face a changing wind. That they are there at all, however, gives them significance (Fig. 5). The *Nuremberg Chronicle* was published in the late fifteenth century, part of the increasingly popular genre of world chronicles published especially in Germany at the time. A series of woodcuts illustrated the people, places, and unusual weather systems mentioned by the text. Most of the plates were reused multiple times throughout the book, illustrating two or three different cities with the same image, for example. Only the largest cities and most important people warranted their own specific plates. Thus it is particularly significant that windmills show up in the images of Rhodes and Constantinople, as place-specific images, and in plates that were *not* re-used for other cities. They help to gives those cities visually-specific identities.

The exposed location required for functional reasons thus became one of the major reasons for which the structure was used, for both navigational and artistic reasons. Their frequent presence in religious artwork is the result of both the windmill's associations with Christ and its functional location on the top of a hill. The symbolic baggage borne by mills was integral to the ways in which artists incorporated them into their work, work which, in turn, is a major source of information about the appearance and use of this technology for modern historians. Yet while the placement and appearance of mills reflects their actual location and structure, other factors affects these elements as well. In images of the life of Christ, six-vaned windmills may have been excluded even if present in the landscape because they do not convey the same symbolic effect as four-vaned, cross-like ones do. Human-powered mills did not require the labor of twelve, as the mystic mill required twelve apostles (or four rivers) to function. The power of the *sampo* to grind forth wealth is not purely fiction, but reflects the value of grain and milling in an agriculturally-based society. That value is further reflected in

Figure 5: **Rhodes [top] and Constantinople [bottom] from the**
Nuremberg Chronicle **(1493);** from Carol Belanger Grafton, *Medieval
Woodcut Illustrations: City Views and Decorations from the Nuremberg
Chronicle* (New York: Dover Publications, 1999), pp. 5 and 32.

Figure 6: **Pieter Bruegel the El-der, "Gluttony" (after 1557);** from H. Arthur Klein, *Graphic Worlds of Peter Bruegel the Elder* (New York: Dover Publications, 1963), p. 203.

all of the mills which appear as analogies for transformation, whether physical, textual, or spiritual.

Familiar instances of negative associations with mills, such as Chaucer's cor-rupt Miller and Dante's confusion between a windmill and Satan, may give the appearance that mills were laden with problematic associations in this period.[47] In his 1557 series of prints, the *Seven Deadly Sins*, Peter Brueghel used a bloated windmill-person as a symbol of gluttony, playing off the voracious mechanical maw of a millstone (and perhaps also off the greed of millers) (Fig. 6). But these are exceptional instances. A corrupt Miller does not imply that mills themselves were inherently evil. Nor does Dante's parallel between Satan's shape and the shape of a windmill, for not only does the author use the turning of a millstone as an analogy in the *Paradiso*, but he analogizes all of the giants in the *Inferno* to large buildings, the only structures large enough to conjure an apt image in his readers' minds.

Most images from this period associate mills of all kinds with transformation and with the creation of virtue. In the Vézelay capital, the New Testament is created by purifying—grinding—the grain of the Old Testament. In the *Windmill Psalter*, a mill is used as a symbol of Solomon's Judgment. Beginning in the early fifteenth century, the mill developed into a symbol of Christ and the Church in the mystic mill genre. The mystic mill images also informed the "new iconography" of the Cardinal and Theological Virtues which also developed in the mid-fifteenth century. The mechanisms which helped to make bread possible, a major portion of diet and daily survival, were closely associated with virtue.

Each text, each image, must be considered in their larger context to be correctly understood, and symbolic analysis and iconography play crucial roles in explaining the agenda of the materials which modern historians rely on for information on the location and appearance of technologies. Text and imagery are multivalent; not all is as it seems with the four-vaned hilltop windmill, or with the silhouette which seems to be one looming in the mist. To paraphrase Freud, sometimes a mill is just a mill, but oftentimes it is a great deal more.

Notes

[1] Such as meat and stews: *The Didascalicon of Hugh of St. Victor: The Medieval Guide to the Arts*, trans. Jerome Taylor (1961; New York: Columbia University Press, 1991), p. 77.

[2] At least 90 percent of medieval mills were agricultural: Adam R. Lucas, "Industrial Milling in the Ancient and Medieval Worlds: A Survey of the Evidence for an Industrial Revolution in Medieval Europe," *Technology and Culture* 46.1 (2005): 6, n. 11. J. Salmon, "The Windmill in English Medieval Art," *Journal of the British Archaeological Association*, 3rd ser. 6 (1941): 88-102 inventories a large number of English representations of windmills, many of which are shown in agrarian contexts.

[3] In John Heywood's *The Play of the Wether*, the Water-Miller describes windmills as located on "hylles and downes whyche partes are moste barayne": Vicki Knudsen Robinson (ed.), *A Critical Edition of The Play of the Wether by John Heywood*, The Renaissance Imagination 27 (New York: Garland Publishing, 1987), p. 231, l. 700.

[4] I am unaware of any literary or artistic instances of tide mills from this period.

[5] Martin Watts, *The Archaeology of Mills and Milling* (Stroud: Tempus, 2002), p. 14.

[6] "Est revolutio orbis sicut revolutio molae" [Al-Farghani, *Liber de aggregationibus stellarum*]. See Romeo Campani (ed.), *Il libro dell'aggregazione delle stelle: (Dante, Convivio, II.6.-134) secondo il Codice Mediceo-Laurenziano, Pl. 29, Cod. 9* (Trent: La Finestra, 2003).

[7] Dante Alighieri, *Paradiso*, Canto 3.1-8 [from *The Divine Comedy of Dante Alighieri: Paradise*, trans. Henry Wadsworth Longfellow (Project Gutenberg E-text #1003)]; Dante, *Convivio*, III.5.14: "Mary must necessarily see the Sun… circling around the world, below the earth, or rather the Ocean, like a millstone not more than half of whose mass can be seen." See M.A. Orr, *Dante and the Astronomers* (London: Wingate Press, 1956), p. 186; A. Oliviero, "La composizione dei cieli in Restoro d'Arezzo e in Dante," *Dante e la scienza*, in P. Boyde and V. Russo (eds.), Interventi Classici 16 (Ravenna: Longo, 1995).

[8] Giorgio De Santillana and Hertha von Dechend, *Hamlet's Mill: An Essay on Myth and the Frame of Time* (Boston: Gambit Inc., 1969), p. 24.

[9] Edward Kealey, *Harvesting the Wind: Windmill Pioneers in Twelfth-Century England* (Berkeley: University of California Press, 1987), p. 23.

[10] Aristotle, *Meteorologica*, Bk. III. Cambridge University Library MS Ee. 2.31, fol. 130; Kealey, *Harvesting the Wind*, pp. 23-24.

[11] She notes that several earlier scholars believed that the windmill was key to the owner's identity: Adelaide Bennett, "The Windmill Psalter: The Historiated Letter E of Psalm One," *Journal of the Warburg and Courtauld Institutes* 43 (1980): 52. See also David Marshall, "John Ball's Revolutionary Windmill: "The Letter of Jakke Mylner" in the English Rising of 1381," ch. 9 of this volume.

[12] 1 Kings 3:16-28.

[13] Bennett, "The Windmill Psalter," p. 63.

[14] Psalms 1:4.

[15] Luke 17:35. This image is quite common in 16-18th century emblemata.

[16] Bennett, "The Windmill Psalter", p. 63.

[17] Kirk Ambrose, "The 'Mystic Mill' Capital at Vézelay," ch. 10 of this volume. Ambrose argues that the Vézelay column has been previously misinterpreted as an early version of a mystic mill. The image was carved a good three centuries before any other instance of a mystic mill, and there is nothing integral to the image which requires it to be read as a eucharistic transformation.

[18] Elias Lönrot and Keith Bosley (eds.), *The Kalevala* (1989; rpt. Oxford: Oxford University Press, 1999), pp. 112-13. For a more in-depth discussion of this mill, see Clive Tolley, "The Mill in Norse and Finnish Mythology," *Saga-Book* 24.2-3 (1995): 63-82. It is also treated extensively in De Santillana, *Hamlet's Mill* (note 8).

[19] Another version is found in Snorri's *Edda*: a powerful quern is constructed, named Grotti, which only two giant maidens, Fenja and Menja, are strong enough to turn. They were abused by the mill's owner, and in retaliation, ground out an army instead of the gold, peace, and prosperity they had been assigned. In the end, like the quern in the *Kalevala*, Grotti is commanded to grind forth salt, and it does so so copiously that the weight of the salt sinks the ship.

[20] Tolley, "The Mill in Norse and Finnish Mythology," p. 65.

[21] All quotations from the *Inferno* come from Dante Alighieri, *The Divine Comedy*, trans. by Allen Mandelbaum (London: Everyman's Library, 1995).

[22] Dante elsewhere uses a watermill as an analogy: in the *Inferno*, he compares the speed with which Virgil moves being faster than the fastest flow of water through a mill's sluice gate [Canto 23:46-51].

[23] A 1492 series of woodcuts includes a portrait of the Miller, identified in part by the post mill standing on a hill behind him: Geoffrey Chaucer, *The Canterbury Tales* (London: Richard Pynson, 1492), sig. g8ʳ [ESTC 5084].

[24] Robert Allen Watson, *A Windmill under a Walnut Shell: Chaucer's "House of Fame" on the Illusionist Rhetoric of Systems*, Ph.D. dissertation, Stanford University, 1988, p. 3.

[25] F.N. Robinson (ed.), "The House of Fame," in *The Works of Geoffrey Chaucer* (Boston: Houghton Mifflin, 1957), §3.1282-86.

[26] Watson, *Windmill under a Walnut Shell*, p. 3.

[27] *Ibid.*, p. 89.

[28] The *Hostienmühle* miniature, dated to *c*.1414, is in a manuscript from Kloster Menen now Bayerische Staatsbibliothek München, *cod. lat.* 8201, fol. 372. This image is discussed at length in Peter Heimann, "Mola Mystica: Wandlungen eines Themas mittelalterlicher Kunst," *Zeitschrift für Schweizerische Archäologie und Kunstgeschichte* 39.4 (1982): 229-52.

[29] Martin Schawe, "Zur 'Alltagsseite' des Göttingen Barfüsseraltares von 1424," *Niederdeutsches Beiträge zur Kunstgeschichte* 27 (1988): 63-84 at 64.

[30] "Unde etiam panes propositionis fiunt, quos soli sacerdotes edunt, quibus puriorem panem manducare praescriptum est, illum utique qui descendit e caelo": Ambrose, *In expositionem evangelii secundum Lucam admonitio* 8, in Jacques P. Migne (ed.), *Patrologiae cursus completus. Series latina* (Paris: Garnier Frères, 1844-65), XV: col. 1781b.

[31] Other articles on mystic mills include M.F. de Lasteyrie, "Notice sur quelques représentations allégoriques de l'Eucharistie," *Mémoires de la Société Nationale des Antiquaires de France*, 4ᵗʰ ser. 9 (1878): 73-86; Christine Göttler, "Das älteste Zwingli-Bildnis?– Zwingli als Bild-Erfinder: Der Titelholzschnitt zur 'Beschribung der götlichen müly,'" *Unsere Kunstdenkmäler* 35.3 (1984): 297-309.

[32] See James Smith Pierce, "The Windmill on the Road to Calvary," *New Lugano Review* 11-12 (1976): 48-55, 99; and Ann Tzeutschler Lurie, "A Newly Discovered Eyckian St. John the Baptist in a Landscape," *Bulletin of the Cleveland Museum of Art* 68.4 (1981): 86-119.

[33] Pierce, "The Windmill on the Road to Calvary," p. 49.

[34] Salmon, "Windmill in English Medieval Art" (note 2), pp. 93-94.

[35] Alois Thomas, "Die Mystiche Mühle," *Die Christliche Kunst* 31 (1934-5): 129-39.

[36] Pierce, "The Windmill on the Road to Calvary," pp. 48-55, 99.

[37] Emile Mâle, *Religious Art in France: The Late Middle Ages* (Princeton: Princeton University Press, 1986), p. 294. Rosemond Tuve, *Allegorical Imagery* (Princeton: Princeton University Press, 1966), pp. 71-77; Rosemund Ture, "Notes on the Virtues and Vices," *Journal of the Warburg and Courtauld Institutes* 26.3/4 (1963): 264-303 at 283-89.

[38] Lynn White, Jr. hypothesized that Temperance's attributes formed a praise of recent technological inventions. The tower mill, mechanical clock, rowel spurs, and eyeglasses were all medieval inventions, although the bridle was not. His explanation seems improbable due to lack of contemporary awareness of these objects as recent inventions. Additionally, the

explanation does not account for the attributes given to the rest of the cardinal virtues: "The Iconography of *Temperantia* and the Virtuousness of Technology" in *Medieval Religion and Technology: Collected Studies* (Berkeley: University of California Press, 1978). See discussion of White's argument in Shana Worthen, *The Memory of Medieval Inventions, 1200-1600: Windmills, Spectacles, Sandglasses, and Mechanical Clocks*, Ph.D. dissertation, University of Toronto, 2006.

[39] Alois Thomas, Matthias Zender, and Franz Josef Heyen, *Die Darstellung Christi in der Kelter: eine theologische und kulturhistorische Studie, zugleich ein Beitrag zur Geschichte und Volkskunde des Weinbaus* (Düsseldorf: Schwann, 1935).

[40] On another note, St. Victor of Marseilles was said to have been crushed to death between two millstones; thus, he is usually shown holding a millstone or a windmill. The story makes the millstones both implements of torture and means to martyred salvation: Salmon, "The Windmill in English Medieval Art" (note 2), p. 95.

[41] Margaret Schlauch, "The Palace of Hugon de Constantinople," *Speculum* 7.4 (1932): 500-14 at 505-11.

[42] *Ibid.*, p. 504; Michael J.T. Lewis, "The Greeks and the Early Windmill," *History of Technology* 15 (1993): 141-89 at 156-8.

[43] "le fait turner cum arbre de mulin": Glyn S. Burgess and Anne Elizabeth Cobby (eds. and trans.), *Voyage de Charlemagne à Jérusalem et à Constantinople*, Garland Library of Medieval Literature 47 (New York: Garland 1988), part 21 [pp. 46-47].

[44] Meliteniotes, "Poème allégorique de Meliténiote," *Notices et Extraits des Manuscrits de la Bibliothèque Imperiale* [Paris] 19.2 (1858): 1-138.

[45] Schlauch, "The Palace of Hugon de Constantinople," pp. 503-4, 507-8.

[46] *Miscellany; Rutter, or pilot-book for coastal waters of Britain*, 1449-1461 [New York, Pierpont Morgan Library, ms M.775, fol. 130v].

[47] See Tim Sistrunk, "The Right to the Wind in the Later Middle Ages," ch. 6 of this volume.

LIST OF CONTRIBUTORS

Kirk Ambrose is an assistant professor at the University of Colorado at Boulder and has published many articles on medieval art in journals including the *Gazette des Beaux Arts*, *Source*, *Traditio*, and *Word & Image*. His book, *The Nave Sculpture of Vézelay: The Art of Monastic Viewing*, will appear in 2006 from the Pontifical Institute of Mediaeval Studies. Among other projects, he is currently co-editing a volume on Romanesque Sculpture Studies.

Niall Brady is Project Director of the Discovery Programme's Medieval Rural Settlement Project in Dublin, and a director of The Archaeological Diving Company Ltd. His particular research interests lie in agrarian technology and underwater archaeology.

George Brooks is professor of Humanities at Valencia Community College in Orlando, Florida. He holds a doctorate from Florida State University in Medieval Studies and History of Technology. Having finished his dissertation, *The Mechanization of the Middle Ages: An Intellectual History of Medieval Machine Building*, Dr. Brooks now teaches humanities at his first alma mater and spends his spare time engaged in the reconstruction of historical technology. He also sponsors a festival called "Catapult Day" in which students show off their own historical reconstruction projects, eat period food, and marvel at the power of a medieval trebuchet hurling cantaloupes to their destruction.

Thomas F. Glick is professor of History and Geography at Boston University and president of the Northeast Chapter of the Society for the Preservation of Old Mills (SPOOM). He has written extensively on irrigation and hydraulic technology in medieval Spain, including *Irrigation and Hydraulic Technology: Medieval Spain and its Legacy* (Aldershot: Variorum, 1996), and is, with Steven J. Livesey and Faith Wallis, an editor of *Medieval Science, Technology, and Medicine: an encyclopedia* (Routledge, 2005).

Janet S. Loengard is professor of history emerita at Moravian College. She works primarily in medieval and sixteenth-century English legal history and is interested in aspects of the law of property varying from the concept and treatment of nuisance to married women's property rights. She has published in both areas and is currently working on the right to light and air in pre-modern London.

Adam Lucas, MsSoc, MA (Hons), PhD in History and Philosophy of Science, University of New South Wales, is a researcher and policy analyst in the New South Wales Cabinet Office. He is currently on secondment to the NSW Department of Aboriginal Affairs. His academic publications have been in the sociology of science and technology and the history of technology. His book, *Wind, Water, Work: Ancient and Medieval Milling Technology*, recently appeared from Brill. He is currently working on a book expanding on the research conducted for his PhD as summarised in the paper included in this volume.

Roberta Magnusson is an Associate Professor of History at the University of Oklahoma. After working on medieval archaeological excavations in Britain and Italy, she received a Ph.D. in history from the University of California, Berkeley. She is a contributor to *Working with Water in Medieval Europe: Technology and Resource Use* (Brill, 2000), and is the author of *Water Technology in the Middle Ages: Cities, Monasteries, and Waterworks after the Roman Empire* (Johns Hopkins, 2001).

David Marshall is completing a dissertation at Indiana University entitled *Reformers, Miscreants, and Mutuality: England and Nation, 1370-1400* that examines the literary expressions of collective identity as imaginings of an English nation in the years surrounding the Revolt of 1381. He holds an M.A. in Medieval Studies from the University of York, England, where he researched early medieval ideas of sanctity and cultural identity.

Luis Pablo Martinez is Inspector of Cultural Patrimony of the Generalitat Valenciana. Along with Thomas F. Glick and Enric Guinot, he edited a volume on the history of water mills in the medieval Kingdom of Valencia: *Els molins hidràulics valencians: Tecnología, història i context social* (Valencia, 2000).

D. Fairchild Ruggles is Associate Professor in the Department of Landscape Architecture at the University of Illinois, Urbana-Champaign. Her book, *Gardens, Landscape, and Vision in the Palaces of Islamic Spain* (2000), which won the 2002 Eleanor Tufts Award from the American Society for Hispanic Art Historical Studies, documented the profound transformation of the Iberian landscape from the eighth century advent of Islam until 1492. Her next book, *Islamic Gardens and Landscape*, is forthcoming from the University of Pennsylvania Press.

Tim Sistrunk received a Ph.D. in Medieval History from the University of Kansas in 1995 and teaches in the Department of History at California State University, Chico. He is currently working on a monograph that treats the legal understanding of the natural world engendered by scientific and technological changes in the twelfth through the fourteenth centuries.

Steven A. Walton holds degrees in engineering and the history of science and technology and teaches in the intercollege program in Science, Technology, & Society at Penn State University. Keenly interested in tools, machines, and processes, his work focusses on the intersection of technology and users—whether invetors or consumers—and especally on these areas as they relate to military technologies.

Shana Worthen recently defended her dissertation, "The Memory of Medieval Inventions, 1200-1600: Windmills, Spectacles, Sandglasses, and Mechanical Clocks", at the Institute for the History and Philosophy of Science and Technoloogy (IHPST) at the University of Toronto. She is currently a visiting scholar at the Center for the History of Science, Technology and Medicine (CHoSTM) at Imperial College in London. She works on the intellectual history of medieval and early modern technology.

Index

Some index entries are grouped under master headings; those with more than one level of subheading are rendered in BOLD: see "rulers", "Popes", "Saints", "Bible", and "rivers", as well as individual country names for sites therein (also see "Islamic Empire" for west Asian site names). As a significant portion of this volume concerns mills, there is also a main heading for "mills" as well as other headings for specific references to "watermills", "windmills", and "tidemills".